Test Bank

INVESTMENTS: A GLOBAL PERSPECTIVE

First Edition

Jack C. Francis

Robert Ibbotson

Marianne Plunkert
University of Colorado at Denver

Pearson Education

Upper Saddle River, New Jersey 07458

Executive editor: Mickey Cox
Assistant editor: Beth Romph
Production editor: Carol Zaino
Manufacturer: Bradford & Bigelow

ISBN 0-13-060454-2

10 9 8 7 6 5 4 3 2 1

INTRODUCTION

This test bank contains a minimum of 20 multiple choice and 5 short answer questions for each of the chapters 2-29, inclusive. Because of the nature of Chapter 1, there is no separate test bank for it; however, questions pertaining to the material found in Chapter 1 are included in the test bank questions for Chapter 2. In addition to the normal notation designating the correct answer for each multiple choice question, the instructor will find a thorough explanation for each answer in the "Solution Guidelines" section, which immediately follows the test questions for the chapter. It is my hope that this will eliminate the frustration that sometimes occurs when an instructor's answer does not correspond with the given answer to a problem, often because of a typographical error. Instructors who wish to give only "short answer" type questions should also find this feature useful since the entire solution, and not simply the correct multiple choice answer, is provided.

The construction of the "Solutions Guidelines" sections served as self-check for myself. In addition, James Brown of Delta State University checked the material for accuracy, so it is my hope that this test bank is totally error-free.

Marianne Plunkert

CHAPTER TWO: RATES OF RETURN

I.   MULTIPLE CHOICE QUESTIONS

1.   Investors who have the investment goal of maximizing their wealth

      a.   are greedy, and society is harmed by such behavior.
      b.   are usually disappointed since they lose money more often than not.
*   c.   actually benefit society in general, so long as they are law-abiding.
      d.   both "a" and "b"
      e.   both "b" and "c"

2.   A basic difference between investing, gambling, and speculation is that

*   a.   as a rule of thumb, investing is associated with a longer holding period than either gambling or speculation.
      b.   both gambling and speculation involve artificial risks rather than the risks that result from normal activity while investing does not.
      c.   investing does not involve any risk whereas gambling and speculation do.
      d.   neither gambling nor speculation involve a rational risk-return tradeoff decision; only investing does.
      e.   There is no real difference. Investing and speculation are just types of gambles.

3.   Which of the following describes a gambling situation?

      a.   An investor invests in a six-month Treasury bill.
      b.   An investor invests in the initial public offering of a stock in hopes of selling it within a week at a much higher price.
      c.   A day-trader invests in thousands of shares of a stock that is unknown to him, based only on its current bid-ask spread, in hopes of earning substantial profits with a minor move in the bid-ask spread for the stock.
      d.   An investor purchased Frontier Airlines when it was selling for $3 a share, and sold it only six-months later when it rose to $12 a share.
*   e.   None of the above are truly gambling scenarios.

4.   An investor's cost of capital can be thought of as

        I.   how much it costs him to borrow money.
        II.   what he could earn on an alternative investment.
        III.   what the investor must earn if his wealth is to be increased.

        a.   I only
        b.   II only
        c.   I and II only.
        d.   II and III only.
    *   e.   I, II, and III.

5.   The required rate of return on a corporate bond can be calculated as the sum of

        a.   the riskless rate and the intermediate horizon premium.
        b.   the riskless rate and the long horizon premium.
    *   c.   the riskless rate, the long horizon premium, and a default risk premium.
        d.   the riskless rate, the long horizon premium, a default risk premium, and a size premium, which depends on the size of the issuing corporation.
        e.   the riskless rate, the intermediate horizon premium, and a size premium, which depends on the size of the issuing corporation.

6.   Another name for an investor's cost of capital is the

    *   a.   required rate of return.
        b.   single-period rate of return.
        c.   expected rate of return.
        f.   range of returns.
        e.   none of the above.

7.   Which of the following statements about the different rates of return is *true*?

        a.   The expected rate of return is synonymous with the required rate of return.
        b.   An investor's wealth will be increased so long as his expected rate of return is greater than his required rate of return.
        c.   An investor's wealth will only be increased if his single-period rate of return is greater than his expected rate of return.
    *   d.   An investor's wealth will only be increased if his single-period rate of return is greater than his required rate of return.
        e.   An investor should only undertake an investment if his required rate of return is greater than his expected rate of return.

8. Kim paid $9,750 for a 6-month Treasury bill that had a face value of $10,000. Her 6-month rate of return and the equivalent 1-year rate of return were

   a.   9.80% and 19.6% respectively.
   b.   1.02% and 2.05% respectively.
* c.   2.56% and 5.19% respectively.
   d.   5.0% and 10.25% respectively.
   e.   none of the above.

9. Sefeytin purchased 100 shares of GAP, Inc. for $32 a share. One year later, he sold his shares for $38 a share, having first received $0.32 a share in dividends. Seyfetin's 1-year rate of return was

* a.   19.75%.
   b.   18.75%.
   c.   16.63%.
   d.   17.75%.
   e.   none of the above.

10. Bao purchased a $1,000 Treasury bond that had one-year left to maturity for $985. He collected $80 in interest income and received the bond's face value when it matured. His 1-year rate of return was

   a.   3.63%.
   b.   1.04%.
   c.   4.67%.
* d.   9.64%.
   e.   none of the above.

The following information is supplied for Questions 11 and 12:

Juan has collected the following information on the historical returns on the stock of the Narnia Corporation:

Year	Return
1	30%
2	-10%
3	15%
4	6%

3

11. The arithmetic mean return for Narnia is

    a. 11.40%.
    b. 9.28%.
*   c. 10.25%.
    d. 15.25%.
    e. none of the above.

12. The standard deviation of the returns for Narnia is

    a. 210.19%.
*   b. 14.50%.
    c. 115.44%.
    d. 29.09%.
    e. 6.86%.

13. You have collected the following historical data for the returns on the stock of the KeyPack Corporation:

Year	Return
1	10%
2	-2%
3	14%

    KeyPack's geometric mean return is

    a. 8.4%.
*   b. 7.3%.
    c. 22.0%.
    d. 33.2%.
    e. none of the above.

14. An opportunity cost is *best* defined as

    a. the brokerage fees that must be paid.
    b. an implicit, immeasurable cost.
*   c. the amount that could be earned on the highest paying alternative use.
    d. the sum of all out-of-pocket costs involved in a transaction.
    e. the risk-free rate.

15.   The following are the historical annual total returns on small company stocks for the period from 1987 through 1996:

Year	Total return	Year	Total return
1987	-9.3%	1992	23.3%
1988	22.9%	1993	21.0%
1989	10.2%	1994	3.1%
1990	-21.6%	1995	34.5%
1991	44.6%	1996	17.6%

The arithmetic average return on small company stocks for the 10-year period was

    a.   20.81%.
*   b.   14.63%.
    c.   12.98%.
    d.   112.98%.
    e.   none of the above.

The following information is supplied for Questions 16 and 17:

Instrument	Total returns (1987 - 1996)
Long-term (20-year) U.S. Treasury coupon bond	9.4%
Intermediate-term (5-year) U.S. Treasury coupon bond	7.8%
Short-term (30-day) U.S. Treasury bill	5.5%
Large company stocks	15.3%
Long-term corporate bonds	9.5%

16.   The historical default risk premium for the 1987-1996 period was

*   a.   0.1%.
    b.   1.7%.
    c.   4.0%.
    d.   5.8%.
    e.   9.8%.

17.   The historical short-horizon equity risk premium for the 1987-1996 period was

    a.   5.9%.
*   b.   9.8%.
    c.   4.0%.
    d.   1.7%.
    e.   7.5%.

18. Which of the following statements is (are) *true* regarding the standard deviation?

    a. It is simple to calculate since only the two extreme values need to be used.
    b. It considers every outcome.
    c. It is a measure of dispersion around the average value, and is a good measure of the variability of return.
    d. It will always be in the same units as the expected value.
    * e. Selections "b," "c," and "d" are all true.

19. Rank the following investments from the *least* risky to the *most* risky:

    I. small company stocks
    II. U.S. Treasury bills
    III. long-term corporate bonds
    IV. large company stocks
    V. U.S. Treasury bonds

    a. V, II, IV, I, III
    b. I, III, V, IV, II
    c. II, V, IV, III, I
    * d. II, V, III, IV, I
    e. V, II, III, IV, I

20. Which of the following statements is (are) *true* regarding the selection of a sample to minimize sampling errors?

    a. The sample should use all the available data, including that from fifty years ago.
    b. The sampling period should be no longer than one year in order to reflect the most current market conditions.
    * c. The sampling period should be long enough to smooth out temporary market conditions, such as bubbles, collapses, and spikes.
    d. both "a" and "b"
    e. both "b" and "c"

II. SHORT ANSWER QUESTIONS

1. What are the advantages associated with using the standard deviation as a measure of risk?

2. Distinguish among investing, speculating, and investing.

3. Dave purchased a 3-month Treasury bill that had a $10,000 face value for $9,900. Calculate his 3-month rate of return and his equivalent annual rate of return.

4.   Sonya purchased 100 shares of Abbott Lab stock for $34 1/2 a share. She received $0.60 a share in dividends and sold the stock after one year for $40 a share. Calculate her one-year rate of return.

5.   Carlos has collected the following data on the historical returns of Seamic Corporation:

Year   Return
1   12%
2   -5%
3   6%
4   10%

Calculate the compound average annual rate of return for Seamic.

CHAPTER TWO: SOLUTION GUIDELINES

Multiple Choice

1. **c**:   Investors do invest to maximize their wealth, based on their risk-return tradeoff. Society benefits from this. Firms receive their funding from these investors and will offer the highest quality goods at the lowest cost, good locations and shopping hours, and courteous service in order to maximize their value, which, in turn, maximizes the wealth of their owners (shareholders).

2. **a**:   Gambling, investing, and speculation all involve risk. Both investing and speculation involve a rational risk-return trade-off, however, and gambling involves artificial risk. The general rule-of-thumb that differentiates investment from speculation is the longer holding period typically involved with an investment.

3. **e**:   Although day-traders border on gambling since they usually have no idea of what company they are investing in, they do invest in hopes of receiving a positive risk-return tradeoff, unlike gamblers who have negative expected returns. Day-traders are probably best classified as speculators.

4. **e**:   An investor's cost of capital may be an explicit interest expense on borrowed capital, an explicit cash dividend payment that a stock issuer pays to its shareholders, or an implicit opportunity cost. Regardless, it is what the investor must earn if his wealth is to be increased.

5. **c**:   A corporate bond must offer at least the riskless rate, which is the Treasury bill yield. Additionally, it must offer a horizon premium for its longer time to maturity and a default risk premium since, unlike issues of the U.S. government, corporate bonds can, and do, default.

6. **a**:   An investor's cost of capital is the return he must require on an investment in order to increase his wealth.

7. **d**:   An investor may expect a return that is higher or lower than his actual single-period rate of return and higher or lower than his required rate of return. However, an investor's wealth will increase only if his actual single-period rate of return is higher than his required rate of return.

8. **c**:   Kim's 6-month rate of return is $r = (\$10,000 - \$9,750)/\$9,750 = 2.56\%$. This is equivalent to an annual rate of return of $(1.0256)^2 - 1 = 5.19\%$.

9. **a**:   Sefeytin's return on GAP = $[(\$38 + \$0.32) - \$32]/\$32 = 19.75\%$.

10. **d**:   Bao's rate of return on the Treasury bond is $[(\$1,000 + \$80) - \$985]/\$985 = 9.64\%$.

11.   **c**:   The arithmetic mean return for Narnia is $[30 + (-10) + 15 + 6]/4 = 10.25\%$.

12.   **b**:   The standard deviation of the returns on Narnia

is $\sigma = \sqrt{\dfrac{(30-10.25)^2 + (-10-10.25)^2 + (15-10.25)^2 + (6-10.25)^2}{4}} = 14.50\%$.

13.   **b**:   The geometric mean return for KeyPack's stock is

$\sqrt[4]{(1.10)(0.98)(1.14)(1.08)} - 1 = 7.3\%$.

14.   **c**:   This is the definition of an opportunity cost.

15.   **b**:   The arithmetic average of the returns on small company stocks is $[-9.3\% + 22.9\% + 10.2\% + -21.6\% + 44.6\% + 23.3\% + 21.0\% + 3.1\% + 34.5\% + 17.6\%]/10 = 14.63\%$.

16.   **a**:   The default risk premium is calculated as the difference between the total return on corporate bonds and the total return on long-term government bonds. $9.5\% - 9.4\% = 0.1\%$.

17.   **b**:   The short-horizon equity risk premium is the difference between the total returns on large company stocks and the return on U.S. Treasury bills. $15.3\% - 5.5\% = 9.8\%$.

18.   **e**:   The standard deviation considers every outcome. It measures the dispersion around the average value and, therefore, fits the definition of risk as the variability of return. It will always be in the same units as the expected value.

19.   **d**:   Treasury bills are the least risky investment, followed by U.S. Treasury bonds, which are longer-term investments. Long-term corporate bonds are even riskier because they have default risk. However, the bondholders have a priority claim over common stockholders, so large company stocks are riskier than corporate bonds. Stocks of smaller firms are even riskier.

20.   **c**:   Including data from fifty years ago may not provide a good representation of recent market conditions. However, using just the current year's data may bias the sample, giving undue emphasis on bubbles, spikes, and collapses that may have occurred during the year. To minimize sampling errors, a long enough period should be used so that these temporary factors are smoothed out.

Short Answer

1.   There are four advantages to using the standard deviation as a measure of risk:

      1.   The standard deviation considers every outcome, unlike the range that considers only the two extreme values.

2. The standard deviation is a well-known statistic, and many hand calculators and computers are programmed to calculate it.

3. The standard deviation measures the dispersion around the average value; thus, it corresponds to the variability-of-return definition of risk.

4. The standard deviation and the variance are equivalent risk measures. Taking the square root of the variance does not alter the risk ranking and allows us to express risk in the same units as the expected value. (The variance is expressed in square units.)

2. A gamble is over more quickly than a speculation or an investment. Rational people gamble as a form of entertainment, not to generate income. Gambling also creates risk artificially via the rules of the game. These risks do not follow the risk-return tradeoff that is the basis for rational economic behavior. Gambles have negative expected returns. Speculations, on the other hand, typically last longer than gambles, but are briefer than investments. Rational people speculate in hopes of making a quick profit. Speculations have positive expected returns. Investing is defined by the U.S. Treasury to be a market asset that has a holding period that is greater than one year. However, an investment may be undertaken for a shorter holding period, such as an investment made in a 90-day Treasury bill. To differentiate between investing, speculation, and gambling, one must examine the investor's intent when the venture was undertaken.

3. Dave's 3-month rate of return is $r = \dfrac{\$10,000 - \$9,900}{\$9,900} = 1.01\%$. Since there are four 3-month periods in a year, his equivalent annual return is $(1.0101)^4 - 1 = 4.10\%$.

4. Sonya's rate of return on her investment in Abbot Lab is $r = \dfrac{(\$40 + \$0.60) - \$34.50}{\$34.50} = 17.7\%$.

5. The compound average rate of return for Seamic is its geometric mean return: $\sqrt[4]{(1.12)(0.95)(1.06)1.10)}1- = 5.5\%$.

CHAPTER THREE: INTRODUCTION TO VALUATION

I.   MATCHING QUESTIONS

Match the following words and phrases with their correct definitions.

Word or Phrase		Definition or Description
1. Price per share *(B)*	A.	The value and price fluctuate randomly together.
2. Passive investment management *(C)*	B.	A value determined by market processes that can sometimes be irrational.
3. Value per share *(E)*	C.	A buy and hold without trading strategy.
4. Continuous equilibrium *(A)*	D.	The appropriate decision when an underpriced security is discovered.
5. Buy a security *(D)*	E.	A value that is estimated by an informed security analyst.

II.   MULTIPLE CHOICE QUESTIONS

1.   A certain stock is currently selling for $63.50. Based on John's estimates, its value is $50.00. If John's estimate of its value is accurate, John should

      a.   buy the stock; it is underpriced.
*   b.   short sell the stock; it is overpriced.
      c.   make no trade since he will realize no profit from either buying or selling it.
      d.   buy the stock and simultaneously enter a short sale order to hedge his position.
      e.   do either "b" or "d."

2.   Yoshito wants to do a short sale on Sysco stock. He can do so if the most recent trades are at which of following consecutive prices?

      a.   27.25, 27.13, 27.13
      b.   27.25, 27.13, 27.06
      c.   27.25, 27.38, 27.50
      d.   27.25, 27.38, 27.38
*   e.   either "c" or "d"

3. Consider the following information:

Company	Market price of stock	Estimated value per share
Acme Corporation	$87.75	$90.00
Baker, Inc.	$11.13	$13.00
Crown Corporation	$31.75	$40.00
Delta Corporation	$19.50	$19.50
Evans Corporation	$44.25	$30.00

For which company's stock would an information trader be most likely to issue a buy order?

   a. Acme Corporation
   b. Baker, Inc.
* c. Crown Corporation
   d. Delta Corporation
   e. Evans Corporation

4. The term "short interest" refers to

* a. the total number of shares that brokers have listed in their accounts as being sold short.
   b. stocks which are not very liquid and may pose problems for short sellers.
   c. a temporary flurry of interest in a particular stock due to recent significant information entering the market about it.
   d. the taking of a long position and a short position in the same stock.
   e. market frictions that reduce the return on an investment.

5. Ian has established a perfectly hedged position. This means that Ian can expect

   a. to earn a return equal to the risk-free rate; no less, no more.
   b. to receive the maximum profits possible from his investments.
   c. to earn a modest arbitrage profit.
   d. potential profits, but no losses on his investments.
* e. to earn zero profits, but also zero losses.

6. Judy purchased 100 shares of GAP at $38 a share. Subsequently, she entered an order to short sell 100 shares of GAP when the stock was selling for $42. Judy can expect to earn

   a. neither profits nor losses on these positions since they represent a perfect hedge.
* b. an invariant profit equal to $400.
   c. an invariant profit, but the amount is indeterminable.
   d. an invariant loss equal to $400.
   e. an invariant loss, but the amount is indeterminable.

7. Haluk purchased 100 shares of Caterpillar stock at $50 a share. Subsequently, he short sold 100 shares of the stock when it was selling for $47.50. Haluk can expect to earn

    a. neither profits nor losses on these positions since they represent a perfect hedge.
    b. an invariant profit equal to $250.
    c. an invariant profit, but the amount is indeterminable.
*   d. an invariant loss equal to $250.
    e. an invariant loss, but the amount is indeterminable.

8. Terry purchased 200 shares of American Electric Power (AEP) AEP at $45 a share. After one year, he received $2.40 a share in dividends and sold the stock for $60. His holding period return was

*   a. 38.7%.
    b. 29.0%.
    c. 28.0%.
    d. 21.0%.
    e. none of the above.

9. An issue of Armco preferred stock pays a $2.10 dividend annually. If Trevor wants an 8% annual return on this investment, he should pay no more than

*   a. $26.25 a share.
    b. $22.68 a share.
    c. $20.00 a share.
    d. $38.10 a share.
    e. All of the above prices are too high.

10. Prasad is considering the purchase of some Amerigas stock, which is currently selling for $20.50. He projects that the annual dividend of $2.20 a share will remain constant for the next three years, after which he plans to liquidate his position. If he wants a 12% return on this investment, he should buy Amerigas only if he expects the price at the end of year three to be at least

    a. $28.80.
*   b. $21.38
    c. $22.20
    d. $23.59
    e. none of the above.

11. Celeste short sold 100 shares of Paccar stock at $52. Subsequently, Celeste covered her short position by purchasing the shares when Paccar was selling for $43. However, while her short position was open, Paccar paid an $0.80 a share dividend. Celeste's holding period return was

    a.   18.8%.
    b.   19.1%.
    c.   22.8%.
*   d.   15.8%.
    e.   none of the above.

12. A bond has a $1,000 face value, a coupon rate of 9%, with interest paid annually, and matures in eight years. John believes he should require a 10% return on this investment. The maximum price he should pay for the bond is, therefore,

    a. $1,000.00.
    b. $1,100.00.
    c. $1,186.52.
*   d. $ 946.65.
    e. $ 659.43.

13. Liu Chen is interested in a stock that recently paid a dividend of $1.20 a share. Liu estimates that this dividend will continue to grow at 5% a year indefinitely. If Liu requires a 16% return on this investment, the maximum price he should pay for it is

    a. $10.01.
    b. $ 7.50.
    c. $ 7.88.
    d. $12.65.
*   e. $11.45.

14. Joan is considering the purchase of a stock that currently pays a $0.70 annual dividend and sells for $28.00. She estimates that the dividend will grow at an annual rate of 10% indefinitely. If she purchases this stock at the current price and her estimate is correct, what annual return will she be receiving?

    a.   10.00%
    b.   2.50%
    c.   12.50%
*   d.   12.75%
    e.   It cannot be determined with the information provided.

15. Tristan purchased 100 shares of CFB Capital at $25.75 and subsequently short sold 100 shares of the stock when it was selling for $30.00. CFB paid a $2.22 a share dividend before Tristan liquidated both his long and his short positions. Tristan's profit (loss) was

*   a. $425 profit.
    b. $425 loss.
    c. $647 profit.
    d. $203 profit.
    e. $203 loss.

16. A certain bond has a $1,000 face value, a coupon rate of 11%, with annual payments, and matures in 5 years. If its yield-to-maturity is 10%, the bond is selling for

    a. $ 440.00.
*   b. $1,037.91.
    c. $ 620.92.
    d. $ 990.00.
    e.   none of the above.

17. A short sale may be done to

    a.   earn speculative profits if you expect the price of a security to increase.
    b.   earn speculative profits if you expect the price of a security to decrease.
    c.   hedge your risk if you own shares of the stock you are short selling.
    d.   create an arbitrage position.
*   e.   Selections "b," "c," and "d" are all correct.

18. Josie purchased a $1,000 bond that pays no coupons, but matures in four years, for a price of $680.00. Her expected average annual rate of return on this investment is

    a.   11.8%.
    b.   8.1%.
*   c.   10.1%.
    d.   11.0%.
    e.   none of the above.

19. A technical analyst spends hours plotting charts of past prices for each stock he follows. He believes by doing so, he can find underpriced and overpriced securities. This analyst must believe that security markets are

    a.   weakly efficient.
    b.   semi-strong efficient.
    c.   perfectly efficient.
*   d.   totally inefficient.
    e.   dominated by information traders.

20.   If security markets are at least semi-strong efficient, then the implication is that

      a.   you are likely to find underpriced and overpriced securities by reading *The Wall Street Journal* daily.

      b.   you can determine when to buy or to sell a security by studying the pattern of its historical prices.

      c.   you cannot expect to find underpriced or overpriced securities even if you are privy to inside information.

*   d.   trading on information that you read in *The Wall Street Journal* is unlikely to allow you to purchase securities that are significantly underpriced or significantly overpriced.

      e.   Both "c" and "d" are correct.

II.   SHORT ANSWER QUESTIONS

1.   A security analyst has made the following projections for the Judd & Merkle (J&M) Corporation:

Year	Dividend (paid at end of year)
1	$1.10
2	$1.15
3	$1.18

     J&M is currently selling for $30 a share, and she estimates that its price at the end of year three will be $43 a share. She believes the stock should offer a 15% return, given its risk level. Which buy-sell decision rule will she apply? Why?

2.   Trevor is considering the purchase of a beach house in Florida as a rental property. He estimates that he'll be able to net $30,000 annually, after paying for maintenance expenses and property taxes. He plans to keep the property for five years, at which point he expects to be able to sell it for $380,000. If Trevor believes he should earn a 20% return on this investment, and the house is on the market for $250,000, should he offer full market price for it?

3.   Janice is considering purchasing a small business operation that has generated annual cash flows of $25,000 for the last three years. Janice believes she'll be able to increase the cash flows to the business by at least 5% a year indefinitely, given her entrepreneurial talents. She believes the risk of this endeavor should offer her an average annual return of at least 22%. What is the maximum price she should pay for the business?

4.   Distinguish between the price of an investment and the value of an investment. Discuss how the buy-sell decision rules are applied, based on the relationship between price and value.

5.   What two conditions must exist to establish a perfect hedge position?

CHAPTER THREE: SOLUTION GUIDELINES

Multiple Choice

1.   **b**:   The stock is overpriced, based on John's estimates. Therefore, he should short sell it in anticipation of a price decrease. He would never want to buy a stock that he believes is overpriced.

2.   **e**:   Short sales may only be done on an uptick or a zero uptick.

3.   **c**:   While both Baker, Inc. and Crown Corporation are selling at prices that are below their estimated values, when commission costs are considered, an investment in Baker is unlikely to generate abnormal returns. Information traders look for significant deviations between the estimated value and the market price of the stock, as is the case for Crown Corporation.

4.   **a**:   This is the definition of "short interest."

5.   **e**:   A perfect hedge is one for which there are no profits or losses. The gains and losses from the long and short positions cancel each other out.

6.   **b**:   Since Judy short sold shares of a stock that she owned, she can cover the short position by using her existing shares, purchased at a price of $38 a share.

Purchase price of Gap	($3,800)
Sale price of Gap	$4,200
Profit	$ 400

7.   **d**:   Since Haluk short sold shares of a stock that he owned, he can cover the short position by using his existing shares. However, because he short sold the stock for less than his purchase price, he will experience a loss equal to the difference between the selling price and the purchase price, regardless of how low the price of Caterpillar stock drops.

Purchase price of Caterpillar	($5,000)
Sale price of Caterpillar	$4,750
Loss	($ 250)

8.   **a**: $r = \dfrac{(P_1 - P_0) + CF}{P_0} = \dfrac{(\$60 - \$45) + \$2.40}{\$45} = 38.7\%$.

9.   **a**: Price = Present value = $\dfrac{dividend}{interest\ rate} = \dfrac{\$2.10}{0.08} = \$26.25$.

10.   **b**:   Since the current price of $20.50 must equal the present value of the expected future cash flows if the stock is currently priced, we can solve the following equation to get the price at the end of three years:

$$\text{Price} = \$2.20 \sum_{t=1}^{3} \frac{1}{(1.12)^t} + P_3\left[\frac{1}{(1.12)^3}\right] = \$20.50$$

$$\$5.28 + P_3\left[\frac{1}{(1.12)^3}\right] = \$20.50$$

$$P_3\left[\frac{1}{(1.12)^3}\right] = \$15.22$$

$$P_3 = \$21.38$$

11.   **d**: $r = \dfrac{(P_1 - P_0) - CF}{P_0} = \dfrac{(\$52 - \$43) - \$0.80}{\$52} = 15.8\%.$

12.   **d**: $\text{Price} = \$90\sum_{t=1}^{8} \dfrac{1}{(1.10)^t} + \$1,000\left[\dfrac{1}{(1.10)^8}\right] = \$946.45.$

13.   **e**:   The constant growth model can be used here:

$$\text{Price} = \frac{(\text{cash dividend}_0)(1 + \text{growth rate})}{\text{discount rate} - \text{growth rate}} = \frac{\$1.20(1.05)}{0.16 - 0.05} = \$11.45.$$

14.   **d**:   The constant growth model is solved to find the discount rate:

$$\text{Price} = \frac{(\text{cash dividend}_0)(1 + \text{growth rate})}{\text{discount rate} - \text{growth rate}}$$

$$\text{Discount rate} = \frac{\text{cash dividend}_1}{\text{Price}_0} + \text{growth rate} = \frac{\$0.70(1.10)}{\$28} + 0.10 = 12.75\%.$$

15.   **a**:
Proceeds from short sale	$3,000
Purchase price of CFB Capital	($2,575)
Dividends (wash)	0
Net profit	$ 425

16.   **b**: $\text{Price} = \$110\sum_{t=1}^{5} \dfrac{1}{(1.10)^t} + \$1,000\left[\dfrac{1}{(1.10)^5}\right] = \$1,037.91.$

17.   **e**:   Short sales can be done in hopes of producing profits if the price of a security decreases, to hedge a long position, or to create an arbitrage position. If the stock price increases, losses, not profits, will result.

18.   **c**:   The expected average rate of return on the bond can be determined by using the time value of money formula.

$$FV = PV(1 + k)^t$$
$$\$1,000 = \$680(1 + k)^4$$
$$k = \sqrt[4]{\frac{\$1,000}{\$680}} - 1 = 10.1\%.$$

19.   **d**:   If the markets are only weakly efficient, the implication is that abnormal returns cannot be made by studying past price information since this information is fully and accurately reflected in current prices. Therefore, an analyst who studies past prices does not believe that markets are even weakly efficient.

20.   **d**:   Semi-strong efficient markets are those in which all publicly available information is fully and accurately reflected in current prices. Therefore, an investor should not expect to find mispriced securities by studying publicly available information, such as that which appears in the *Wall Street Journal*. However, the semi-strong efficient markets hypothesis does not conclude that an investor would be unable to find mispriced securities if he were privy to inside information as suggested by selection "c."

Short Answer

1.   Based on the analyst's expectations and her required rate of return, the fair market value of the stock is calculated as follows:

$$\text{Price} = \frac{\$1.10}{(1.15)^1} + \frac{\$1.15}{(1.15)^2} + \frac{\$1.18 + \$43}{(1.15)^3} = \$30.88.$$

Although the analyst's estimate of J&M's value is slightly more than its current market price, she would not expect a profit from either buying or selling this stock once transaction costs are factored in, so she would be expected to follow the **don't trade** rule.

2.   Based on Trevor's estimates, the fair market value of the beach house is calculated as follows:

$$\text{Price} = \$30,000 \sum_{t=1}^{5} \frac{1}{(1.20)^t} + \$380,000 \left[\frac{1}{(1.20)^5} \right] = \$242,432.$$

Trevor should not, therefore, be willing to pay the asking price for the house. The most he should offer is $242,432.

3.   The constant growth model can be employed to determine the fair market value of the business, based on Janice's estimates.

$$\text{Price} = \frac{\$25,000(1.05)}{0.22 - 0.05} = \$154,412.$$

Therefore, $154,412 is the maximum price she should be willing to pay for the business.

4.   The *price* of an investment is what it is actually selling for while the *value* of the investment is the present value of the expected future cash flows from the investment. If the price of an investment is below its value, then it is underpriced and should be purchased and held in order to profit from expected price gains. If the price of the investment is equal to its value, then the investment is correctly priced, and no profits or gains should be expected from either buying or selling it. Therefore, the "don't trade" rule should be followed. If the price of the investment is greater than its value, it is overpriced. If the investment is owned, it should be sold to avoid expected losses when the price falls to the level of its true value. If it is not owned, then it can be sold short in order to profit from the future price decline.

5.   In order for a perfect hedge position to be established, the dollar commitments to both the short and long positions must be identical, and the price at which the short sale is executed must exactly equal the purchase price for the long position. If either of these conditions is not met, then the hedge will be imperfect, and the risk is not totally eliminated.

CHAPTER FOUR: ANALYSIS OF FINANCIAL STATEMENTS

I. MULTIPLE CHOICE QUESTIONS

1. Which of the following statements is most correct?

    a.   The debt ratio is a good measure of a firm's profitability.

*   b.   If a firm has a high cash flow interest coverage, it probably will be able to meet its debt obligations.

    c.   Having a high current ratio and a high quick ratio is always a good indication that a firm is measuring its liquidity well.

    d.   A decline in the inventory turnover ratio suggests that the firm's liquidity position is improving.

    e.   All else equal, a decrease in the use of debt will increase the return on equity.

2. Which of the following types of ratios measures the productivity of money invested in the firm?

    a.   Turnover ratio

    b.   Coverage ratio

    c.   Common stock share data

    d.   Solvency ratio

*   e.   Profitability ratio

3. Which of the following will not affect the quick ratio?

    a.   Inventory is sold on credit for a profit.

    b.   Cash is used to pay dividends.

*   c.   A new piece of equipment is purchased using a five-year note.

    d.   Inventory is purchased on credit.

    e.   Neither of the scenarios described in "c" or "d" will affect the quick ratio.

4. A firm has a total debt-to-assets ratio of 0.30. Its financial leverage ratio is

    a.   0.70.

    b.   3.33.

    c.   0.77.

*   d.   1.43.

    e.   none of the above.

5.   The accounts receivable turnover ratio is a measure of

*   a.   how timely the firm's credit customers are in paying their bills.
       b.   the number of uncollectable accounts.
       c.   the expected level of bad debt losses .
       d.   the profitability of credit sales.
       e.   none of the above.

6.   A firm has a total debt-to-assets ratio of 0.43. Its financial leverage ratio is

       a.   0.57.
*   b.   1.75.
       c.   2.33.
       d.   0.70.
       e.   none of the above.

7.   A firm has a net profit margin of 4%, a total asset turnover ratio of 5, and a financial leverage ratio of 1.20. Its return on equity is

       a.   16.7%.
*   b.   24.0%.
       c.   10.0%.
       d.   0.24%.
       e.   none of the above.

8.   A firm has a net profit margin of 10%, a total asset turnover ratio of 3, and a total debt-to-assets ratio of 35%. Its return on equity is

       a.   10.5%.
       b.   85.7%.
       c.   8.57%.
*   d.   46.2%.
       e.   none of the above.

9.   Which of the following transactions will cause the total debt-to-assets ratio to decrease?

       a.   Equipment is purchased using a five year note.
*   b.   Inventory is sold for a profit.
       c.   Additional inventory is purchased on credit.
       d.   A new bond issue is sold.
       e.   none of the above

10. A firm has a collection period of 36 days. Its annual sales are $3,600,000. Assuming a 360 day year, its average accounts receivable balance is

     a. $277,777.
*   b. $360,000.
     c. $129,600.
     d. $100,000.
     e.   none of the above.

11. Which of the following transactions will cause an immediate increase in the return on equity?

     a.   A new issue of stock is sold.
     b.   New equipment is purchased.
*   c.   A new issue of bonds is sold.
     d.   An increase in dividends is announced.
     e.   none of the above

12. Which of the following collection periods would you expect to be typical for a grocery store?

     a.   60 days
*   b.   5 days
     c.   30 days
     d.   40 days
     e.   90 days

13. A firm has a return on assets of 15% and a total asset turnover of 1.2 times. Its net profit margin is

*   a.   12.5%.
     b.   18.0%.
     c.   8.0%.
     d.   15.0%.
     e.   none of the above.

14. A bond covenant stipulates that the Bye-bye Corporation must maintain a minimum current ratio of 2.5. Bye-bye's present current ratio is 2.3. To meet the bond covenant Bye-bye can

    a.   stimulate sales by selling inventory below cost.
    b.   increase its collection efforts on its accounts receivable.
    c.   issue a 3-year note and use the proceeds to pay off its suppliers.
    d.   sell a new issue of stock.
*   e.   Both "c" and "d" will increase Bye-bye's current ratio.

15. You read in the stock pages of the *WALL STREET JOURNAL* that a certain company has a price-earnings ratio of 5 and a closing stock price of $20. What are the annual earnings per share for the company?

    a. $1.00
    b. $2.00
    c. $3.00
*   d. $4.00
    e. $5.00

16. A high current ratio relative to other firms in the same industry may indicate

    a.   that the firm is more liquid than other firms in the industry.
    b.   that the firm is investing in lower earning assets and is therefore generating lower returns on assets.
    c.   that the firm is less liquid than other firms in the industry.
*   d.   Selections "a" and "b" are both correct.
    e.   Selections "b" and "c" are both correct.

17. The Inmar Corporation has an interest expense of $20,000, operating earnings of $100,000, and sales of $500,000. What is Inmar's times-interest-earned ratio?

    a.   4 times
*   b.   5 times
    c.   6 times
    d.   25 times
    e.   none of the above

18. The Inmar Corporation has $100,000 of cash, $200,000 of accounts receivable, $300,000 in inventory, and current liabilities of $200,000. The current ratio of Inmar is

    a.   1.0.
    b.   1.5.
    c.   2.0.
    d.   2.5.
*   e.   3.0.

19. The Inmar Corporation has $100,000 of cash, $200,000 of accounts receivable, $300,000 in inventory, and current liabilities of $200,000. Its quick ratio is

    a.   1.0.
*   b.   1.5.
    c.   2.0.
    d.   2.5.
    e.   3.0.

20. The following information is available for the Jeanjac Corporation:

net income	$2,800,000	current liabilities	$3,000,000
tax rate	39%	long-term debt	$15,000,000
interest expense	$3,000,000	preferred stock	$1,000,000
		common equity	$25,000,000

Jeanjac can borrow funds at the current rate of 15%. Based on this information,

    a.   its long-term pre-tax rate of return is 14.9%, which means that the firm is not earning enough to pay off its debts.
    b.   its long-term pre-tax rate of return is 20%, which means that the firm is earning enough to pay off its debts although the coverage is not ample.
*   c.   its long-term pre-tax rate of return is 18.5%, which means that while the firm is earning enough to pay off its debts, there is not a lot of room for errors on the part of management.
    d.   its long-term pre-tax rate of return is 14.9%, which means that the firm can comfortably pay off its debts and should have a strong quality rating on its bonds.
    e.   nothing can be concluded about the firm's ability to cover its debt obligations since one does not know the level of the firm's operating profits.

II.   SHORT ANSWER QUESTIONS

1. Mr. McKay is a loan officer for SureBank. He is considering an application for a short-term loan submitted by NerdCo, a firm that manufactures computer peripheral devices. Why might Mr. McKay be more concerned with NerdCo's quick ratio than with its current ratio when evaluating NerdCo's liquidity?

2. Two firms in the fast-food industry have similar profit margins and asset turnover ratios. However, Sushi Sizzler has a much higher return on equity than does Delightful Dogs. What is the likely explanation for this difference?

3. The most recent balance sheets for Skies 'R Us, a regional airline company, are as follows:

Skies 'R Us
Balance Sheet
as of December 31,

(amounts in thousands)

	2000	1999
Cash and cash equivalents	$ 3,600	$10,300
Accounts receivable	$14,000	$ 9,500
Inventories	$ 3,000	$ 5,000
Other current assets*	$12,000	$ 8.500
Total current assets	$32,600	$33,300
Plant, property and equipment	$16,200	$15,400
Total assets	$48,800	$48,700
Accounts payable	$ 6,000	$ 8,000
Notes payable	0	$ 9,000
Other current liabilities	$ 5,200	$ 3,300
Total current liabilities	$11,200	$20,300
Long-term debt	$ 5,800	$ 1,200
Total liabilities	$17,000	$21,500
Common equity	$31,800	$27,200
Total liabilities and equity	$48,800	$48,700

*includes maintenance deposits

Construct common size balance sheets for Skies 'R Us. Discuss any significant changes in the sources and uses of funds by the company in the two-year period.

4. The following income statement information was revealed in Forefront Semiconductor Corporation's must recent annual report:

ForeFront Semiconductor Corporation
Income Statement
for the years ending December 31,

(amounts in thousands)	2000	1999
Net sales	$63,000	$45,000
Cost of sales	40,000	30,000
Gross profit	$23,000	$15,000
Operating expenses:		
Research and development	9,300	6,500
Sales and marketing	8,300	4,900
General and administrative	4,300	3,000
Total operating expenses	$21,900	$14,400
Operating income	$ 1,100	$ 600
Interest expense	900	300
Earnings before tax	$ 200	$ 300
Taxes	80	120
Net income	$ 120	$ 180

Prepare common-size income statements. Use them to identify the primary reasons that net income decreased in 2000 from its 1999 level.

5. The following data is available for Starlite Corporation for the most recent two years:

	2000	1999
Sales	$6,800,000	$4,500,000
Net income	$ 612,000	$ 382,500
Total assets	$1,900,000	$1,300,000
Total debt	$ 722,000	$ 495,000
Dividend payout ratio	25%	25%

a. What has happened to Starlite's return on equity over the two-year period? Use the DuPont system to explain the change.

b. Assuming that Starlite obtains no additional external financing, at what rate do you expect the firm to be able to grow over the next year?

CHAPTER FOUR: SOLUTION GUIDELINES

Multiple Choice

1. **b**: Firms with high cash flows available to meet interest payments are best able to weather bad times. The debt ratio reflects nothing about the profitability of the firm. Liquidity ratios that are much higher than average are just as bad as those that are too low since it may indicate that the firm is investing more in current assets, which tend to offer lower returns. If anything, a decline in the inventory turnover ratio may mean the firm is less, not more liquid. Finally, an examination of the components of the return on equity reveals that the return on equity decreases, not increases, with a decrease in the use of debt, all else equal.

2. **e**: Profitability ratios measure the amount of money that a firm earns per dollar of investment. Turnover ratios measure the asset management of the firm. Coverage ratios measure how well a firm is able to meet its fixed payments. Common stock share data indicate the amount that a shareholder owning a single share is entitled to receive, and solvency ratios measure the ability of a firm to meet its short-term debt obligations.

3. **c**: Neither equipment nor five-year notes are included in the calculation of the quick ratio. Inventory that is sold for a profit will increase cash or accounts receivable, and will increase the ratio. If cash is used to pay dividends, the ratio will decrease due to the decrease in the cash account. If inventory is purchased on credit, accounts payable will increase, resulting in a decrease in the quick ratio.

4. **d**: The financial leverage ratio is calculated as total assets/total equity and the total debt-to-assets ratio is total debt/total assets. Since total assets = total debt + total equity, 1 - total debt-to assets ratio = total equity- to- assets. The reciprocal of this is total assets/total equity. Therefore, the financial leverage ratio is equal to 1/(1 - total debt-to-assets), and 1/(1 - 0.30) = 1.43.

5. **a**: The accounts receivable turnover ratio measures how many times a year receivables turn over and, therefore, how timely the firm's credit customers are in paying their bills. The higher the ratio, the more timely the payments. It does not indicate how many of the accounts may be uncollectable or end up as bad debt losses; nor does it indicate the profitability of credit sales.

6. **b**: The financial leverage ratio is calculated as total assets/total equity and the total debt-to-assets ratio is total debt/total assets. Since total assets = total debt + total equity, 1 - total debt-to assets ratio = total equity- to- assets. The reciprocal of this is total assets/total equity. Therefore, the financial leverage ratio is equal to 1/(1 - total debt-to-assets), and 1/(1 - 0.43) = 1.75.

7. **b**: Return on equity = net profit margin x total asset turnover x financial leverage ratio = 4% x 5 x 1.20 = 24.0%.

8. **d**:   The financial leverage ratio = 1/(1 - total debt-to-assets ratio) and is, therefore, equal to 1/(1 - 0.35) = 1.54. Return on equity = net profit margin x total asset turnover x financial leverage ratio = 10% x 3 x 1.54 = 46.2%.

9. **b**:   If inventory is sold for a profit, total assets will increase and total debt is unaffected, so the total debt-to-assets ratio will decrease. Since the total debt-to-assets ratio must be less than 1.0, the purchase of new equipment with debt will cause the ratio to increase as will the purchase of inventory on credit. A new bond issue increases both debt and total assets (cash, most immediately) and also causes an increase in the debt ratio.

10. **b**:   The collection period = accounts receivable/average daily credit sales; therefore, the accounts receivables = collection period x average daily credit sales. Assuming all the sales are credit sales, accounts receivable = 36 x $3,600,000/360 = $360,000.

11. **c**:   Return on equity = net profit margin x total asset turnover x financial leverage ratio. Therefore, an increase in debt will increase the return on equity since this will increase the financial leverage ratio, leaving the other two factors unchanged. A new issue of stock will decrease the return on equity since it increases the equity account. The purchase of new equipment will have the immediate effect of decreasing total asset turnover and, therefore, decreasing the return on equity. The announcement of an increase in dividends has no effect on any of the factors.

12. **b**:   Since grocery stores do not sell goods on credit (the use of a bank card is considered a cash sale for the store), one would expect the average collection period to be zero, or close to it, allowing for credit sales to employees perhaps.

13. **a**:   The return on assets = net profit margin x total asset turnover, so the net profit margin = return on assets/total asset turnover = 15%/1.2 = 12.5%.

14. **e**:   The issuance of a 3-year note to pay off accounts payable will decrease current liabilities, thereby increasing the current ratio. A new stock issue will increase the cash account, a current asset, and also increase the current ratio. Selling inventory at a loss will decrease current assets, and the collection of accounts receivable will have no effect on current assets.

15. **d**:   The price-earnings ratio = market price of stock/earnings per share, so earnings per share = market price of stock/price-earnings ratio = $20/5 = $4.00.

16. **d**:   A high current ratio indicates more liquidity, which is not necessarily good if it is due to the firm's investing more in current assets, which offer a lower return than longer-term investments.

17. **b**:   The times-interest-earned ratio = operating profit/ interest expense = $100,000/$20,000 = 5 times.

18. **e**: The current ratio = current assets/current liabilities = ($100,000 + $200,000 + $300,000)/$200,000 = $600,000/$200,000 = 3.0.

19. **b**: The quick ratio = (current assets - inventory)/current liabilities = ($100,000 + $200,000)/$200,000 = $300,000/$200,000 = 1.5.

20. **c**: Long-term capital = long-term debt + preferred stock + common stock. The long-term capital pre-tax rate of return = (interest + pre-tax earnings)/(capitalization). Jeanjac's pretax earnings are $2,800,000/(1 - 0.39) = $4,590,164. Therefore, the long-term capital pre-tax rate of return = ($3,000,000 + $4,590,164)/($15,000,000 + $1,000,000 + $25,000,000) = $7,590,164/$41,000,000 = 18.5%. While this ratio is greater than the current market interest rate of 15% and, therefore, indicates that the firm is earning enough to pay off its debts, it is not comfortably higher and does not allow room for much error.

Short Answer

1. The industry in which NerdCo operates, the computer peripheral device industry, has a high obsolescence factor. Therefore, Mr. McKay may rightly assume that not all the inventory will be salable. The quick ratio eliminates inventory from the equation when evaluating a firm's liquidity.

2. Return on equity = net profit margin x total asset turnover x financial leverage ratio. Since Sushi Sizzler and Delightful Dogs have similar net profit margins and asset turnover ratios, the difference between their returns on equity lies in the use of debt. Since Sushi Sizzler has a higher return on equity, it must be using more debt than Delightful Dogs.

3.   The common size balance sheets for Skies 'R Us is provided below:

Skies 'R Us
Balance Sheet
as of December 31,

(amounts in thousands)

	2000	**% of total assets**	**1999**	**% of total assets**
Cash and cash equivalents	$ 3,600	7.4%	$10,300	21.1%
Accounts receivable	$14,000	28.7%	$ 9,500	19.5%
Inventories	$ 3,000	6.1%	$ 5,000	10.3%
Other current assets*	$12,000	24.6%	$ 8.500	17.4%
Total current assets	$32,600	66.8%	$33,300	68.4%
Plant, property and equipment	$16,200	33.2%	$15,400	31.6%
Total assets	$48,800	100.0%	$48,700	100.0%
Accounts payable	$ 6,000	12.3%	$ 8,000	16.4%
Notes payable	0	0.0%	$ 9,000	18.5%
Other current liabilities	$ 5,200	10.7%	$ 3,300	6.8%
Total current liabilities	$11,200	23.0%	$20,300	41.7%
Long-term debt	$ 5,800	11.9%	$ 1,200	2.5%
Total liabilities	$17,000	34.9%	$21,500	44.1%
Common equity	$31,800	65.1%	$27,200	55.9%
Total liabilities and equity	$48,800	100.0%	$48,700	100.0%

*includes maintenance deposits

Skies 'R Us has significantly decreased its use of short-term debt financing. Its current liabilities as a percent of total assets is nearly halved. While "other current liabilities" has increased as a percent of total assets, the firm paid off its notes payable in full and has also reduced its accounts payable. It is using a greater percentage of long-term debt and common equity financing and has significantly reduced its cash account as well as its inventories.

The uses of funds include the repayment of short-term debt obligations, a greater investment in accounts receivable and "other current assets," which includes maintenance deposits. Plant, property, and equipment increased only slightly.

4.   The common size income statements for Forefront Semiconductor are presented below:

ForeFront Semiconductor Corporation
Income Statement
for the years ending December 31,

(amounts in thousands)	2000	% of sales	1999	% of sales
Net sales	$63,000	100.0%	$45,000	100.0%
Cost of sales	40,000	63.5%	30,000	66.7%
Gross profit	$23,000	36.5%	$15,000	33.3%
Operating expenses:				
Research and development	9,300	14.8%	6,500	14.4%
Sales and marketing	8,300	13.2%	4,900	10.9%
General and administrative	4,300	6.8%	3,000	6.7%
Total operating expenses	$21,900	34.7%	$14,400	32.0%
Operating income	$ 1,100	1.7%	$ 600	1.3%
Interest expense	900	1.4%	300	0.7%
Earnings before tax	$ 200	0.3%	$ 300	0.7%
Taxes	80	0.1%	120	0.3%
Net income	$ 120	0.2%	$ 180	0.4%

Although Forefront's cost of sales decreased, its operating expenses increased.
Specifically, the firm is investing more in "sales and marketing" as a percent of sales. Its
research and development and general and administrative expenses increased only
slightly. Too, it appears the firm is using more debt since both its raw interest expense
and the interest expense as a percent of sales has increased significantly, the latter having
doubled.

5a.   The ROE for Starlite for the two years is calculated first using the following formula:
ROE = net income/total equity.

	2000	**1999**
ROE	$612,000/$1,178,000	$382,500/$916,000
	= 52%	= 41.8%

Using the DuPont System to analyze the reason for the increase, we break the return on
equity down into its three components:

ROE = net profit margin x asset turnover x financial leverage ratio
2000:   52% = (612/6,800 = 9%) x (6,800/1,900 = 3.58) x (1,900/1,178 = 1.61)
1999:   41.8% = (382.5/4,500 = 8.5%) x (4,500/1,300 = 3.46) x (1,300/805 = 1.61)

The financial leverage of Starlite has remained constant for the two years. While the
asset turnover increased slightly in 2000 from its 1999 level, it is clear from this analysis
that the biggest reason for this increase is the improved profit margin.

b.   g = ROE x retention rate = 52% x 0.75 = 39%.

CHAPTER FIVE: PRIMARY SECURITIES

I.   MULTIPLE CHOICE QUESTIONS

1.   Preferred stock differs from common stock in that

    a.   preferred stock dividends are legal obligations of the corporation; common stock dividends are not.

    b.   preferred stockholders have voting rights; common stockholders do not.

*   c.   preferred stockholders have a prior claim over common shareholders if a firm is liquidated.

    d.   common shareholders receive a fixed dividend whereas the preferred stock dividends will increase with the earnings of the firm.

    e.   Both "c" and "d" are true.

2.   Which of the following debt securities would you expect to offer the highest before-tax return?

*   a.   a debenture of a large corporation

    b.   a bond of a U.S. government agency

    c.   a revenue bond issued by a state to finance a turnpike

    d.   a general obligation bond

    e.   a Treasury bill

3.   Receipts for shares of foreign stock held in a trust are called

    a.   Eurodollar receipts

    b.   Yankee certificates of deposit

*   c.   American depository receipts

    d.   Bankers' acceptances

    e.   Fixed foreign share trusts

4.   A pre-emptive right

    a.   gives the holder of a debt security the right to sell the bond back to the issuer at a specified price.

    b.   gives the bond issuer the right to redeem the bond at a prespecified price prior to maturity.

    c.   gives creditors the right to sell property that has been pledged to secure a bond and use the funds from the sale to satisfy the debt's unpaid interest or principal.

    d.   gives the holder of preferred stock the right to exchange the preferred stock for shares of common stock.

*   e.   gives the owner of common stock the right to maintain his proportionate ownership in the firm.

5. Which of the following statements is *true* regarding money market securities?

    a. Money market securities have maturities of no more than six months.
    b. Money market securities trade in the over-the-counter market.
    c. Money market securities have maturities of no more than one year.
    d. Money market securities are not very actively traded.
*   e. Both "b" and "c" are true.

6. Commercial paper

    a. is used primarily to finance international trade.
    b. has maturities of one to two years.
    c. is secured by the assets of a commercial bank.
*   d. is short-term, unsecured debt of a large, creditworthy corporation.
    e. is both "a" and "b".

7. A revenue bond is

    a. a tax-exempt bond backed by the full faith and credit of the issuer.
    b. a bond issued by an agency of the federal government.
    c. riskier than a general obligation bond of the same issuer.
    d. a type of municipal bond, and therefore its interest payments are exempt from federal taxation.
*   e. Both "c" and "d" are characteristics associated with revenue bonds.

8. The U.S. Treasury recently sold a new, $10,000, 90-day Treasury bill at a discount of 5%. This means that an investor could have purchased the bill at a price

    a. of $9,500.
*   b. greater than $9,500.
    c. less than $9,500.
    d. of $10,500.
    e. of none of the above.

9. Jim purchased a 90-day, $10,000 Treasury bill for $9,685 and held it until it matured. His rate of return was

*   a. 3.25%.
    b. 3.15%.
    c. 8.13%.
    d. 2.93%.
    e. indeterminable with the information supplied.

10.   Which of the following is *not* a capital market security?

*   a.   commercial paper
        b.   common stock
        c.   preferred stock
        d.   a 30-year Treasury bond
        e.   All of the above are capital market securities.

11.   Tracking stock refers to

        a.   shares of stock in a mutual fund that track the S&P 500 Index.
*   b.   an equity security that is issued by a corporation and represents ownership
                in a division of the corporation only.
        c.   an issue of preferred stock that is convertible to shares of the common stock of the
                corporation.
        d.   an issue of preferred stock that is non-cumulative.
        e.   an issue of preferred stock that pays an adjustable rate dividend.

12.   Paul is in the 28% income tax bracket and is trying to decide between two investments:
        (a) a tax-exempt municipal bond that is yielding 8%, or (b) a similar-risk corporate bond
        that is yielding 11%. Paul should

        a.   invest in the corporate bond since he will earn a 15.3% after-tax return on it,
                compared to the 8% after-tax return on the municipal bond.
        b.   invest in the corporate bond since it offers the higher return for the same level of
                risk.
*   c.   invest in the municipal bond since its after-tax return is 8% while the
                corporate bond's after-tax return is only 7.92%.
        d.   invest in the corporate bond since its after-tax return is 7.92% compared with the
                5.76% after-tax return on the municipal bond.
        e.   invest in the corporate bond; only investors in the highest marginal tax brackets
                should consider investing in municipal bonds.

13.   Which of the following instruments is a *secured* debt instrument?

        a.   debenture
        b.   commercial paper
*   c.   repurchase agreement
        d.   general obligation bond
        e.   none of the above

14. A type of preferred stock that is re-issued with a new cash dividend rate on a very frequent basis is called

   a. participating preferred stock.
   b. cumulative preferred stock.
* c. money market preferred stock.
   d. callable preferred stock.
   e. convertible preferred stock.

15. The Calmark Corporation invested in an issue of preferred stock that pays an 8% dividend. If Calmark pays taxes at the marginal rate of 39%, its after-tax return on this investment is

   a. 4.88%.
   b. 13.11%.
   c. 5.60%.
* d. 7.93%.
   e. none of the above.

16. An arrangement in which firms make periodic repayments of principal to the trustees of a bond issue, who then use the funds to purchase outstanding bonds according to a set schedule, is referred to as a

* a. sinking fund.
   b. mortgage bond.
   c. convertible bond.
   d. collateral trust bond.
   e. debenture arrangement.

17. A corporation has 500,000 share outstanding. You own 500 shares. The firm has an eight-member board of directors and six director positions are up for election. If cumulative voting exists, you have

   a. 4,000 votes.
   b. 1,000 votes.
* c. 3,000 votes.
   d. 500 votes.
   e. none of the above.

36

18. Which of the following statements about zero-coupon bonds is (are) *true*?

   a. They can be issued only by the U.S. government or agencies of the U.S. government.
   b. They are considered to be money market instruments since they always sell at a discount from face value.
   c. The difference between the face value of the bond and the price paid for the bond is treated as capital gain income and may be taxed preferentially, depending on the current tax laws.
   d. The difference between the face value of the bond and the price paid for the bond is considered to be interest income, which is taxed when the bond matures.
   * e. The difference between the face value of the bond and the price paid for the bond is considered to be interest income, and the investor must pay tax on the implied interest income each year, even though no interest payment is received.

19. Which of the following statements regarding stock splits and stock dividends is (are) *true*?

   a. A stock dividend increases the return earned by the shareholder, but a stock split is merely an accounting change and does not affect returns.
   b. Stock splits and stock dividends affect only the aggregate value of the firm; per share values are unchanged.
   c. Stock splits and stock dividends affect the per share values of the firm, but the aggregate value of the firm remains unchanged.
   d. Neither stock splits nor stock dividends affect the returns earned by the shareholder; they are merely accounting changes.
   * e. Both "c" and "d" are true statements.

20. Which of the following instruments pays interest income that is exempt from federal income taxes?

   a. U.S. Treasury bills
   b. government agency debt
   * c. municipal bonds
   d. all of the above
   e. "a" and "c" only

II. SHORT ANSWER QUESTIONS

1. The Tremont Corporation has 1 milliion shares outstanding and sells for $33 a share. You own 500 shares.

   a. What is the current market value of your investment?

b.   Determine the new price per share, the new number of shares you will own, and the new market value of your investment if
(1) the firm declares a 3 for 1 split.
(2) the firm pays a 10% stock dividend.

2.   You own 200 shares of Up-for-Grabs Corporation. There are eleven members on the board of directors, seven of whom are up for re-election. How many votes can you cast for your favorite candidate, Mr. Fisch, if

a.   ordinary voting is used?
b.   cumulative voting is used?

3.   What does it mean to hold your securities in a "street name?" Discuss the advantages and disadvantages of doing so.

4.   "Preferred stock is a hybrid security." Discuss the meaning of this statement.

5.   Mary Nichols is a portfolio manager for a certain life insurance corporation. She is trying to decide on one of two investments: (a) a municipal bond that is yielding 9%, or (b) an issue of preferred stock that offers a dividend yield of 10%. Mary has assessed the risk of each of the alternatives and found them to be similar. Which one should she choose if her firm pays taxes at the marginal rate of 34%?

CHAPTER FIVE: SOLUTION GUIDELINES

Multiple Choice

1.   **c**:   Preferred shareholders have a prior claim over common shareholders if a firm is liquidated. Its dividends, however, are not legal obligations of the firm. Preferred shareholders cannot force a firm into bankruptcy if dividends are missed. Preferred shareholders typically have no voting rights and typically receive fixed dividend payments.

2.   **a**:   The higher the risk of an investment, the higher is the expected return. Bonds of government agencies, while not specifically guaranteed by the U.S. government, are considered fairly free of default risk. Likewise, a Treasury bill is considered default free. Revenue bonds and general obligation bonds pay interest that is free from federal taxation, and thus offer a lower return. Therefore, the debenture issued by a large corporation will offer the highest expected return.

3.   **c**:   This is the definition of an American depository receipt (ADR).

4.   **e**:   This is the definition of a pre-emptive right.

5.   **e**:   Money market securities have less than or equal to one year to maturity and are actively traded in the over-the-counter market.

6.   **b**:   This is the definition of commercial paper.

7.   **e**:   A revenue bond is a type of municipal bond that offers interest payments that are free from federal taxation. The revenue bond is backed by the proceeds of a particular project, and is not backed by the full faith and credit of the issuing government. It is, therefore, riskier than a general obligation bond of the same issuer, which *is* backed by the full faith and credit of the issuing government.

8.   **b**:   The price of the T-bill that is selling at a discount of 5% is $9,875. While this chapter does not provide students with the method for calculating the actual price, they should recognize that because money market calculations are based on a 360-day year, the price will be greater than $9,500. They should also be able to eliminate the price of $10,500 since T-bills sell at a discount from face value.

9.   **a**: $$r = \frac{P_1 - P_0}{P_0} = \frac{\$10,000 - \$9,685}{\$9,685} = 3.25\%.$$

10.   **a**:   Capital market instruments are those with greater than one year to maturity. By definition, commercial paper has less than one year to maturity (more specifically, they are issued with maturities from 5 days to 270 days) and is not a capital market instrument.

11.   **b**:   This is the definition of tracking stock.

12.   **c**:   Paul's after-tax return on the corporate bond is 11%(1 - 0.28) = 7.92%. Since he can earn 8% on the municipal bond, it is the better deal for him.

13.   **c**:   A debenture is long-term, unsecured debt while commercial paper is short-term, unsecured debt. A general obligation bond is a type of municipal bond that is backed by the taxing power of the issuing government, but is unsecured. The securities that are purchased in a repurchase agreement serve as collateral for the loan.

14.   **c**:   This is the definition of money market preferred stock.

15.   **d**:   Since Calmark receives a 70% dividend income exclusion, only (0.39)(0.30) = 11.7% of the 8% dividend it receives is taxed. 1 - (0.117)(0.08) = 99.064% of the 8% dividend can be kept by the company. (0.99064) x 8% = 7.925%.

16.   **a**:   This is the definition of a sinking fund.

17.   **c**:   The number of votes that a shareholder receives under cumulative voting is equal to the number of shares owned times the number of board seats up for election. 500 x 6 = 3,000 votes.

18.   **e**:   Zero coupon bonds are issued by corporations as well as the U.S. government and its agencies. They are capital market instruments since they have more than one year to maturity. The difference between the face value of the bond and the price paid for the bond is considered to be interest income, and the investor must pay taxes on the implied interest income each year, even though no interest payments are received.

19.   **e**:   Both stock splits and stock dividends affect the per share values, but not the aggregate value of the firm or the wealth of the investor. They are merely accounting changes.

20.   **c**:   Only municipal bonds pay interest that is exempt from federal taxation. Interest earned on Treasury bills or on the debt of government agencies is fully taxable at the federal level.

Short Answer

1a.   500 x $33 = $16,500

b.   (i) If Tremont declares a 3 for 1 split, you will own 3 times as many shares, or 1,500 shares. The new price per share will be $33/3 = $11, so the new market value of your investment is $11 x 1,500 = $16,500.

(ii) If the firm pays a 10% stock dividend, you will own 500(1.10) = 550 shares. The new price per share will be $33/1.10 = $30, and the new market value of your investment will be $30 x 550 = $16,500.

2a.   If ordinary voting is used 1 vote = 1 share, so you will have 200 votes.

b.   If cumulative voting is used, your number of votes equals the number of shares you own times the number of seats being elected, or 200 x 7 = 1,400 votes.

3.   Holding your securities in "street name" means that they are registered in the name of the brokerage rather than in your name. By doing so, you do not risk losing the securities or having them stolen, which is important if they are bearer, rather than registered, securities. You can sell your securities more easily; it requires only a phone call to your broker. If you take position of the securities, you must deliver them to the broker in order to sell them. Cash dividends and/or interest income can easily be swept into an interest-bearing account in your name at the brokerage firm, so you start earning interest immediately. Holding securities in street name also allows the brokerage firm to cut costs by reducing its paperwork.

On the other hand, it may take weeks (or months) to move your securities to another brokerage firm if they are held in street name. You will not be able to take advantage of the opportunity to buy commission-free securities directly from the firm through plans such as payroll deduction plans. You may find it more difficult to negotiate lower commissions from another broker. Too, if the investment is for a child, the child may benefit from being able to see and touch the securities he owns.

4.   Preferred stock is sometimes referred to as a hybrid securities because it has many of the characteristics of debt, even though it is an equity investment. Preferred stock generally pays a fixed dividend, which is similar to the fixed coupon paid on debt instruments, and may have call or convertible provisions, just as many debt issues have. Additionally, preferred stockholders, like debtholders, have priority over common stockholders with respect to earnings and also with respect to their claim on the assets of the firm in the event of bankruptcy. However, preferred stockholders have a lower priority claim than bondholders. Like common stockholders, they may have more control than bondholders, if they receive any voting rights.

5.   The life insurance company earns an after-tax return on the municipal bond of 9% since the income is exempt from federal taxation. Since the life insurance corporation can exclude 70% of its dividend income from taxation, only 30% is taxable. This means that 0.30 x 0.34 = 10.2% of the preferred stock yield of 10% must be given up to pay taxes. This leaves 1 - (0.102)(0.10) = 1 - 0.012 = 98.98% of the 10% yield, or 9.898%, for the insurance company. Since this is greater than the after-tax return on the municipal bond, Mary should choose the preferred stock investment.

CHAPTER SIX: THE GLOBAL STOCK MARKET

I.   TRUE-FALSE QUESTIONS

F   1.   The Securities and Exchange Commission (SEC) selects which stocks are to be listed on the New York Stock Exchange (NYSE).

F   2.   The over-the-counter (OTC) stock market is smaller than the New York Stock Exchange (NYSE).

T   3.   Nasdaq has a central computer that connects thousands of over-the-counter (OTC) brokers and dealers from all around the U.S. and makes them into one unfragmented market for securities.

F   4.   The stocks of no large or important companies are traded over-the-counter (OTC); the major firms are all listed on organized exchanges.

F   5.   A "margin call" occurs when the market price of a security that was purchased on credit rises so high that the initial margin is no longer sufficient to meet the maintenance margin requirement.

F   6.   The over-the-counter (OTC) market is located in Chicago, Illinois.

F   7.   An order-crossing network is a continuous, 24-hours-per-day, auction market.

T   8.   Instinet operates in the fourth market.

F   9.   SEC approval of a prospectus means that, at least initially, the security is a safe investment.

F   10.   Nasdaq is not as liquid a market as the New York Stock Exchange (NYSE) because it lacks spatial consolidation.

II.   MULTIPLE CHOICE QUESTIONS

1.   Which of the following is a voluntary organization of security dealers that performs a self-regulating function for the over-the-counter (OTC) market?

    a.   American Stock Exchange (AMEX)
    b.   Security Exchange Commission (SEC)
    c.   Security Investors Protection Corporation (SIPC)
    d.   National Quotation Bureau (NQB)
*   e.   National Association of Security Dealers (NASD)

2.   When an investor requests that a security be traded at the best possible price as soon as the order reaches the trading floor of the exchange, he is giving his broker a

*   a.   market order.
     b.   limit order.
     c.   stop loss order.
     d.   stop limit order.
     e.   good till cancelled order.

3.   Which of the following is usually designed to either protect a customer's existing profit or to reduce the amount of loss?

     a.   market order
     b.   limit order
*   c.   stop order
     d.   fill or kill order
     e.   short sale

4.   Which of the following functions is not performed by an investment banker?

     a.   advising clients
     b.   administrative work
     c.   risk-bearing
*   d.   collection of deposits
     e.   Neither c nor d is performed by an investment banker.

5.   The Securities Investor Protection Act

*   a.   established an insuring agency for brokerage firms.
     b.   required the registration of investment advisors.
     c.   required a registration statement for new securities.
     d.   provided for treble damages to be assessed against violators of securities laws.
     e.   Selections "a," "b," and "d" were all part of the Securities Investor Protection Act.

6.   Which of the following categories of assets is the most liquid?

     a.   corporate bonds
     b.   real estate
     c.   municipal bonds
     d.   NYSE-listed stocks
*   e.   U.S. Treasury bonds

7.   Individuals who own seats on the New York Stock Exchange (NYSE) and buy
      and sell securities for the clients of brokerage houses are termed

      a.   specialists.
      b.   block positioners.
      c.   investment bankers.
*   d.   floor brokers.
      e.   registered representatives.

8.   Which of the following is an example of a transaction that would take place in the
      primary market?

      a.   A broker buys 100 shares of Spiegel stock in the over-the-counter market for a
            client.
      b.   A broker buys 100 shares of Hasbro stock, trading on the American Stock
            Exchange, for a client.
      c.   An investor buys a 90-day Treasury bill that has one month remaining to maturity.
*   d.   Pacific Bell sells a new issue of 7 3/8% debentures that mature in 2043.
      e.   Both "c" and "d" are primary market transactions.

9.   The Intermarket Trading System (ITS) is

      a.   a computerized system that allows American investors to invest in foreign
            securities and foreign investors to invest in American securities.
*   b.   an electronic trading network that links the various U.S. markets in order to
            facilitate trading between them.
      c.   the term given to the largest, most actively traded securities in the NASDAQ
            system.
      d.   a unified European capital market created by the European Economic
            Community.
      e.   none of the above.

10.   Which of the following types of orders has the advantage of guaranteed
      execution?

      a.   limit order
*   b.   market order
      c.   stop loss order
      d.   stop limit order
      e.   fill or kill order

11.   The minimum initial margin requirement is set by

*   a.   the Board of Governors of the Federal Reserve.
        b.   the firms listed on the NYSE.
        c.   the president and vice-president of the NYSE.
        d.   the National Association of Security Dealers (NASD)
        e   the Security Investors Protection Corporation (SIPC)

12.   Which of the following is *not* an advantage associated with an order-crossing network?

        a.   A trader's variable trading costs may be reduced to zero.
        b.   Impact costs are minimized.
*   c.   Continuous liquidity is provided.
        d.   Buyers and sellers remain anonymous.
        e.   All of the above are advantages associated with an order-crossing network.

13.   Which of the following is (are) *not* a characteristic of a call market?

        a.   A verbal auction can be used for more actively traded issue and a written auction
                for less active issues.
        b.   An auction for every stock listed may be held just once a day.
        c.   Timing costs are minimized.
        d.   Anonymity is guaranteed.
*   e.   Neither "c" nor "d" is a characteristic associated with a call market.

14.   Optimark is an example of a(n)

        a.   call market.
        b.   organized exchange in the U.S.
        c.   organized exchange in Sweden.
*   d.   order-crossing network.
        e.   regulatory agency for the over-the-counter market.

15.   Steve called his broker and placed an order to purchase 10,000 shares of Quality
        Semiconductor, Inc.(QSI), a small firm which sells on Nasdaq. The order caused
        the price of QSI to increase significantly prior to the execution of Steve's order.
        This is an example of a(n)

        a.   opportunity cost.
        b.   timing cost.
*   c.   impact cost.
        d.   commission cost.
        e.   agency cost.

16. Ms. Chang called her broker and placed an order to sell some shares of Truex Corporation, an over-the-counter stock with very low trading activity. Two weeks passed before a dealer was found who agreed to buy the shares. This is an example of a(n)

    a.   impact cost.
*   b.   timing cost.
    c.   opportunity cost.
    d.   commission cost.
    e.   agency cost.

17. Trudy purchased 100 shares of IBM on margin when the stock was selling for $160 a share. The initial margin requirement was 55% and the maintenance margin was 35%. If IBM subsequently fell to $142 a share, Trudy will get

    a.   a margin call for $1,800.
    b.   a margin call for $4,970.
    c.   a margin call for $2,790.
    d.   a margin call for $3,830.
*   e.   no margin call.

18. Phillip has purchased some shares of Texaco for $80 a share. He is confident that the stock will do well and is looking forward to enjoying huge capital gains from this investment, but he would like to limit his losses if he is wrong. To do so, Phillip can enter a

    a.   stop loss buy order at $75.
    b.   limit order to sell at $82.
    c.   market order to sell.
*   d.   stop loss sell order at $75.
    e.   stop loss sell order at $82.

19. Jean is interested in purchasing 300 shares of a stock that is currently selling for $23 a share. The initial margin requirement is 55% and the maintenance margin requirement is 35%. How much cash does Jean need to have to make this investment?

    a. $3,105
*   b. $3,795
    c. $2,415
    d. $4,485
    e.   none of the above

20.   Paul owns some shares of Frontier Airlines, which he purchased when the stock
       was selling for $3.50 a share. The stock price rose to $9.50 a share, and
       Paul wanted to protect his profits in case the stock took a nose dive. He entered a
       stop loss sell order at $8.88. That same day, the stock dropped to $8.50 at one
       point, but ended up closing at $9. Paul ended up

*   a.   selling his shares; when the price dropped to $8.88 (or lower), the order became a
             market order and was executed at the next available price.
       b.   still owning his shares since the stock closed at $9.
       c.   selling his shares for a price of $8.88 or better.
       d.   selling his shares for a price of $8.50.
       e.   still owning his shares since the price dropped below $8.88; his order was passed
             over and never executed.

III.   SHORT ANSWER QUESTIONS

1.   Mr. Chen purchased 500 shares of Hasbro stock when it was selling for $30 a
       share, using all the available margin. The initial margin requirement was 60%.
       By the end of the year, Hasbro's price had increased to $38 a share, and Mr. Chen
       received a $0.32 a share dividend. The interest rate on the borrowed funds was
       8%. What was Mr. Chen's rate of return on this investment?

2.   Cheryl purchased 200 shares of a stock that was selling for $80 a share, using all
       the available margin. The initial margin requirement was 50%, and the
       maintenance margin requirement was 30%. To what price can the stock drop
       before there is a margin call?

3.   Camille purchased 1,000 shares of Vintage Petroleum (VPI) at $18 a share, using all the
       available margin. The initial margin requirement was 55%, and the maintenance margin
       requirement was 30%. Subsequently, the price of the stock fell to $14. Will there be a
       margin call? If so, for how much?

4.   What is a stop loss order? What are the advantages and disadvantages associated with
       this type order?

5.   An investment banking firm agreed to underwrite an IPO for Fledgling Corporation. It
       was determined that the shares would be offered to the public at an initial price of $22,
       and that the underwriting spread would be 12%. As it turned out, one and a half million
       shares were sold at a price of $25. The investment banker incurred $650,000 in
       administrative expenses associated with the issue.
       a.   What were Fledgling's proceeds from the IPO?
       b.   Calculate the investment banker's gain or loss.

CHAPTER SIX: SOLUTION GUIDELINES

True-False

1.   **False:** Firms may apply for listing on the NYSE and will be listed if they meet the listing requirements of the exchange.

2.   **False:** The over-the-counter market has a greater number of issues than the NYSE. Some NYSE-listed stocks are also traded in the over-the-counter market in what is known as the third market. All government bonds, and most corporate bonds also trade in the over-the-counter market.

3.   **True:** Nasdaq is a computerized network of geographically dispersed dealers.

4.   **False:** Even some firms that can meet the listing requirements of the NYSE choose to be traded only in the over-the-counter market.

5.   **False:** A margin call occurs when the price of a security that was purchased on credit drops so that the ratio of the equity position of the trader to the total value of the portfolio drops below the maintenance margin requirement.

6.   **False:** The over-the-counter market has no central location; it is a network of geographically dispersed dealers.

7.   **False:** An order-crossing network is an electronic communication network (ECN) that matches buy and sell orders off the floor of a securities exchange. They are not continuous, 24-hours-per-day, auction markets, and sometimes such a network is not available when needed.

8.   **True:** Instinet uses telephone lines to connect over 5,000 subscribers' computer terminals around the world, who negotiate securities trades between themselves.

9.   **False:** SEC approval means only that enough information has been provided for a rational investor to judge the quality of the issue for herself.

10.   **False:** Nasdaq is every bit as liquid as the NYSE. It does not lack spatial consolidation, but provides a different type than that offered by the NYSE. Nasdaq links geographically dispersed dealers together in a single market-making computer system. This maximizes the competition between market-makers.

Multiple Choice

1.   **e:**   Although the SEC regulates the over-the-counter market as well, the NASD is the self-regulatory agency for the over-the-counter market.

2.   **a:**   This is the definition of a market order.

3.   **c:**   A stop loss sell order is placed below the current market price to protect the customer's existing profit on a long position or to reduce the amount of loss that a customer may experience. A stop loss buy order is placed to limit losses or protect profits on a short position in the stock. Market orders are orders to buy or sell at the prevailing price. Limit orders are placed above the current market price in hopes of selling at a favorable price, or below the current market price in hopes of buying at a favorable price. A fill or kill order is an order for immediate execution and does not protect profits. A short sale is the sale of borrowed stock.

4.   **d:**   An investment banker advises firms on the type of security to issue, the timing of the issue, and other such matters. The investment banker also does the necessary paperwork to register the security with the SEC, and in a firm commitment underwriting agreement, purchases the securities from the issuing firm, thus bearing the risk if the issue does not sell at the offer price. Investment bankers do not have anything to do with deposits.

5.   **a:**   The Securities Investor Protection Act established the SIPC, which indemnifies investors against losses that they might incur if their brokerage firm goes bankrupt.

6.   **e:**   Issues of the U.S. Treasury are more liquid than any other type of asset.

7.   **d:**   This is the definition of a floor broker.

8.   **d:**   Primary market transactions refer to the sale of new securities. Securities selling on exchanges are secondary market transactions, and a 3-month Treasury bill that has one month remaining to maturity is obviously not a new issue.

9.   **b:**   This is the definition of the Intermarket Trading System (ITS).

10.   **b:**   A market order will be executed at the prevailing price. Limit orders, stop loss orders, and stop limit orders may never be executed if the specified price is not reached. A fill or kill order will not be executed if it can not be executed immediately.

11.   **a:**   The Board of Governors of the Federal Reserve sets the minimum initial margin requirement.

12.   **c:**   An order-crossing network is an ECN that matches buy and sell orders off the floor of a securities exchange. Impact costs are minimized when publicly unidentified buyers and sellers who are compatible turn up in the crossing network at the same time. Traders may pay a fixed annual cost, making their variable costs zero. However, order-crossing networks are not continuous, 24-hour-a-day auction markets.

13.   **e:**   A call market is one in which buy and sell orders for a particular stock are batched for simultaneous execution at a single price when an auction for that stock is called.

Therefore, timing costs can be high. Buyers and sellers do not remain unidentified, so anonymity is not guaranteed.

14.   **d:**   Optimark, headquartered in Durango, Colorado, is an electronic order-crossing system that has a crossing for every stock in the system every 90 seconds.

15.   **c:**   Impact costs are the costs associated with disadvantageous market movements that are associated with the presentation of the order to the market.

16.   **b:**   Timing costs refer to the costs associated with the movement of the market price between the time that the order is entered and when it actually gets executed.

17.   **e:**   The total value of the portfolio is 100($160) = $16,000. Since the initial margin requirement is 55%, Trudy will have to deposit a margin of 0.55($16,000) = $8,800. If IBM drops to $142 a share, the portfolio and Trudy's margin drops by $1,800 ($18 x 100 = $1,800). This reduces the margin to 49%.

$$\frac{\$8,800 - \$1,800}{\$16,000 - \$1,800} = 49\%$$

Since this is greater than the maintenance margin of 35%, there will be no margin call.

18.   **d:**   If Texaco falls to $75 a share, the stop loss sell order will become a market order, and Phillip's shares will be sold at the prevailing price, which will be close to $75 a share, limiting his losses to around $5 a share. A limit order to sell at $82 would never be executed if Texaco's stock price drops; nor would a stop loss sell order for $82. The market order to sell would be executed immediately at the prevailing price.

19.   **b:**   The total value of Jean's stock is 300 x $23 = $6,900. She must deposit 55% of that as an initial margin, so she will need 0.55($6,900) = $3,795.

20.   **a:**   When a stop loss sale order has been placed and the stock price drops to the price specified on the order, the order becomes a market order and is executed at the prevailing price. Since the price of Frontier Airlines dropped below $8.88, it would have become a market order, and Paul's shares would have been sold.

Short Answer

1.   The total value of the Hasbro stock was $30(500) = $15,000. Mr. Chen was required to make an initial investment of $15,000(0.6) = $9,000. Therefore, he borrowed $15,000 - $9,000 = $6,000. The interest on these funds was 0.08($6,000) = $480. Mr. Chen's profit was 500($38) - 500($30) + 500($0.32) - $480 = $3,680 on his investment of $9,000. This is a return of $3,680/$9,000 = 40.9%.

2.   The total value of Cheryl's purchase is $80(200) = $16,000. Cheryl had to deposit 0.50($16,000) = $8,000 to meet the initial margin requirement. The maintenance margin requirement is 30%, therefore, we can determine the amount per share that her stock can drop before there is a margin call by solving the following:

$$\frac{\$8,000 - 200P}{\$16,000 - 200P} = 0.30$$

$$\$4,800 - 60P = \$8,000 - 200P$$

$$\$140P = \$3,200$$

$$P = \$22.86 \text{ a share drop}$$

Therefore, the stock price can drop to $80 - $22.86 = $57.14 per share before there will be a margin call.

3.   Camille's initial margin requirement is 0.55($18,000) = $9,900. If the stock price drops to $14, she has lost $4,000 a share. Her new equity position is

$$\frac{\$9,900 - \$4,000}{\$18,000 - \$4,000} = \frac{\$5,900}{\$14,000} = 42.1\%$$

Since this is greater than the maintenance margin requirement of 30%, there will be no margin call.

4.   A stop loss order is an order to buy or sell that becomes a market order when the specified price on the order is reached. The specified price is less than the current market price on a stop loss sell order and greater than the current market price on a stop loss buy order. Thus, an investor with a long position in a stock can enter a stop loss sell order and limit his losses while an investor with a short position in a stock can enter a stock loss buy order to limit his losses. However, because the order becomes a market order when the specified price is reached, an investor may sell (buy) a stock when the dip (rise) in the price is only temporary, in which case the investor may have wished to maintain his position in the stock.

5a.   Since the underwriting spread was 12%, Fledgling would receive (0.88)($22)(1,500,000) = $29,040,000 from the sale of the stock.

b.   The investment banker received $25(1,500,000) = $37,500,000 from the sale. It paid Fledgling $29,040,000 for the shares and incurred $650,000 in administrative expenses, so its net gain was $37,500,000 - $29,040,000 - $650,000 = $7,810,000.

CHAPTER SEVEN: STATISTICAL ANALYSIS AND THE SML

I.   MULTIPLE CHOICE QUESTIONS

1.   The variability of return that an investor experiences due to inflation is referred to as

      a.   interest rate risk.
      b.   market risk.
*   c.   purchasing power risk.
      d.   liquidity risk.
      e.   domestic political risk.

2.   The risk that arises from alternating bull and bear markets is referred to as

      a.   interest rate risk.
*   b.   market risk.
      c.   purchasing power risk.
      d.   liquidity risk.
      e.   domestic political risk.

3.   Which of the following is a measure of *undiversifiable* risk?

      a.   coefficient of variation
      b.   standard deviation
      c.   variance
*   d.   beta
      e.   skewness

4.   Which of the following statements regarding the analysis of a security's return is *true*?

      a.   The analyst will obtain the same results regardless of whether he uses annual rates of return or monthly rates of return, so long as they both cover the same time period.
      b.   The analyst should be careful to break the investment horizon into a series of consecutive, but overlapping, sub-periods for which the rates of return are computed.
      c.   A three-year time period is usually a sufficient amount of time over which to examine the returns of a security.
*   d.   Ideally, a representative sample period should include both bull and bear market conditions.
      e.   Selections "c" and "d" are both true statements.

5.	The stock of Static Corporation has a beta of 0.7. If the return on the market is expected to increase 15%, the expected return on Static Corporation should increase

*	a.	10.5%.
	b.	7.0%.
	c.	8.0%.
	d.	indeterminable without knowing the risk-free rate.
	e.	none of the above.

6.	Dominant assets have which one of the following characteristics?

	a.	the highest rate of return
	b.	the lowest risk
*	c.	the highest rate of return for their level of risk
	d.	the lowest beta
	e.	none of the above

7.	Which of the following best defines the *total risk* of an investment?

	a.	negative skewness in the returns--i.e., returns that are distributed asymmetrically so that there is more probability of a return that is below the expected return than there is of getting a return that is above the expected return
*	b.	the variability of the single period rates of return
	c.	a wide range between the best possible return and the worse possible return
	d.	the cumulative probability attached to all possible returns that are negative
	e.	the investment's beta

8.	Which of the following portfolios is undesirable because it is a dominated investment?

	Portfolio	Expected return	Standard deviation
* a.	W	12%	20%
b.	X	5%	7%
c.	Y	15%	36%
d.	Z	12%	15%

	e.	All of the above portfolios are equally desirable, depending on the individual investor's risk-return trade-off.

The following information is supplied for the Hindle Corporation, referred to in Questions 9 and 10:

Probability of return	Return
0.50	10%
0.30	15%
0.20	20%

9.   Based on the above probability distribution, the expected return for the Hindle
       Corporation is

    a.   5.1%.
    b.   4.5%.
    c.   10.5%.
    d.   15.5%.
*   e.   13.5%

10.   Based on the above probability distribution, the standard deviation of the possible returns
       for the Hindle Corporation is

    a.   10.1%
    b.   4.2%.
    c.   17.3%.
*   d.   3.9%.
    e.   0%.

11.   Which of the following is an example of market risk?

*   a.   the risk that the economy will enter a recession
    b.   the risk that a certain airline company will file for bankruptcy
    c..   the risk that a company will win a lawsuit it has filed against a competitor for
        patent violations
    d.   the risk that there will be a war in the country that produces the majority of the
        raw materials needed to produce a certain industry's product
    e.   "b," "c," and "d" only

The following information is supplied for Questions 12, 13, 14, 15, 16, and 17:

Probability	Return on Security A	Return on the S&P 500 Index
0.3	12%	14%
0.6	10%	15%
0.1	-5%	6%

12.   The expected returns on Security A and the S&P 500 Index are

*   a.   9.1% and 13.8% respectively.
    b.   9.0% and 11.7% respectively.
    c.   5.7% and 11.7% respectively.
    d.   10.1% and 13.8% respectively.
    e.   none of the above.

13. The standard deviations of the returns on Security A and the S&P 500 Index are

       a.   23.9% and 7.0% respectively.
*   b.   4.8% and 2.6% respectively.
       c.   3.7% and 7.0% respectively.
       d.   1.9% and 2.6% respectively.
       e.   none of the above.

14. The covariance of the returns on Security A and the S&P 500 Index is

*   a.   0.0012.
       b.   0.0118.
       c.   0.0004.
       d.   0.
       e.   0.1218.

15. The beta of Security A is

       a.   0.05.
       b.   0.02.
       c.   0.50.
*   d.   1.78.
       e.   0.56.

16. The correlation coefficient for the returns of Security A and the S&P 500 Index is

       a.   0.
*   b.   0.9615.
       c.   0.1062.
       d.   0.0012.
       e.   none of the above.

17. How much of the variance in Security A's return is explained by simultaneous market movements?

       a.   94.19%
       b.   12.00%
*   c.   92.45%
       d.   100.0%
       e.   none of the above

18. The returns of which of the following pairs of companies would you expect to have the lowest covariance?

    a. United Airlines and American Airlines
    b. United Airlines and Hilton
    c. Ford Motor Company and General Motors
    d. Sherwin Williams and Home Depot
 * e. Abbott Laboratories and Disney

19. Rank the following four securities according to their level of systematic risk, with the *least* risky security listed first:

	Expected return	Standard deviation	Beta
Security A	13.2%	3.4%	0.8
Security B	18.6%	6.8%	1.4
Security C	15.0%	7.0%	1.0
Security D	14.1%	5.8%	0.9

 * a. A, D, C, B
    b. A, D, B, C
    c. D, A, B, C
    d. C, B, A, D
    e. B, C, D, A

20. Which of the following statements regarding the skewness statistic is correct?

    a. Because most investments have asymmetric probability distributions, ignoring the skew statistic in investment decision-making is a grievous error.
    b. The dominance principle fully incorporates the concept of skewness.
 * c. Since most investments have symmetric probability distributions, the skewness statistic contains no valuable information.
    d. Both "a" and "b" are correct statements.
    e. None of the above statements are correct.

II. SHORT ANSWER QUESTIONS

1. John had obtained a beta value for a particular stock from *Value Line Investment Survey*. He was surprised to note, however, that when he looked up that same stock's beta value on an internet source, it was similar, but different. How would you explain this difference to John?

2.   The following probability distribution was estimated for the stock of Amor Corporation:

Probability	Return
0.2	5%
0.7	10%
0.1	18%

a.   Calculate the expected return for Amor.
b.   Calculate the standard deviation, the second moment, of Amor's returns.
c.   Calculate the skew, the third moment, for Amor's probability distribution.

3.   The returns on Security J and Security M are expected to have the following probability distributions:

Probability	Return on J	Return on M
0.5	15%	10%
0.3	10%	12%
0.2	18%	14%

a.   Calculate the expected return for each security.
b.   Calculate the standard deviation of the returns for each security.
c.   Calculate the covariance of the returns on the two securities.
d.   Calculate the correlation coefficient of the returns on the securities.
e.   If the return on Security J increases, how safe would you feel in predicting that the return on Security M will also increase, based solely on the movement of Security J?

4.   The statistical concept of skewness is ignored in the dominance principle, which focuses only on the statistical measures of expected return and variance (or standard deviation). In doing so, isn't a piece of valuable information being discarded? Explain.

5.   The conditional expectation for the returns of security i is presented as
$E(r_i | r_m, \alpha, b) = \alpha_i + b_i r_m$. Explain the meaning of the α_i and b_i terms.

CHAPTER SEVEN: SOLUTION GUIDELINES

Multiple Choice

1. **c**: This is the definition of purchasing power risk.

2. **b**: This is the definition of market risk.

3. **d**: Undiversifiable risk is the systematic risk, which is measured by beta. All of the other statistics measure total risk.

4. **d**: Ideally, the sample period should include both bull and bear markets. Smaller sample periods are likely to result in unacceptably large sampling errors. Three years is probably too small a sampling period since the average business cycle is seven years. The time intervals should not be overlapping if the analyst wishes to obtain statistically independent rates of return. Different results will be obtained depending on the subperiods used.

5. **a**: The beta of Static Corporation of 0.7 means that if the market increases by a certain percentage, the expected return on Static will increase by 0.7 times that percentage. $(0.7)(15\%) = 10.5\%$.

6. **c**: This is the definition of a dominant asset.

7. **b**: The total risk of an investment is measured by the variability of the single period rates of return.

8. **a**: Portfolio W has the same expected return as Portfolio Z but a higher level of risk, as measured by the standard deviation. Therefore, Portfolio Z dominates Portfolio W.

9. **e**: $E(r_{Hindle}) = 0.50(10\%) + 0.30(15\%) + 0.20(20\%) = 13.5\%$.

10. **d**:
$$\sigma_{Hindle} = \sqrt{(0.5(10 - 13.5)^2 + 0.3(15 - 13.5)^2 + 0.2(20 - 13.5)^2} = 3.9\%.$$

11. **a**: Market risk is a risk that affects all firms to one degree or another.

12. **a**: $E(r_A) = 0.3(12\%) + 0.6(10\%) + 0.1(-5\%) = 9.1\%$.
$E(r_{S\&P}) = 0.3(14\%) + 0.6(15\%) + 0.1(6\%) = 13.8\%$.

13. **b**:
$$\sigma_A = \sqrt{0.3(12\% - 9.1\%)^2 + 0.6(10\% - 9.1\%)^2 + 0.1(-5\% - 9.1\%)^2} = 4.8\%.$$
$$\sigma_{S\&P} = \sqrt{0.3(14\% - 13.8\%)^2 + 0.6(15\% - 13.8\%)^2 + 0.1(6\% - 13.8\%)^2} = 2.6\%.$$

14. **a**: $COV(A, S\&P) = 0.3(0.12 - 0.091)(0.14 - 0.138) +$
$0.6(0.10 - 0.091)(0.15 - 0.138) + 0.1(-0.05 - 0.091)(0.06 - 0.138) = 0.0012.$

15. **d**: $\beta = \dfrac{COV(A, S\&P)}{VAR(S\&P)} = \dfrac{0.0012}{(0.026)^2} = 1.78.$

16. **b**: $\rho = \dfrac{COV(A, S\&P)}{\sigma_A \sigma_{S\&P}} = \dfrac{0.0012}{(0.048)(0.026)} = 0.9615.$

17. **c**: $\rho^2 = (0.9615)^2 = 0.9245 = 92.45\%.$

18. **e**: Firms that are in the same industry or in related industries are more likely to have returns that move together.

19. **a**: Beta is the measure of systematic risk. Security A has the lowest beta and Security B the highest.

20. **c**: The dominance principle does not incorporate the concept of skewness; however, since most investments have symmetric probability distributions, the skewness statistic does not provide any valuable information.

Short Answer

1. Different financial services firms may use different data when determining the beta of a firm. They may use different lengths of time, for example. Even if the same length of time is used, they may use different subperiods (i.e., monthly data versus quarterly data). They may also use different proxies for the market portfolio. Some may use the S&P 500 Index, others the NYSE Composite Index, and still others the Wilshire 5000 Equity Index. Some financial services firms report the historical beta while others adjust the beta that is determined using the historical information. Any of these differences will produce different results.

2a. $E(r_{AMOR}) = 0.2(5\%) + 0.7(10\%) + 0.1(18\%) = 9.8\%.$

b.
$\sigma_{AMOR} = \sqrt{0.2(5\% - 9.8\%)^2 + 0.7(10\% - 9.8\%)^2 + 0.1(18\% - 9.8\%)^2} = \sqrt{11.36} = 3.37\%.$

c. $SKEW(r_{AMOR}) = 0.2(5 - 9.8)^3 + 0.7(10 - 9.8)^3 + 0.1(18 - 9.8)^3 = 33.024$

3a. $E(r_J) = 0.5(15\%) + 0.3(10\%) + 0.2(18\%) = 14.1\%.$
$E(r_M) = 0.5(10\%) + 0.3(12\%) + 0.2(14\%) = 11.4\%.$

b.

$$\sigma_J = \sqrt{0.5(15\% - 14.1\%)^2 + 0.3(10\% - 14.1\%)^2 + 0.2(18\% - 14.1\%)^2} = \sqrt{8.49} = 2.91\%.$$

$$\sigma_M = \sqrt{0.5(10\% - 11.4\%)^2 + 0.3(12\% - 11.4\%)^2 + 0.2(14\% - 11.4\%)^2} = \sqrt{2.44} = 1.56\%.$$

c.   COV(J, M) = 0.5(15 - 14.1)(10 - 11.4) + 0.3(10 - 14.1)(12 - 11.4) + 0.2(18 - 14.1)(14 - 11.4) = 0.66

d. $$\rho = \frac{0.66}{(2.91)(1.56)} = 0.145.$$

e.   You should not feel very secure. The correlation of the returns of the two securities is, albeit positive, very weak. In fact, it is very close to zero. in which case observing the movement of the returns on Security J would give you no information about the movement of the returns on Security M.

4.   This would be the case if the probability distributions for investment returns were asymmetric (skewed); however most investments have returns that are symmetric. Therefore, no valuable information is being discarded.

5.   The alpha value, α_i, is the y-intercept of the characteristic line; it is the point at which the line intersects the y-axis. It is also an estimate of the ith asset's rate of return when the market is stationary--$r_{M,t} = 0$. The b_i term is the beta coefficient, which measures the systematic, or undiversifiable, risk of the asset. It is an indicator of how closely the securities returns move with the market.

CHAPTER EIGHT: EFFICIENT CAPITAL MARKETS AND ANOMALIES

I.   MULTIPLE CHOICE QUESTIONS

1.   Which of the following statements about the weekend effect is *true*?

       a.   Proponents of the weekend effect would buy a security on Friday and sell it during the first hour of trading on the following Monday.

       b.   The weekend effect appears to occur only in the U.S. stock markets; there is no support for its existence in the stock markets of other countries.

       c.   Lawrence Fisher's study of the weekend effect indicated that by the end of the day, Monday's trading resembles that of the other four days of the week.

       d.   Proponents of the weekend effect might choose to buy a security during the first hour of trading on Monday.

*   e.   Both "c" and "d" are true statements.

2.   Which of the following anomalies violates the weakly efficient markets hypothesis?

       a.   the size effect

*   b.   the January effect

       c.   the stock split effect

       d.   the insider effect

       e.   None of the above violate the weakly efficient markets hypothesis.

3.   The semi-strong form efficient markets hypothesis implies that

       a.   investors can expect securities to be fairly priced according to their risk most of the time.

       b.   an investor will never earn an abnormal return on his investment if he is only privy to publicly available information.

       c.   investors can expect new information about a firm to be rapidly reflected in its stock price.

       d.   only those with insider information should invest in the stock market.

*   e.   Both "a" and "c" are implications of the semi-strong form efficient markets hypothesis.

4.   Which of the following is (are) *consistent* with the concept of semi-strong efficient markets?

     a.   Mr. E. Wave plots the past prices of stocks and uses the charts to decide when to buy and sell his stock. He claims that by using this method, he always earns abnormal profits.
     b.   Ms. S. Tracker believes that if she buys the stock of firms that she reads have announced stock splits, she can earn abnormal profits.
     c.   Mr. R. Gym, a New York cab driver, overhears two of his fares talking about a takeover attempt that their firm plans to initiate on another firm. Mr. Gym calls his broker and buys shares of the planned target and earns an abnormal profit on his investment.
     d.   Ms. R. Ketchum decides to invest in some bonds of an airline that has filed for bankruptcy since the bonds are offering an extremely high yield due to the high risk involved. Fortunately for Ms. Ketchum, the airline overcomes its financial difficulties and the bond payments are made as scheduled, so Ms. Ketchum enjoys a high return on her investment.
*   e.   Both "c" and "d" are consistent with the concept of semi-strong form efficient markets.

5.   According to the empirical studies, which of the following seems to violate the semi-strong efficient markets hypothesis?

     a.   Most mutual funds do not outperform the S&P 500 Index on a risk-adjusted basis.
*   b.   Small stocks, on average, earn returns that are greater than their risk level would justify.
     c.   On average, investors who invest in the stock of a firm on the day it announces a stock split can not expect to earn abnormal returns.
     d.   Investors with inside information tend to earn abnormal returns on their investments.
     e.   Both "b" and "d" violate the semi-strong form efficient markets hypothesis.

6.   Statistically measuring a security's serial correlation should detect which of the following patterns in security prices?

     a.   head and shoulders
     b.   trends
     c.   reversals
*   d.   both "b" and "c"
     e.   all of the above

7. If securities markets are semi-strong efficient, which of the following activities would *not* be profitable to perform?

    a.   charting prices

    b.   buying common stocks when a stock dividend or a stock split is announced.

    c.   studying Moody's or Standard and Poor's to get hot tips.

    d.   using a filter rule to decide when the best time to buy or sell a security is

*   e.   None of the above would prove to be profitable endeavors if the markets are semi-strong efficient.

8. Which of the following statements correctly describes conditions in a market that is strongly (or perfectly) efficient?

    a.   Only a few technical analysis tools would provide valuable insights.

    b.   No one could earn trading profits in excess of the return from a naïve buy-and-hold strategy, except for an occasional lucky fool.

    c.   Stock prices would always equal their true economic values as they fluctuate randomly together.

*   d.   Both "b" and "c" describe conditions that would exist in a perfectly efficient market.

    e.   All of the above describe conditions that would exist in a perfectly efficient market.

9. Which of the following statements is *true* regarding value managers and growth managers?

    a.   Value managers look to buy stocks that are currently enjoying high growth rates in earnings and are expected to continue to have high earnings growth.

*   b.   Value investors tend to outperform growth investors.

    c.   Value managers tend to invest in stocks issued by corporations that have high earnings growth, low current yields and high P/E ratios.

    d.   Both "b" and "c" are true statements.

    e.   All of the above are true statements.

10. If security markets in the U.S. were all strongly (or perfectly) efficient, which of the following would be true?

    a.   It would be easy for unethical traders to manipulate securities' prices.

*   b.   The markets must also be both weakly and semi-strong efficient if they are perfectly efficient.

    c.   Playing the market would be both fun and profitable for many.

    d.   Some profitable patterns could be detected in graphs of stock price movements.

    e.   All of the above statements would be true if securities markets were strongly efficient.

11. Anomalous evidence that violates the weakly efficient markets hypothesis includes which of the following?

    a.   the weekend effect
    b.   the holiday effect
    c.   the January effect
*   d.   all of the above
    e.   "a" and "c" only

12. Evidence exists that security rates of return are statistically independent if which of the following statements are true?

*   a.   Serial correlations are zero.
    b.   Runs of all signs are zero.
    c.   Filter rules earn zero returns.
    d.   The returns are distributed according to a normal probability distribution.
    e.   All of the above.

13. Stock splits can best be described by which of the following statements?

    a.   an accounting change that does not change the price per share or the value of the stock
    b.   a good way to guarantee that the price will increase after the split is announced
*   c.   the economic equivalent of a stock dividend
    d.   all of the above
    e.   "a" and "c" only

14. The results of event studies have indicated that unusually large returns can be earned, even after considering transactions and other costs, by

    a.   buying a stock when the firm has announced an increase in its dividend per share.
    b.   buying stocks that have high earnings growth rates that are expected to continue in the future.
    c.   buying a stock once it has hit a low and has rebounded by at least 1%.
*   d.   buying the stock of a firm that has a low market capitalization.
    e.   None of the above will result in unusually large returns once transactions and other costs are considered.

15. Studies of mutual fund performance have indicated that

    a.   larger funds perform better than smaller funds.
*   b.   load funds perform slightly worse than no-load funds.
    c.   most actively managed mutual funds tend to earn higher returns than passively managed index funds.
    d.   the best performing funds are also those that charge the highest management fees.
    e.   none of the above.

16.   A study on insider trading by Jeffrey Jaffe concluded that

      a.   insiders who have the shortest holding periods earn the highest returns.

      b.   outsiders who conduct trades based on the information supplied in the SEC's *Official Summary of Insider Transactions* can earn the same high returns as insiders.

*   c.   average insider's gains are maximized if the insider has a holding period of about eight months.

      d.   the greater the plurality of insiders who bought or sold, the greater the returns that were earned.

      e.   All of the above are conclusions reached by Jaffe.

17.   In order for a test of any of the efficient markets hypotheses to conclude that investors can earn abnormally high returns by using a particular strategy, the test should incorporate

      a.   commission costs.
      b.   taxes.
      c.   dividends.
      d.   the risk level of the investment.

*   e.   all of the above.

18.   Which of the following would be used to test the weakly efficient markets hypothesis?

      a.   runs test
      b.   filter rule test
      c.   event studies
      d.   all of the above

*   e.   "a" and "b" only

19.   If markets are at least semi-strong form efficient,

      a.   investors should passively manage their portfolios to minimize transactions costs.

      b.   the only way for an investor to increase his return is to accept higher levels of systematic risk.

      c.   technical analysis is a waste of time.

*   d.   all of the above

      e.   "a" and "b" only

20. In which of the following stocks would a growth manager be most likely to invest?

	Cash dividend yield	Earnings growth rate	Price-earnings ratio	Beta
I.	0%	20%	80X	1.98
II.	0.5%	18%	121X	2.50
III.	8.0%	10%	20X	0.62

    a.   I only.
    b.   II only.
    c.   III only.
*   d.   I and II.
    e.   I, II, and III.

II. SHORT ANSWER QUESTIONS

1. Justin used a 2% filter to time the purchases and sales of his securities and found that his portfolio returned 25% in one year's time. He noted that the S&P 500 Index returned only 16% during the same period of time and concluded that the weakly efficient markets hypothesis was violated. Comment on Justin's conclusion.

2. Discuss the differences in the strategies used by growth managers and value managers. Is there any evidence that one strategy is superior to the other?

3. What is a *run*? How have runs tests been used to test the weakly efficient markets hypothesis and what were the results of these tests?

4. Describe the January effect. If an investor believes the results of the studies supporting the January effect, what might she do to capitalize on it?

5. What level of market efficiency seems to exist in the U.S. stock markets? Explain.

CHAPTER EIGHT: SOLUTION GUIDELINES

Multiple Choice

1.　　**e**:　　The weekend effect refers to the fact that, on average, the stock market tends to fall on Monday's relative to the preceding Friday's closing price. This effect seems to occur in foreign markets as well. Harris' study concluded that Monday's trading finishes up like the other four days of the week, and that most of the negative returns on the average Monday occur in the first hours of trading. Therefore, an investor who chose to trade on the results of these studies would buy a security early Monday morning when its price would be lower.

2.　　**b**:　　The January effect suggests that investors can earn unusually high returns by buying a stock near the end of December and selling it in January. Thus, investors are using past price information to generate abnormal returns, and this violates the weakly efficient markets hypothesis. The size effect violates the semi-strong efficient markets hypothesis. Trading on stock split announcements does not appear to generate unusual returns, and insiders use information that is not historical.

3.　　**e**:　　Semi-strong market efficiency suggests that investors will not be able to earn unusual returns using only publicly available information. They will receive only a return that rewards them for the risk level taken. This does not mean that they should not invest in the stock market; it means only that they should not expect to earn abnormal returns from doing so.

4.　　**e**:　　Semi-strong market efficiency says that all publicly available information is rapidly incorporated into current stock prices. Therefore, Mr. Wave should not be able to earn abnormal returns by charting past price information, and Ms. Tracker should not be able to earn abnormal returns by buying the stock of firms that have announced splits. Mr. Gym, however, has insider information. His ability to earn an abnormal return on it (before legal costs for trading on insider information) does not violate semi-strong form efficiency. Nor does the fact that Ms. Ketchum ends up earning a high return on her bonds. The market incorporated the news about the airlines into the current price of the bonds as the news became available.

5.　　**b**:　　Trading on stock split announcements does not appear to offer any abnormal returns; nor do most mutual funds appear to outperform the S&P 500 on a risk-adjusted basis. Both of these are consistent with the semi-strong efficient markets hypothesis. While some studies have concluded that insiders can earn abnormal returns, the semi-strong efficient markets hypothesis does not suggest that prices reflect private information, only public information. Investing in the stocks of small firms has, however, been shown to provide higher returns than the risk levels of these investments would mandate.

6. **b**: Serial correlations measure the correlations in time-series of security prices with the same security's past prices, lagged by some preset amount of time. This will detect trends and reversals. Runs tests are used to determine any irregular trends in price changes. The head and shoulders pattern has been shown to be no different from that which can be generated using random numbers.

7. **e**: Semi-strong efficient markets are those in which all publicly available information is reflected in the securities' prices, so using any of the listed strategies would not result in abnormal profits.

8. **d**: Strongly efficient markets are those in which all information, both public and private, is reflected in a security's price. Therefore, no technical analysis tool, which utilizes past information, would provide any valuable insight. No one should expect to earn unusual profits although occasionally some investor may get lucky--just as a gambler might hit a jackpot upon inserting a quarter in a slot machine. Prices and values will always equal each other in a strongly efficient market since both will respond together to any new information that enters the market.

9. **b**: Value managers tend to outperform growth managers. Value managers look for stocks with low earnings growth, high current yields, and low P/E ratios.

10. **b**: If markets are perfectly efficient, securities' prices will fully reflect all information, both public and private, so obtaining abnormal profits would not be possible regardless of the amount or type of information to which you were privy. Unethical traders would not be able to manipulate securities' prices either. Weakly efficient markets and semi-strong efficient markets must also exist if the markets are perfectly efficient since they are actually subsets of perfectly efficient markets.

11. **d**: The weekend effect, the holiday effect, and the January effect all violate the weakly efficient markets hypothesis since investors are using only information regarding past price movements to earn higher than normal returns on their investments.

12. **a**: If serial correlations are zero, then there is no relationship between a security's past price and its current price. A zero run indicates that the price has remained flat for a period of time, but does not indicate anything about statistical independence, nor does the fact that the use of a filter rule earns zero returns. Stock returns do tend to be normally distributed in the long-run, but this does not necessarily mean that the returns are statistically independent.

13. **c**: Stock splits and stock dividends have no effect on the value of the firm, but they do reduce the price per share of the stock. There is no evidence that either results in price increases after the split is announced. While the accounting rules for dealing with them differ slightly, the two are economic equivalents.

14. **d**:   Growth investors, who buy stocks with high earnings growth rates, tend to underperform value investors. Buying a stock of a firm that has announced an increase in its dividend per share does not appear to yield any abnormal returns. Studies on filter rules have concluded that, even with the smallest filters, no abnormal profits are earned after considering transactions costs. However, the size effect seems to produce abnormal profits even after adjusting for such costs.

15. **b**:   Investors in load mutual funds tend to earn slightly less than those in similar no-load funds. There is no evidence that the performance of a fund differs based on its size. Passively managed funds tend to meet, and sometimes beat, the performance of actively managed funds. Funds that charge high management fees tend to perform a little worse than funds with lower management fees.

16. **c**:   Jaffe's study concluded that insiders who have holding periods of less than eight months earn lower returns than those who hold their investments for about eight months. It also stipulated that as the plurality increase from three or four to five or more, the returns on insider trades were lower. Outsiders who traded on information regarding insider trading that is made publicly available by the SEC earned lower returns than the insiders, possibly due to the time lag.

17. **e**:   Efficient markets tests should adjust returns for commission costs, taxes, and dividends (on both long and short positions). They should also adjust for the risk level of the investment in order to determine whether the return is truly abnormal.

18. **e**:   Runs tests can determine if a particular pattern of prices is any different from what one could generate using a random number series, and filter rules tests determine if investors can use past price information to time their trades in order to generate unusual profits. Event studies, however, are used to test the semi-strong efficient markets hypothesis.

19. **d**:   If markets are semi-strong form efficient, technical analysis, which involves the study of past price information, is a waste of time since this information is already incorporated into current stock prices. Investors who are privy only to publicly available information can expect to increase their returns by investing in stocks that have higher levels of systematic risk (i.e., higher betas). They should passively manage their portfolios so that transactions costs do not eat up the returns that they are able to achieve.

20. **d**:   Growth managers tend to invest in stocks that have low cash dividend yields, high earnings growth rates, high price-earnings multiples, and high betas.

Short Answer

1.   Justin's portfolio may have performed better than the S&P 500 Index because it was riskier. He also may have failed to adjust for transaction costs when

calculating his return. Even if his observation adjusts for risk and transaction costs, this does not necessarily violate the weakly efficient markets hypothesis. His success could be the result of blind luck rather than something that he can expect to repeat by following the same trading rule.

2. Value managers look to buy stocks that are selling at prices that are below their values. They then hold the stocks until the prices increase prior to selling them. They usually buy stocks that are issued by below-average sized firms, have low price-earnings ratios, below-average earnings growth rates, high cash dividend yields, low price-to-book-value ratios, and low betas. They often buy stocks that are unpopular. Growth managers look for stocks with high earnings growth rates that are expected to continue. They generally buy stocks with low cash dividend yields, high rates of return on equity, high price-to-book-value ratios, and high betas. They typically invest in glamour stocks that are issued by large corporations. A number of studies have concluded that value managers tend to outperform growth managers.

3. A *run* refers to something that happens in a series of numbers whenever the changes between consecutive numbers switch direction. Runs can be used to determine if a series of price changes for a security is any different from what would be observed in a series of randomly generated numbers. The runs tests that have been published suggest that the price changes are not significantly different from changes produced by randomly generated numbers. Hence, the conclusion is that stock prices move randomly.

4. The January effect refers to the fact that the average stock's return in the month of January is over five times larger than the mean monthly return obtained by averaging over all 12 months. An investor who wished to capitalize on this would buy a stock in the last week or so of December and sell it after the price jumped up in January.

5. The bulk of the evidence supports the semi-strong efficient markets hypothesis. This means that security prices fully and accurately reflect all publicly available information, but not private information. With the exception of the size effect and value investing, investors do not appear to be able to earn abnormal profits from studying publicly available information. The jury is out regarding whether the markets are, in fact, perfectly efficient. Studies by Jaffe, Seyhun, and Meulbroek, among others, have concluded that abnormal profits are made on trades by insiders. However, the modest size of these profits, suggests that most private information is reflected in security prices as well.

CHAPTER NINE: FUTURES AND OPTIONS

I.   MULTIPLE CHOICE

1.   A futures contract differs from an option in that

*   a.   Futures contracts involve legal obligations to buy or sell the underlying asset; the owner of an option can simply let the option expire.
        b.   The future price at which the underlying asset can be bought or sold is specified in the futures contract, but it is not specified in the option.
        c.   The future price at which the underlying asset can be bought or sold is specified in the option, but it is not specified in the futures contract.
        d.   The futures contract has a stated expiration date whereas the option does not.
        e.   Options involve legal obligations to buy or sell the underlying asset; the owner of a futures contract can simply let the contract expire.

2.   Which of the following is (are) *true* regarding the differences between forward and futures contracts?

        a.   Futures contracts have counterparty risk; forward contracts do not.
*   b.   Futures contracts are more liquid than forward contracts.
        c.   Futures contracts can be customized to the investor's needs; forward contracts are standardized instruments.
        d.   Delivery is guaranteed with a forward contract; a long position in a futures contract could lose a lot if the investor who sold the contract defaults.
        e.   Both "a" and "b" are true statements.

3.   Mike had read that a number of hurricanes that had hit the southeastern United States had severely damaged the orange orchards in that area and reasoned that the price of orange juice could be expected to rise with the lower supply. In early October, he decided to enter a long position in one contract (15,000 pounds) of January orange juice futures at a price of $0.9265 per pound. Mike was required to deposit a 10% margin of $1,390 with his broker when he entered the contract. By December, the price of the January futures in orange juice had risen to $0.9450 per pound, and Mike entered a reversing trade. What was Mike's rate of return on this investment?

        a.   -80.0%
        b.   + 2.0%
        c.   + 9.2%
*   d.   +20.0%
        e.   none of the above

4.   Sheila noted that the corn harvest was expected to be exceptional and reasoned that the price of corn would fall. In July, she entered a short position in one September corn contract (5,000 bushels) at $2.055 a bushel, and had to deposit a 10% margin with her broker. In August, September corn was selling for $2.10 a bushel, and Sheila entered a reversing trade. Calculate Sheila's rate of return on this investment.

*   a.   -21.9%
        b.   +22.0%
        c.   - 2.2%
        d.   -78.1%
        e.   +75.0%

5.   Which of the following statements regarding options is (are) *true*?

        a.   Options are linear instruments because their prices move in a linear one-to-one relationship with the market price of the underlying.
        b.   Option holders are obligated to exercise their options, but option writers have no such obligation.
*   c.   American options can be exercised at any time, up to and including the day they expire.
        d.   European options are traded only in foreign markets.
        e.   Both "c" and "d" are true statements.

6.   Which of the following is *not* a function performed by the clearing house of a futures exchange?

        a.   tracking the details of each transaction
        b.   guaranteeing delivery of the underlying
        c.   expediting the delivery process
*   d.   finding buyers and/or sellers for the contracts
        e.   All of the above functions are performed by the clearing house.

7.   Which of the following positions might an investor who expected stock prices to increase take?

*   a.   enter a long position in an S&P 500 Index futures contract
        b.   enter a short position in an S&P 500 Index futures contract
        c.   write a call option on the S&P 500 Index
        d.   buy a put option on the S&P 500 Index
        e.   both "a" and "c"

8.   A call option on Texaco has an exercise price of $60 and is selling for $4. The current market price of Texaco is $63. The intrinsic value of this call is

      a. $ 0.
      b.   -$3.
*   c.   +$3.
      d.   +$56.
      e.   cannot be determined with the information provided

9.   Steve wrote a put option for 100 shares of IBM when it was selling for $173. The exercise price on the option was $175, and Steve received the option premium of $2.75 per option share. At the time of expiration, IBM was selling for $180. Steve's profits (or losses) from his position were

      a.   a loss of $225.
*   b.   a profit of $275.
      c.   a loss of $275.
      d.   a loss of $75.
      e.   a profit of $775.

10.   The premium on a call option will be higher,

      a.   the lower the level of market interest rates.
*   b.   the greater the volatility of the underlying stock's returns.
      c.   the shorter the time to expiration.
      d.   the lower the price of the underlying.
      e.   the higher the exercise price of the option.

11.   Which of the following is *not* an advantage of buying a put option over short selling a stock if you expect the stock price to fall?

      a.   Losses on the put option are limited to the option premium.
      b.   The put buyer is not responsible for any dividend payments made on the stock prior to the expiration date of the option.
      c.   A put can be purchased at any time; short sales can be done only on an uptick.
*   d.   Put options can expire while a short position can remain open indefinitely.
      e.   All of the above are advantages of the put option.

12.   The option premium is determined by all of the following *except*

*   a.   the expected return on the underlying stock.
      b.   the volatility of the underlying stock.
      c.   the time to expiration on the option.
      d.   the level of market interest rates.
      e.   All of the above are factors in determining the price of an option.

13. An investor might choose to write a call option on a stock she owned in order to earn additional income for her portfolio if she expected

    a.   the stock price to increase.
    b.   the stock price to decrease, but she wanted to continue to hold the stock.
    c.   the stock price to remain fairly stable.
*   d.   both "b" and "c"
    e.   none of the above

14. In August, Shayla purchases a call option on Amazon stock, which expires in September, for $6 7/8. The exercise price on the option is $125. Amazon's stock price is $119 1/4. Calculate the intrinsic value and the time value of this option.

    a.   intrinsic value = $6.875; time value = 0
    b.   intrinsic value = $5.75; time value = $1.125
*   c.   intrinsic value = 0; time value = $6.875
    d.   intrinsic value = $6.875; time value = $5.75
    e.   cannot be determined without information on the risk-free rate

15. In September, Tim purchases a put option on Dell Computer, which expires in October, for $5 1/8. The exercise price on the option is $50, and Dell Computer is selling for $46 1/4. Determine the intrinsic value and the time value of this option.

    a.   intrinsic value = 0; time value = $5.125
*   b.   intrinsic value = $3.75; time value = $1.375
    c.   intrinsic value = $5.125; time value = 0
    d.   intrinsic value = $3.75; time value = 0
    e.   cannot be determined without information on the risk-free rate

16. Lori purchased a call option for 100 shares of AT&T stock with an October expiration for $3 per optioned share. The exercise price on the option was $45, and the market price of AT&T was $46. Prior to expiration, AT&T was selling for $50 a share, and Lori decided to sell her option. Calculate the minimum profit (loss) that Lori earned.

    a. $500 profit
    b. $300 loss
*   c. $200 profit
    d. $100 profit
    e. $800 loss

17. Which of the following is (are) *true* regarding the differences between a warrant and a call option?

    a. The owner of a warrant is obligated to exercise the warrant, whereas the owner of a call option has no such obligation.

    b. The exercise price of a warrant moves in unison with the underlying stock price; the exercise price of a call option is fixed.

    c. The exercise of a warrant will increase the number of shares outstanding for a firm; the exercise of a call option will not.

    d. The writer of a warrant is the corporation that has issued the stock on which the warrant is written; the writer of a call option is simply another investor.

    * e. Both "c" and "d" are true statements.

18. Elliott has noted that the TriValley Communications Corporation (TCC) has an issue of callable bonds outstanding that are also convertible into 1 share of TCC's common stock. The bonds have 10 years to maturity and pay a coupon rate of 10%. He does some research and discovers that non-callable, non-convertible bonds of similar risk, with the same coupon and maturity are selling for $98. He has also determined that long-term call options on TCC's stock are selling for premiums of $2 a share and that the interest rate call on TCC's bonds is valued at $1. Use the building block approach to determine the price of TCC's convertible bonds.

    a. $ 97

    b. $101

    * c. $ 99

    d. $100

    e. $ 95

19. In September, Josie wrote a call option on Compaq stock, which expires in January. Josie did not own the stock and decided not to buy it. Compaq was selling for $23 1/4 and the exercise price of the option was $25. The option premium was $3 1/2. Prior to expiration, Compaq was selling for $28. What was Josie's profit (loss) per share on this transaction?

    a. $3.50 loss

    b. $6.50 profit

    c. $6.50 loss

    * d. $0.50 profit

    e. $3.50 profit

20.   Jake simultaneously purchased 100 shares of the stock of Gateway Corporation at a price of $97 and purchased a put on the stock of Gateway Corporation for $3 1/8. The exercise price of the put, with a September expiration date, was $95. At expiration, Gateway's price had risen to $100. Jake should

       a.   exercise his option to recoup part of his option premium.
*   b.   let his option expire.
       c.   sell his option for its intrinsic value of $5 per optioned share.
       d.   sell his option for its intrinsic value of $2 per optioned share.
       e.   execute a reversing trade to get out of his option contract.

II.   SHORT ANSWER

1.   Discuss the similarities and differences between a long position in a futures contract and a call option.

2.   How does a warrant attached to a bond differ from a bond with a convertible feature?

3.   Hans Wolff owns The Heidleberg, a shop that specializes in German imports. His peak season is from early November through Christmas, and he receives the bulk of his inventory in September. Hans must pay for his order in deutschemarks and has observed that for the last three years, the dollar depreciated against the mark between the time he placed his order in early June and the time he paid for the shipment in October. This year when Hans places his order, he notes that the exchange rate is at $0.5405 per deutschemark. He also observes that a futures contract on deutschemarks for September delivery is trading at $0.5414, which he feels will allow him to achieve the profit margin he desires. The contract is for DM125,000, and Hans estimates he will need DM250,000 to pay for his order. Demonstrate how Hans can lock in the $0.5414 exchange rate by illustrating his cash flows in September if the exchange rate is then (a) $0.5800, or (b) $0.5175.

4.   In September, Jeremy Tillman purchased 100 shares of AmericaOnline (AOL) stock at $91 5/16. He simultaneously wrote a call with a January expiration and a $90 strike price. The option premium was $16 1/2. Calculate Jeremy's rate of return if AOL increases in price to $115 prior to expiration.

5.   A warrant on the stock of PrimaTek Corporation has an exercise price of $30 and entitles the holder to purchase five shares of the firm's stock. Calculate the intrinsic value of the warrant when PrimaTek is selling for (a) $25 a share, and (b) $35 a share.

CHAPTER NINE: SOLUTION GUIDELINES

Multiple Choice

1.   **a**:   The future price at which the underlying asset can be bought or sold is specified on both the futures contract and the option. However, in order to get out of a futures contract, the investor must do a reversing trade. The option investor can simply let his option expire.

2.   **b**:   Forward contracts are negotiated individually between two parties and can be customized to meet the needs of the parties involved whereas futures contracts are standardized instruments that trade on exchange floors. The clearing house of the exchange guarantees each party that the delivery (of the underlying asset and the funds) will take place as promised. Therefore, futures contracts do not have the counterparty risk involved in a forward contract and are much more liquid since there is an active secondary market for them.

3.   **d**:   Mike's profit = $0.9450(15,000) - $0.9265(15,000) = $277.50. The rate of return on his investment of $1,390 is r = $277.50/$1,390 = 20%.

4.   **a**:   Sheila's margin = 0.10(5,000)($1.055) = $1,028. Her loss on the transaction was $2.10(5,000) - $2.055(5,000) = ($225). Her rate of return was, therefore, -$225/$1,028 = -21.9%.

5.   **c**:   American options can be exercised at any time; European options can only be exercised at expiration, but they are traded in the U.S. and other foreign markets as well. Option writers are obligated to perform, but option holders may let their options expire. Options are nonlinear instruments. Their prices do not move in a one-to-one relationship with the market price of the underlying.

6.   **d**:   Futures brokers perform the function of actually finding the buyers and/or sellers for the contracts. The clearing house only tracks the details of the transactions, guarantees delivery, and expedites the delivery process.

7.   **a**:   An investor who expects stock prices to increase will profit from taking a long position in a futures contract, buying (not writing) a call option, or selling (not buying) a put option on the S&P 500 Index if his expectations are upheld.

8.   **c**:   The intrinsic value of the call on Texaco = MAX[0, (Stock price - Exercise price)] = MAX[0, ($63 - $60)] = $3.

9.   **b**:   Steve's put option will only be exercised on him if the price of IBM is less than the exercise price on the option. The exercise price of the option is $175, and IBM's stock price is $180. Therefore, the put holder will let his option expire, and Steve's profit will be the option premium that he received, $275.

10.   **b**:   The premium of a call option will be higher the greater the volatility of the underlying stock's returns since this increases the chance that the option will expire in the money. The premium will also be higher the higher the price of the underlying (more risk for the writer), the lower the exercise price (greater chance to expire in the money), the longer the time to expiration (more time to become more profitable for the owner), and the higher the level of market interest rates (greater opportunity cost).

11.   **d**:   While put options expire while short positions can remain open indefinitely, this is a disadvantage of the put option, not an advantage. For the investor to maintain his position by using put options, a second put option must be purchased when the put expires. The investor then incurs more costs--the option premium and transactions costs.

12.   **a**:   The expected return on the underlying stock is not a factor in determining an option's premium; only the volatility of the returns is a factor, as is the time to expiration and the level of market interest rates.

13.   **d**:   An investor who writes call options on stock that she owns can expect to increase the income to her portfolio with the premiums earned only if the options expire unexercised. If the stock price increases, the options will be exercised, and the investor will be forced to sell her holdings of the stock. If the stock price decreases or remains fairly stable, the options will not be exercised.

14.   **c**:   The intrinsic value of a call option = MAX[0, (Stock price - Exercise price)]. The remainder of the premium is the time value of the option. The intrinsic value of the Amazon option is MAX[0, ($119.25 - $125)] = 0. The time value = $6.875 - 0 = $6.875.

15.   **b**:   The intrinsic value of a put option = MAX[0, (Exercise price - Stock price)]. The remainder of the premium is the time value of the option. The intrinsic value of the Dell Computer put option is MAX [0, ($50 - $46.25)] = $3.75. Its time value is $5.125 - $3.75 = $1.375.

16.   **c**:   The minimum profit on a call option = intrinsic value of the option - option premium. Lori's profit = MAX [0, ($50 - $45)] - $3 = $5 - $3 = $2 per option share, or $200.

17.   **e**:   The exercise price of both options and warrants is fixed at the outset. While the exercise price of a warrant may change according to a preset schedule, it does not move in unison with the underlying stock. Neither the owner of a warrant nor the owner of a call option is obligated to exercise it. However, because the writer of a warrant is the firm that has issued the stock on which the warrant is written, the exercise of a warrant will increase the number of shares outstanding. The writer of a call option is simply another investor and has no effect on the number of shares outstanding for the firm.

18.   **c**:   The building block approach presented in this chapter presents the price of a convertible security as follows:

Price of convertible security	=	Price of equivalent non-convertible security	+ call premium on issuer's stock	- call premium on an equivalent non-convertible security
$99	=	$98	+ $2	- $1

19.   **d**:   Since Compaq was selling for more than the exercise price of $25, the option will be exercised, and Josie will have to buy the stock at $28 in order to fulfill her obligation. Her $0.50 per share profit is calculated below:

Buy Compaq	($28.00)
Sell Compaq at exercise price of $25	$25.00
Received option premium	$ 3.50
Net profit	$ 0.50

20.   **b**:   The intrinsic value of the put option is zero since the exercise price is less than the current market price of Gateway's stock. If Jake no longer wishes to hold Gateway, he should sell the stock at the current market price of $100, not exercise his option, which would allow him to sell it for only $95.

Short Answer

1.   Both a long position in a futures contract and a call option give an investor the right to purchase the underlying asset at some point in the future for a prespecified price. However, the investor in the futures contract is obligated to purchase the underlying asset unless he does a reversing trade whereas the option holder can simply let his option expire. No premium is charged for the futures contract. The investor simply puts up a margin with the broker. The buyer of a call option, however, pays a price for it. The losses of the option holder are limited to the price paid for the option. The losses associated with a long position in the futures contract can (theoretically) be as large as the value of the contract when the long position is entered.

2.   A warrant gives the holder the right to buy a given number of shares of common stock from the issuer for a specified price within a specified time period. If the warrant holder wishes to exercise the warrant, he will pay the issuer cash for the stock, and he will still own the bond. A convertible bond gives the holder the right to exchange the bond for shares of common stock. If the holder chooses to exercise this option, he will exchange the bond for the shares of stock rather than paying cash. He will no longer own the bond.

3. Hans must go long in two futures contracts for September delivery to hedge his position. His cash flows in September are as follows:

Transaction results	DM = $0.5800	DM = $0.5175
Gain (loss)on futures transaction	250,000[$0.5800 - $0.5414] = $9,650	250,000[$0.5175 - $0.5414] = ($5,975)
Pay for merchandise at current exchange rate	($145,000)	($129,375)
Net cash flow	($135,350)	($135,350)

This is a net price of $135,350/250,000 = $0.5414 per deutschemark.

4. If AOL's price rises to $115, the call that Jeremy wrote will be exercised, and he will be forced to sell his shares for $9,000 (= $90 x 100). His net investment was $7, 481.25, calculated as follows:

Buy AOL at $91 5/16	($9,131.25)
Receive option premium	$1,650.00
Net investment	$7,481.25

His rate of return is ($9,000 - $7481.25)/$7,481.25 = 20.3%.

5. The intrinsic value of a warrant = MAX[0, {(Stock price - Exercise price)(Number of shares)}].
    a. Intrinsic value = MAX[0,{($25 - $30)(5)}] = 0(5) = 0.
    b. Intrinsic value = MAX[0, {$35 - $30)(5)}] = $5 (5) = $25.

CHAPTER TEN: CREATING PRICE INDEXES

I.   MULTIPLE CHOICE QUESTIONS

1.   Which of the following is (are) *true* regarding the comparison of the Dow Jones Industrial Average (DJIA) and the S&P 500 Index?

      a.   The S&P 500 Index includes small stocks whereas the Dow Jones Industrial Average uses only blue chip stocks.

      b.   The S&P 500 Index is price-weighted whereas the Dow Jones Industrial Average is value-weighted.

*   c.   The S&P 500 Index is not affected by stock splits, but the Dow Jones Industrial Average is.

      d.   Both "a" and "c" are true statements.

      e.   All of the above are true statements.

2.   Which of the following is (are) *true* regarding the Dow Jones Industrial Average?

      a.   It has a high positive correlation with the S&P 500 Index because both use market values in their computations.

*   b.   If not for the high degree of systematic risk in the U.S. equity markets, the Dow Jones Industrial Average would be a worthless market indicator.

      c.   The Dow Jones Industrial Average has the advantage of using a much more rational basis for selecting the stocks it uses in its calculation than most of the other market indicators.

      d.   The Dow Jones Industrial Average is a superior indicator because it uses a much smaller (and therefore, manageable) sample and a much simpler computational procedure.

      e.   Both "a" and "c" are true statements.

3.   The geometric mean return

      a.   is superior to the arithmetic mean return in calculating an expected single-period return.

      b.   will always be larger than the arithmetic mean return if there is any variability in the returns.

      c.   should be averaged with the arithmetic mean return in determining an expected single-period return.

*   d.   is a better indicator of the long-term performance of an investment than the arithmetic mean return.

      e.   Both "b" and "d" are true statements.

4.   The S&P 500 Index

     a.   is a price-weighted indicator.
     b.   uses only stocks trading on the NYSE and the AMEX, the two major exchanges, in its calculation.
     c.   has a downward bias when a stock splits.
*   d.   is a good representative of the price movements of large company stocks, but not necessarily of small company stock price movements.
     e.   None of the above is a true statement.

5.   The average investor needs to be concerned with

     a.   nominal returns in order to minimize his purchasing power risk.
*   b.   real returns since these measure the purchasing power than is left after the rate of inflation is removed from nominal returns.
     c.   only nominal returns since inflation only affects the very wealthy.
     d.   real returns in times of inflation and nominal returns in deflationary periods.
     e.   Both "b" and "d" are true statements.

6.   A market indicator ideally should be

     a.   composed of all the stocks that are traded in order to be an accurate representation of the markets.
     b.   price-weighted in order to eliminate the size of the firm from biasing the indicator.
*   c.   able to reflect small changes in the underlying prices immediately.
     d.   both "a" and "c".
     e.   all of the above.

7.   Small samples

     a.   should never be used since they are subject to large sampling errors.
     b.   can be used if the elements in the sample are highly positively correlated.
     c.   if you are interested only in a narrowly defined group.
     d.   will lack the quality of representativeness that is necessary for it to be a good sample.
*   e.   Both "b" and "c" are true statements.

8.   Equally weighted indicators

    a.   are appropriate to study the behavior of investors who have no skill and select stocks irrationally.
    b.   give disproportionately large weights to the securities issued by small companies.
    c.   weights each security in proportion to the fraction of total market value represented by the firm's outstanding shares.
    d.   all of the above
*   e.   "a" and "b" only

The following information is supplied for Questions 9 and 10:

Stock	Beginning price	Beginning shares outstanding	Current price	Current shares outstanding
M	$18	12 million	$30	12 million
N	$5	5 million	$15	8 million
P	$80	50 million	$100	75 million

9.   Using the same methodology as that used to construct the Dow Jones Industrial Average, calculate the current value of the 3-stock market indicator.

*   a.   48.3333
    b.   14.0000
    c.   1711.6667
    d.   34.3333
    e.   none of the above

10.   Using the same methodology as that used to construct the S&P 500 Index and assuming an index value of 10, calculate the current value of the 3-stock market indicator.

    a.   2660.000
    b.   9.6880
*   c.   18.8163
    d.   26.6000
    e.   none of the above

11.   The following three stocks are used to calculate a price-weighted indicator:

Stock	Price on Day 1	Shares outstanding on Day 1
J	$32	10 million
K	$48	15 million
L	$84	20 million

Stock L is split 2-for-1 on Day 2. Calculate the value of the indicator on both Day 1 and Day 2.

  a.   Day 1: 3.7333;   Day 2: 0.6462
* b.   Day 1: 54.6667;   Day 2: 40.6667
  c.   Day 1: 54.6667;   Day 2: 82.6667
  d.   Day 1: 3.7333;   Day 2: 7.0857
  e.   none of the above

12.   At the end of 1998, the S&P 500 Index closed at 1229.23, and on June 30, 1999, the S&P 500 Index closed at 1372.71. The 6-month percentage change in the index was

  a.   8.95%.
  b.   10.45%.
* c.   11.67%.
  d.   9.25%.
  e.   none of the above.

13.   The end-of-year close prices for a certain stock that paid no dividends are as follows:

Year 0:	$40.00
Year 1:	$46.00
Year 2:	$44.62
Year 3:	$54.00
Year 4:	$62.63

The annual time weighted return for the four-year period is

  a.   66.26%.
  b.   12.25%.
* c.   11.86%.
  d.   39.14%.
  e.   13.55%.

14. Jim Spencer developed the following price relatives for the quarterly returns on a stock:

Quarter	Price relative
1	0.8812
2	1.0125
3	1.0324
4	0.9800

The quarterly geometric mean rate of return is

    a.   -9.73%.
    b.   1.98%.
    c.   9.03%.
*   d.   -2.53%.
    e.   none of the above.

15. The annual returns on Posser Corporation's stock have been as follows for the past three years:

Year 1	22%
Year 2	-3%
Year 3	10%

Calculate the arithmetic average annual rate of return and the variance of the returns for Posser Corporation.

*   a.   The arithmetic average is 9.67% with a variance of 0.01564.
    b.   The arithmetic average is 9.67% with a variance of 0.00667.
    c.   The arithmetic average is 11.67% with a variance of 0.00410.
    d.   The arithmetic average is 9.67% with a variance of 0.0197.
    e.   The arithmetic average is 11.67% with a variance of 0.0123.

16. The arithmetic average rate of return for the stock of the Milmine Corporation is 14.25% with a variance of 0.0062. The geometric mean rate of return on Milmine's stock is approximately

    a.   13.63%.
    b.   14.56%.
*   c.   13.94%.
    d.   14.87%.
    e.   It cannot be determined with the information given.

17.   Chris earned a 24.2% return on his investment in a Science and Technology Fund during 200X. The inflation rate for that year was 3.1%. Chris' real rate of return was

        a.   17.0%.
        b.   12.05%.
        c.   23.45%.
*   d.   20.50%.
        e.   none of the above.

18.   Andy Chang has collected the historical data on a stock in which he is interested. He has determined that the annual rates of return for the past five years were 15%, 24%, 16%, 5%, and 12%, respectively. Andy wants to use the data to estimate an expected return for year six. The best estimate of the expected return is

        a.   19.45%.
        b.   11.40%.
*   c.   14.40%.
        d.   12.00%.
        e.   18.00%.

19.   According to the results of empirical research on the impact of inflation on securities' returns,

        a.   the real rates of return on common stocks are positively correlated with the rate of inflation.
*   b.   only Treasury bills, Treasury bonds, and corporate bonds provide investors with complete hedges against both expected and unexpected inflation.
        c.   real returns are positively correlated to both the rate of inflation and the money supply.
        d.   investors need only focus on nominal returns in their investment decision making.
        e.   Both "a" and "b" are true statements.

20.   If the nominal rate of return on U.S. Treasury bills in 200X is 5.21% and the real return on U.S. Treasury bills in that year is 1.53%, the rate of inflation in 200X is

*   a.   3.62%.
        b.   9.65%.
        c.   -3.49%.
        d.   1.04%.
        e.   none of the above.

II. SHORT ANSWER

1. Amin has invested his money in a mutual fund that is entirely invested in small cap stocks. He has noted that the S&P 500 Index has increased only 16% while his mutual fund has returned 26% over the same period. Based on this, Amin is recommending this fund to friends. Comment on Amin's recommendation.

2. The following information is supplied for three stocks:

| | **Base period** | | **End of one year** | |
Stock	Price	Shares outstanding	Price	Shares outstanding
Alpha	$18	2 million	$12	2 million
Beta	$26	6 million	$30	6 million
Gamma	$60	15 million	$35	30 million

Calculate the value of a market-value weighted index composed of these three stocks at the end of one year, assuming an index value of 100. Calculate the percentage increase (decrease) in the index for the year.

3. One criticism of the Dow Jones Industrial Average is that it is downward biased when a stock splits. Do you agree with this criticism? Why or why not?

4. Consider the following two stocks:

Stock	Price on day 1	Shares outstanding on day 1
Mars	$100	12 million
Neptune	$45	30 million

Assume that on Day 2 Mars stock decreases in value by 5% while Neptune increases in value by 5%. Explain what will happen to the value of a market indicator composed of these two stocks if the indicator is (a) price-weighted, or (b) value-weighted. Why?

5. The stock of the Villella Bottling Corporation has the following history of returns:

Year	Return
1	- 3%
2	10%
3	18%
4	13%
5	15%

a. Calculate the company's annual compound average rate of return.

b. What is the best estimate of the expected return on the stock of the Villella Bottling Corporation for Year 6?

CHAPTER TEN: SOLUTION GUIDELINES

Multiple Choice

1.   **c**:   Because the S&P 500 Index is a market-value weighted index, both price and shares outstanding are included in the calculation, so a stock split will have no effect on the Index. The Dow Jones Industrial Average, however, uses only prices in its calculation, so a stock split will cause a decrease in a price without a simultaneous increase in the number of shares outstanding. Both the S&P 500 Index and the DJIA use only large stocks in their calculations.

2.   **b**:   The Dow Jones Industrial Average does have a high positive correlation with the S&P 500 Index, but not because they both use market values in their computations. The DJIA uses only prices. The high positive correlation is the result of the large amount of systematic risk that exists in the U.S. equity markets. If the U.S. equity markets were less affected by systematic risk, the DJIA would zigzag chaotically and give some misleading signals. The selection process for the stocks used in calculating the DJIA is anything but rational. AT&T, a utility stock, is included in an average that is supposed to be an *industrial* stock average, for example.

3.   **d**:   The geometric mean return will always be smaller than the arithmetic mean return if there is any variability in returns. It reflects an average compounded rate of return and is a better indicator of the long-term performance of an investment than is the arithmetic mean return. The arithmetic mean return is a better estimate of an expected return over a single holding period.

4.   **d**:   The S&P 500 Index is a market-value weighted indicator that uses stocks from the NYSE, the AMEX, and NASDAQ in its calculation. Because it is market-value weighted, it automatically adjusts for stock splits. It is not a good representative of small company stocks since it uses only the stocks of large companies in its calculation.

5.   **b**:   The average investor should focus on real returns since only real returns reflect his purchasing power.

6.   **c**:   A market indicator should be large enough to exemplify the population of interest; however, if it is too large, it will not be economical to maintain. It should also be market-value weighted or equally weighted, not price-weighted. Ideally it should be able to reflect small changes in the underlying prices immediately.

7.   **e**:   Small samples are fine if the elements in the sample are highly positively correlated or if you are interested only in a narrowly defined group. In the latter case, the sample will be a good representation of the population of interest, even though it is small.

8.   **e**:   When equal weights are used in a market indicator, it represents the equal likelihood of selecting every security. Thus, it represents the behavior of investors who have zero skill and select stocks irrationally or randomly. Equal weighting does give

disproportionately large weights to securities issued by small companies because these securities are given the same weights as those issued by large corporations, even though large corporations provide more investment opportunities in the securities market.

9. **a**: Using the current prices and a price-weighted average, the value is ($30 + $15 + $100)/3 = 48.3333.

10. **c**: The base period value of a market-value weighted index composed of the three stocks is $18(12) + $5(5) + $100(75) = $4,241 million. The current value is $30(12) + $15(8) + $100($75) = $7,980 million. The value of the index is [$7,980/$4241] x 10 = 18.8163.

11. **b**: The value of the price-weighted indicator on Day 1 is ($32 + $48 + $84)/3 = 54.6667. On Day 2, the price of Stock L will be $42 after the 2-for-1 split. The new value of the indicator is, therefore, ($32 + $48 + $42)/3 = 40.6667.

12. **c**: The percentage change in the S&P 500 Index for the six-month period is (1372.71 - 1229.23)/1229.23 = 11.67%.

13. **c**: The annual rates of return are calculated using the following formula: $r = \dfrac{P_1 - P_0}{P_0}$. They are supplied below:

Year	Return
1	15%
2	-3%
3	21%
4	16%

The annual time weighted return is the geometric mean return.

$$GMR = \sqrt[4]{(1.15)(0.97)(1.21)(1.16)} - 1 = 11.86\%.$$

14. **d**: $1 + GMR = \sqrt[4]{(0.8812)(1.0125)(1.0324)(0.9800)} = \sqrt[4]{0.9027} = 0.9747.$
GMR = 0.9747 - 1.0 = -2.53%.

15. **a**: The arithmetic average rate of return is (22% + -3% + 10%)/3 = 9.67%. The variance of these returns is
$$VAR(r) = \frac{(0.22 - 0.0967)^2 + (-0.03 - 0.0967)^2 + (0.10 - 0.0967)^2}{2} = \frac{0.03127}{2} = 0.01564.$$

16. **c**: GMR = Arithmetic average - 0.5VAR(r) = 0.1425 - 0.5(0.0062) = 13.94%.

17. **d**: Chris' real rate of return = {[1 + nominal return]/[1 + inflation rate]} - 1.0; rr = [1.242/1.031] - 1.0 = 20.5%.

18.   **c:**   The best estimate of the expected return for a single holding period is the arithmetic average of the historical returns. Andy should use (15% + 24% + 16% + 5% + 12%)/5 = 14.4% for his expected rate of return in year six.

19.   **b:**   Bodie, Jaffe, and Mandelker and Nelson published studies that concluded that both the nominal and the real rates of return from common stocks were negatively correlated with the inflation rate. A study by Fama and Schwert concluded that only Treasury bills, corporate bonds and government bonds provided investors with complete hedges against both expected inflation and unexpected inflation. Rene Stulz developed a model in which real returns are negatively related to both the inflation rate and the money supply.

20.   **a:**   1 + nominal rate = (1 + real rate)(1 + inflation rate)
             1.0521 = (1.0153)(1 + inflation rate)
             inflation rate = 1.0521/1.0153 - 1.0 = 3.62%

Short Answer

1.   The S&P 500 Index is not an appropriate benchmark for Amin to use to judge the performance of his mutual fund since the S&P 500 Index is comprised only of the stocks of large companies. Amin's fund may have been expected to earn a higher return due to the greater amount of risk involved in small caps. In order to better judge his fund's performance, Amin should compare the performance to that of a small cap index, such as the S&P 600 Small Cap Index.

2.   The base period market value of the three stocks is ($18 x 2) + ($26 x 6) + ($60 x 15) = $1,092 million. The market value at the end of one year is ($12 x 2) + ($30 x 6) + ($35 x 30) = $1,254. The value of the index at the end of the year is [1254/1092] x 100 = 114.8352. The beginning value of the index was [1092/1092] x 100 = 100. The percentage increase is, therefore, [114.8352 - 100]/100 = 14.8352%.

3.   The criticism is a just one. Since the Dow Jones Industrial Average is price-weighted, only prices are incorporated in the index. Typically, it is a higher-priced stock that will split. After the split, its price per share will be lower, even though the aggregate market value of the company is unchanged. Since a lower number (the new price) is now being added in to calculate the DJIA, the DJIA will be lower; hence the downward bias. Additionally, it is the higher priced stocks that control the average; that is, a 1% change in a higher priced stock will affect the average by more than the same percentage change in a lower priced stock. So, when one of the higher priced stocks in the average splits, the resultant percentage decrease in the price of that stock can affect the DJIA dramatically.

4.   Since Mars is the higher priced stock, a change in its price will affect a price-weighted indicator by more than the same percentage change in the lower priced Neptune stock. The decrease in Mars stock price will, therefore, cause a price-weighted indicator to decrease. If the indicator were value-weighted, the stock with the higher market value

would control the indicator. The market value of the Mars stock is $100(12 million) = $1,200 million, and the market value of the Neptune stock is $45(30 million) = $1,350 million. Therefore, the 5% increase in Neptune's stock price will have the greater effect on the indicator, and the value of the market-value indicator will increase.

5a.   Villella Bottling's annual compound average rate of return is found by calculating the geometric mean return.

$$GMR = \sqrt[5]{(0.97)(1.10)(1.18)(1.13)(1.15)} - 1.0 = 10.3\%.$$

b.   The best estimate of the expected return on Villella Bottling Corporation's stock for year six is the arithmetic average of its historical returns:

(-3% + 10% + 18% + 13% + 15%)/5 = 10.6%.

CHAPTER ELEVEN: SELECTED INVESTMENT INDEXES

I.   MULTIPLE CHOICE QUESTIONS

1.   The S&P 500 Index would be *unaffected* by which of the following events:

      a.   The United States enters a war.

      b.   The United States enters a recession.

      c.   The United States enters a period of high inflation.

*   d.   The workers at General Motors, a U.S. corporation that is included in the calculation of the index, go on strike.

      e.   All of the above would have an effect on the S&P 500 Index.

2.   Ibbotson's Large Company Stock Index

      a.   ignores dividend payments.

      b.   ignores brokerage commissions, income taxes and other transactions costs.

      c.   uses the S&P 500 Stocks Composite Index and assumes that dividends thereon are reinvested.

      d.   indicates that large stocks offered an annual average real return of 12.5% from 1926 through 1996.

*   e.   Both "b" and "c" are true statements.

3.   An examination of Ibbotson's U.S. Treasury Bill Index reveals that

      a.   Treasury bills have always offered a return that is slightly above the rate of inflation.

*   b.   In recent decades, the real return on Treasury bills has sometimes been negative.

      c.   In the majority of the years from 1926 to 1996, Treasury bills have offered a return that has been less than the inflation rate.

      d.   Treasury bill returns have usually been higher than the returns on long-term government bonds.

      e.   Both "a" and "d" are true statements.

4.   The reinvestment return component of Ibbotson's large common stock index's total returns

      a.   is small enough that it could easily be ignored when calculating the total returns on the index.

      b.   is always a positive number, although it is larger in some years and negligible in others.

*   c.   has sometimes been negative when reinvested dividends were used to buy stocks that were depreciating in value.

      d.   considers brokerage fees on the reinvested amount.

      e.   Both "a" and "b" are true statements.

5.   Which of the following statements about time diversification is (are) *true*?

      a.   Empirical evidence suggests that time diversification works well for investors in common stocks, but not for bond investors.

      b.   If time diversification benefits indeed exists, then it is better to be a long-term investor than a short-term speculator.

      c.   Time diversification benefits are the result of returns reverting back toward the arithmetic mean returns in a period following extremely high or extremely low returns.

      d.   Empirical evidence suggests that time diversification does not exist.

*   e.   Both "b" and "c" are true statements.

6.   Asset pricing models tend to be based on the assumption that

      a.   the standard deviation of a return is constant through time.

      b.   heteroscedasticity is the norm.

      c.   economic equilibrium exists.

      d.   the standard deviation of a return is unstable through time.

*   e.   Both "a" and "c" are true statements.

7.   A measure of the predictability of one series, conditional on knowing the value of another series, is provided by a(n)

*   a.   cross correlation.

      b.   serial correlation.

      c.   autocorrelation.

      d.   trend analysis.

      e.   either "b" or "c;" the terms are synonymous.

8.   Studies of historical correlations suggest that

      a.   the returns on large company stocks and small company stocks are inversely related.

      b.   the inflation rate fluctuates randomly from year-to-year; thus, it is difficult to make a good short-run forecast of inflation.

*   c.   one cannot forecast future stock prices by looking at the trend in past prices.

      d.   All of the above are true statements.

      e.   Only "a" and "c" are true statements.

9.   Which of the following will provide you with an expected return on small cap stocks?

     a.   expected return on Treasury bills plus micro-cap equity size premium

*   b.   expected return on long-term Treasury bonds plus micro-cap equity size premium plus large corporation's long-horizon equity risk premia

     c.   expected return on Treasury bills plus large corporation's long-horizon equity risk premia plus micro-cap equity size premium

     d.   large corporation's long-horizon equity risk premia plus micro-cap equity size premia

     e.   expected return on long-term corporate bonds plus micro-cap equity size premium plus large corporation's long-horizon equity risk premia

10.   Which of the following is (are) *true* regarding a comparison between the Financial Times Stock Exchange (FT-SE) Index and the MSCI Index for England?

     a.   The MSCI Index reinvests all cash dividends, but the FT-SE Index ignores cash dividends.

*   b.   The MSCI uses a much larger sample than does the FT-SE Index.

     c.   FT-SE includes international tax considerations, but the MSCI Index ignores them.

     d.   FT-SE is price-weighted while the MSCI Index is market-value weighted.

     e.   Both "a" and "b" are true statements.

11.   In 1996, the total return on long-term government bonds was -0.93%. The coupon income return was 6.18%, and the capital appreciation return was - 7.37%. The reinvestment return was

     a.   -2.12%.

     b.   +2.12%.

     c.   +1.06%.

*   d.   +0.26%.

     e.   It cannot be determined with the information supplied.

Use the following information to answer Questions 12 and 13:

Year	Large stock total returns	Small stock total returns
1987	5.23%	-9.30%
1988	16.81%	22.87%
1989	31.49%	10.18%
1990	-3.17%	-21.56%
1991	30.55%	44.63%
1992	7.67%	23.35%
1993	9.99%	20.98%
1994	1.31%	3.11%
1995	37.43%	34.46%
1996	23.07%	17.62%

12.   The covariance of the returns of large company and small company stocks for the decade from 1987 to 1996 is

      a.   183.03.
*   b.   203.36.
      c.   218.66.
      d.   196.79.
      e.   none of the above.

13.   The cross correlation for the returns of large and small company stocks is

      a.   0.
      b.   0.82.
*   c.   0.73.
      d.   0.87.
      e.   0.98.

Use the following information to answer Questions 14 and 15:

The table below provides serial and cross correlations for the historical annual returns of four different asset classes and the rate of inflation for the period 1926 to 1996:

TABLE 11-A

	Large company stocks	Long-term corporate bonds	Long-term govern-ment bonds	Treasury bills	Inflation
Large company stocks	1.00				
Long-term corporate bonds	0.25	1.00			
Long-term government bonds	0.18	0.94	1.00		
U.S Treasury bills	-0.04	0.22	0.24	1.00	
Inflation	-0.02	-0.15	-0.15	0.41	1.00
Serial correlations	-0.01	0.10	-0.01	0.92	0.64

Source: *Stocks, Bonds, Bills, and Inflation 1997 Yearbook,* published by Ibbotson Associates, Chicago. Table 6.3, pg. 114.

14. The information provided in Table 11-A above suggests that

    a.   long-term government bond returns tended to move inversely with inflation, and future annual returns on these bonds could be predicted from observing past returns.

    b.   long-term government bond returns tended to move closely with corporate bond returns, but only the corporate bonds' annual returns could be easily predicted by observing past annual returns.

*   c.   Of the four asset classes, only the returns on Treasury bills tended to move somewhat with the rate of inflation.

    d.   The rate of inflation was a good predictor of the return on large company stocks during the period.

    e.   none of the above

15. Which of the following statements is (are) *true*, based on the information provided in Table 11-A above?

*   a.   Inflation had a large negative effect on the returns of fixed income securities during the period.

    b.   The rate of inflation tended to move randomly during the period.

    c.   The future annual returns on large company stocks could easily have been predicted by looking at the past returns.

    d.   All of the above are true statements.

    e.   Only a and b are true statements.

Use the following information to answer Questions 16 through 20:

The total returns for six different asset classes and the inflation rate for 1996 are provided below:

Large company stocks	23.07%
Small company stocks	17.62%
Long-term corporate bonds	1.40%
Long-term government bonds	-0.93%
Intermediate-term government bonds	2.10%
U.S. Treasury bills	5.21%
Inflation	3.32%

16. The bond horizon risk premium in 1996 was

    a.   -3.6%.

    b.   -13.8%.

    c.   +3.6%.

*   d.   -5.8%.

    e.   +6.2%.

17.   The small stock risk-premium in 1996 was

       a.   4.6%.
*   b.   -4.4%.
       c.   11.8%.
       d.   18.7%.
       e.   -5.5%.

18.   The bond default risk premium for 1996 was

*   a.   2.35%.
       b.   -3.62%.
       c.   -2.30%.
       d.   24.23%.
       e.   0.47%.

19.   The inflation-adjusted long-term government bond return in 1996 was

       a.   -0.93%.
       b.   1.40%.
       c.   -5.84%.
*   d.   -4.11%.
       e.   4.29%.

20.   The large stock risk premium in 1996 was

       a.   4.6%.
*   b.   17.0%.
       c.   24.2%.
       d.   16.6%.
       e.   20.5%.

II.   SHORT ANSWER QUESTIONS

1.   Below are a set of serial correlations for the historical returns of five different asset classes:

       Asset A   +0.002
       Asset B   +0.581
       Asset C   -0.001
       Asset D   -0.350
       Asset E   +0.728

       Indicate which of the assets' returns have been random, which seem(s) to follow a trend and which seem(s) to have frequent reversals.

2.   Scott Solder will receive a distribution from a trust fund when he turns twenty-one in five years. If inflation averages 4% a year between now and the time of the distribution, how much purchasing power will Scott have lost?

3.   Compare and contrast the MSCI Index for England with the Financial Times Stock Exchange ("Footsie") Index.

4.   What is meant by a "reinvestment return?" Will this component of an asset's total return always be positive? Explain.

5.   The following information is provided for the average total returns on four different asset classes from 1926 to 1996:

	Geometric mean	Arithmetic mean
Large company stocks	10.7%	12.7%
Small company stocks	12.6%	17.7%
Long-term government bonds	5.1%	5.4%
U.S. Treasury bills	3.7%	3.8%

a.   Calculate the expected return on a long-horizon Treasury bond.

b.   Calculate the expected return on small company stocks.

CHAPTER ELEVEN: SOLUTION GUIDELINES

Multiple Choice

1.   **d**:   Indexes tend to be unaffected by events that occur within a single firm since bad (or good) news at one firm is offset by good (or bad) news at another.

2.   **e**:   Ibbotson's Large Stock Index is based on the S&P 500 Index and assumes the reinvestment of dividends. It ignores brokerage commissions, income taxes, and other transactions costs. The large stock index grew at a *nominal rate* of 12.5% a year.

3.   **b**:   In recent decades the Treasury bill rate has fluctuated above and below the inflation rate. The returns have usually been lower than that on long-term government bonds, reflecting the risk-return relationship. The average real return on Treasury bills from 1926 to 1996 was positive.

4.   **c**:   The reinvestment return component of an investment's total return is too large to ignore. Negative reinvestment returns occurred during periods when the reinvested cash dividends were used to buy stocks that were depreciating in value at the time of the reinvestment. Brokerage fees are not incorporated.

5.   **e**:   Empirical evidence indicates that the benefits of time diversification exists for every category of assets. These benefits are the result of returns reverting back toward the arithmetic mean returns in the period following extremely high or extremely low returns. This evidence argues in favor of being a long-term investor, rather than a short-term speculator.

6.   **e**:   Asset pricing models are based on the assumption that economic equilibrium exists. These models are static and assume that the standard deviation of a return is constant through time. Heteroscedasticity is a quality that is associated with unstable standard deviations.

7.   **a**:   Cross correlations measure the predictability of one series, conditional on knowing the value of another series. Serial correlations, or autocorrelations, measure the extent to which the values in one time series are related to subsequent values in the same set of data.

8.   **c**:   The serial correlation coefficients for stocks are not statistically different from zero. This indicates that stock prices move randomly and, therefore, that future stock prices cannot be predicted by observing past stock prices. The cross correlations for the returns on large company stocks and small company stocks are positive, indicating a direct relationship. The serial correlation coefficients for the inflation rate are positive, indicating that the inflation rate does not move randomly, but instead follows a trend.

9. **b**: The expected return on small cap stocks can be estimated by adding the expected return on long-term Treasury bonds, the large corporation's long-horizon equity premium, and a micro-cap equity size premium.

10. **b**: Both the MSCI Index for England and the Footsie are market value-weighted indexes, and both assume the reinvestment of cash dividends. Footsie ignores international tax considerations, but the MSCI Index includes them. The MSCI Index samples 46% more stocks than the 100 stocks included in the Footsie.

11. **d**: Total return = coupon income return + capital appreciation return + reinvestment return. Therefore, -0.93% = 6.18% + -7.37% + reinvestment return. Reinvestment return = 0.26%.

12. **b**: The arithmetic mean returns are first calculated to proxy for expected returns. The arithmetic mean return for the large company stocks is 16.038, and the arithmetic mean return for the small stocks is 14.634. The covariance of the returns is calculated as follows:

$$COV(large, small) = \frac{\begin{array}{l}(5.23 - 16.038)(-9.3 - 14.634) + (16.81 - 16.038)(22.87 - 14.634) \\ + (31.49 - 16.038)(10.18 - 14.634) + (-3.17 - 16.038)(-21.56 - 14.634) \\ + (30.55 - 16.038)(44.63 - 14.634) + (7.67 - 16.038)(23.35 - 14.634) \\ + (9.99 - 16.038)(20.98 - 14.634) + (1.31 - 16.038)(3.11 - 14.634) \\ + (37.43 - 16.038)(34.46 - 14.634) + (23.07 - 16.038)(17.62 - 14.634)\end{array}}{9}$$

$$= 203.36.$$

13. **c**: The standard deviation of the returns for the large company stocks and the small company stocks must first be calculated.

$$\sigma_{large} = \sqrt{\frac{\begin{array}{l}(5.23 - 16.038)^2 + (16.81 - 16.038)^2 + (31.49 - 16.038)^2 + (-3.17 - 16.038)^2 \\ + (30.55 - 16.038)^2 + (7.67 - 16.038)^2 + (9.99 - 16.038)^2 + (1.31 - 16.038)^2 \\ + (37.43 - 16.038)^2 + (23.07 - 16.038)^2\end{array}}{9}} = 14.01$$

The correlation coefficient is then calculated, using the covariance calculated in Question 12.

$$\rho_{large, small} = \frac{203.36}{(14.01)(19.78)} = 0.73.$$

14. **c**: The cross correlation coefficient for the long-term government bond returns and inflation is negative, so the bond returns did move inversely with inflation, but the serial correlation coefficient for the long-term government bond returns is very close to zero, indicating no ability to predict future returns from

observing past returns. Similarly, while the cross correlation coefficient for the returns on long-term government bonds and long-term corporate bonds is a high positive number, indicating that they did move closely together, the serial correlation coefficient for the long-term corporate bond returns is a very low positive number. Thus, it would not have been easy to predict future returns by observing the past annual returns on the corporate bonds. The cross correlation coefficient for the returns on large company stocks and inflation is not significantly different from zero, so inflation was not a good predictor of the returns on large company stocks. The cross correlation coefficient for the Treasury bill returns and inflation is the only one that is high enough to indicate that those returns tended to move somewhat with the rate of inflation.

15.   **a**:   The cross correlation coefficients for the returns of both the long-term government bonds and the long-term corporate bonds and inflation is negative, indicating that as inflation increased, the returns of these fixed income securities decreased. The serial correlation coefficient for the inflation rate is a significantly positive number, indicating that the inflation rate did not move randomly; it followed a trend. The serial correlation coefficient for the returns on large company stocks was not significantly different from zero, indicating that these returns followed a random pattern.

16.   **d**:   Bond horizon risk premium =

$$\frac{1 + \text{long - term government bond total return}}{1 + \text{Treasury bill total return}} - 1 = \frac{1 + (-0.0093)}{1.0521} - 1 = -5.8\%.$$

17.   **b**:   Small stock risk premium =

$$\frac{1 + \text{small stock total return}}{1 + \text{large stock total return}} - 1 = \frac{1.1762}{1.2307} - 1 = -4.4\%.$$

18.   **a**:   Bond default risk premium =

$$\frac{1 + \text{long - term corporate bond total return}}{1 + \text{long - term government bond total return}} - 1 = \frac{1.0140}{1 + (-0.0093)} - 1 = 2.35\%.$$

19.   **d**:   Inflation-adjusted long-term government bond return =

$$\frac{1 + \text{long - term government bond total return}}{1 + \text{inflation rate}} - 1 = \frac{1 + (-0.0093)}{1.0332} - 1 = -4.11\%.$$

20. **b**: Large stock risk premium =

$$\frac{1+\text{large stock total return}}{1+\text{Treasury bill total return}} - 1 = \frac{1.2307}{1.0521} - 1 = 17.0\%.$$

Short Answer

1. Serial correlations that are close to zero indicate randomness. Positive serial correlations are indicative of a trend, and negative ones indicate frequent reversals.

Asset	Serial correlation	
A	+0.002	**random**
B	+0.581	**trend**
C	-0.001	**random**
D	-0.350	**reversals**
E	+0.728	**trend**

2. Scott will have lost 82.2% of his purchasing power.

   $$1/(1.04)^5 = 0.822 = 82.2\%$$

3. Both the MSCI Index for England and the Financial Times Stock Exchange Index ("Footsie") are market value indexes. They are total return indexes and both assume the reinvestment of dividends. The MSCI Index, however, does not incorporate any local taxes that are withheld from payments to foreign investors, and no other taxes or transaction fees are deducted from the MSCI returns. Footsie ignores the international tax considerations. MSCI uses a much larger sample than does the 100-stock Footsie Index.

4. The reinvestment return component of the total return on a security is the return earned on dividend or interest income that is assumed to be reinvested in the security rather than taken as a cash flow. This component will not always be positive. If, as was the case after the market crash of 1929, the dividend or interest income is reinvested in securities that are depreciating in value, the reinvestment return will be negative.

5a. The expected return on a long-term government bond equals the expected return on a short-term Treasury bill plus a long-horizon risk premium. Since expected returns are being calculated, the arithmetic means, not the geometric means, are used. The long-horizon risk premium is calculated below.

$$\frac{1+\text{long - term government bond total return}}{1+\text{Treasury bill total return}} - 1 = \frac{1.054}{1.038} - 1 = 1.5\%.$$

The expected return on the long-term government bond is, therefore, 3.8% + 1.5% = 5.3%.

b. The expected return on small company stocks is equal to the expected long-term government bond return plus a large stock equity risk premium plus a small stock risk premium. The equity risk premium for the large company stock is calculated as follows:

$$\frac{1 + \text{large stock total return}}{1 + \text{Treasury bill total return}} - 1 = \frac{1.127}{1.038} - 1 = 8.6\%.$$

The small stock risk premium is 4.4%.

$$\frac{1 + \text{small stock total return}}{1 + \text{large stock total return}} - 1 = \frac{1.177}{1.127} - 1 = 4.4\%.$$

The expected return on small company stocks is, therefore, 5.4% + 8.6% + 4.4% = 18.4%.

CHAPTER TWELVE: USING INDEXES

I.   MULTIPLE CHOICE QUESTIONS

1.   Which of the following statements about closed-end investment companies is (are) *false*?

    a.   Shares of closed-end investment companies are bought and sold on exchange floors.

    b.   Closed-end investment companies have a fixed number of shares that they are authorized to sell; therefore, if an investor wants to buy shares of a closed-end investment company, another investor must be willing to sell the shares.

*   c.   Closed-end investment company shares will always sell for a price that is greater than or equal to the net asset value per share.

    d.   Both "b" and "c" are false statements.

    e.   All of the above are false statements.

2.   A major difference between closed-end investment companies and open-end investment companies is that

    a.   Income earned on an investment in a closed-end investment company is subject to double taxation whereas income earned on an investment in an open-end investment company is taxed only at the investor level.

    b.   Closed-end investment company shares are bought and sold directly through the company whereas open-end investment company shares are traded on exchange floors.

    c.   Open-end investment companies have a termination date that is set at origination; closed-end investment companies have no termination date.

*   d.   The shares of open-end investment companies will be purchased at a price that is greater than or equal to the net asset value per share, but the shares of a closed-end company may sometimes be purchased for less than the company's net asset value.

    e.   Both "a" and "c" are true statements.

3.   Which of the following statements regarding index mutual funds is (are) *false*?

    a.   There is a greater potential for profit since index mutual funds typically have a higher turnover ratio than actively managed funds.

    b.   Index mutual funds usually are more fully invested than actively managed funds.

    c.   Index mutual funds are more tax efficient investments than actively managed funds.

    d.   Index mutual funds are usually load funds.

*   e.   Both "a" and "d" are false statements.

4.   A unit investment trust is a type of

       a.   mutual fund.
       b.   index fund.
*   c.   closed-end investment company.
       d.   iSHARE.
       e.   pyramid scheme.

5.   A tracking error may occur because

       a.   investors must pay taxes on the income received on an index fund.
       b.   management fees reduce investors' returns.
       c.   the indexed portfolio is not invested in all the stocks that make up the targeted index.
       d.   all of the above
*   e.   only "b" and "c"

6.   Which of the following statements regarding SPDRs is (are) *false*?

       a.   A SPDR is a type of closed end investment company.
       b.   A SPDR is a type of unit investment trust.
*   c.   A SPDR is a type of index mutual fund.
       d.   SPDRs are traded continuously on the AMEX.
       e.   Investors can buy and sell odd lots of SPDRs.

7.   Which of the following is *not* an advantage of a SPDR?

       a.   SPDRs can be bought and sold throughout the trading day at market prices that are continuously updated, rather than only at market-at-close prices.
       b.   SPDRs may be sold short, even on a downtick.
       c.   Investors who execute 50,000 share transactions have the option of receiving a basket of the underlying stock rather than cash.
*   d.   SPDRs may use derivatives to reduce the risk of the portfolio.
       e.   Neither "b" nor "c" are advantages associated with SPDRs.

8.   Which of the following statement(s) about iShares is *false*?

*   a.   iShares are unit investment trusts (UITs).
       b.   iShares are passively managed portfolios.
       c.   iShares have relatively low turnover rates.
       d.   iShares are indexed to a non-U.S. stock market index.
       e.   All of the above statements are true.

9. Investors who take a long position in an S&P 500 Index futures contract

    a. enjoy any cash dividend payments made while their contract is open.
    b. have the option of receiving a basket of stocks rather than a cash settlement, which provides them with more tax management capability.
    c. will profit if the value of the S&P 500 Index falls.
*   d. must deposit a minimum margin of at least 3% of the market value of the contract before their order will be executed.
    e. Both "a" and "b" are true statements.

10. An investor who buys a put option on the S&P 500 Index

    a. has the option of receiving a basket of stocks rather than a cash settlement, which provides him with more tax management capability.
    b. has the option of delivering a SPDR if the option is exercised on him.
    c. will only exercise his option if the market value of the S&P 500 Index rises above the exercise price on the option.
*   d. will profit if the value of the S&P 500 Index falls below the exercise price by an amount that is greater than the option premium.
    e. will profit if the value of the S&P 500 Index rises above the exercise price by an amount that is greater than the option premium.

11. A manager of an S&P 500 Index mutual fund can hedge her position by

    a. buying a put option on the S&P 500 Index.
    b. entering a short position in an S&P 500 futures contract.
    c. buying a call option on the S&P 500 Index.
    d. entering a long position in an S&P 500 futures contract.
*   e. doing either "a" or "b".

12. High-yield bond funds invest in

    a. municipal bonds issued by a single or multiple entities.
*   b. junk bonds.
    c. bonds issued by blue-chip corporations.
    d. long-term government bonds.
    e. both corporate bonds and stocks that have high dividend yields.

13. The New America family of funds has 10 million shares outstanding. The current market value of its assets is $620 million and its liabilities are $150 million. The net asset value per share of the fund is

    a. $62.
*   b. $47.
    c. $15.
    d. $53.
    e. It cannot be determined without knowing the percentage load.

14. Penny purchased shares of the MedTech Fund at its net asset value of $9.66 per share. During the year she received dividends of $0.12 a share and capital gain distributions of $0.10 a share. At the end of the year, the net asset value per share of the fund was $12.00. Her one-period rate of return was

*   a.   26.5%.
        b.   21.3%.
        c.   10.1%.
        d.   25.5%.
        e.   none of the above.

15. The NewTech Fund reported an average asset value of $96,263,492 in 200X. During the year, it made purchases of $66,180,868 and received $75,167,243 from the sale of some of the assets in its portfolio. Its turnover rate was

        a.   78%.
        b.   113.6%.
*   c.   68.7%.
        d.   88%.
        e.   none of the above.

The following information is provided for Questions 16 and 17:

Sue Conita has read that the Federal Reserve is expected to decrease interest rates in the next quarter, which she expects to result in a significant increase in stock prices. Sue decides to take a long position in one futures contract on the S&P 500 Index (value = $250 times index) with a delivery date three months from now at a price of 1351. The current value of the S&P 500 Index is 1340. Her initial margin requirement is 5%.

16. To the nearest dollar, how much cash will Sue need to enter this position?

        a. $16,750
        b. $34.250
*   c. $16,888
        d. $33,512
        e. $335,000

17. By the December delivery date on Sue's contract, the S&P 500 Index increased to 1370. Calculate Sue's gain or loss on her position.

        a. $12,138 loss
*   b. $4,750 gain
        c. $7,500 gain
        d. $9,388 loss
        e.   none of the above

18.   Mark heard some analysts claim that the stock market is overpriced. Convinced by their
        arguments, he decided to buy a put on the S&P 500 Index with an exercise price of 1325.
        The option premium was 39 1/4 and the S&P 500 Index was at 1335 when he purchased
        the option. At the expiration of his option, the S&P 500 was at 1328. Calculate Mark's
        gain or loss on this position.

        a. $7 gain
        b. $3 gain
        c. $26.25 loss
        d. $32.25 loss
    *   e. $39.25 loss

19.   Jim Franklin is the manager of an S&P 500 Index mutual fund and has decided to execute
        a protective put position. He buys an at-the-money put with an exercise price of 1350.
        This position

        a.   limits the portfolio's profit potential if the S&P 500 increases in value.
    *   b.   protects against loss if the S&P 500 Index falls below 1350.
        c.   will increase in value, dollar for dollar, as the S&P 500 Index increases in
               value.
        d.   will offer the same returns as writing a call on the S&P 500 Index.
        e.   Both "b" and "d" are true statements.

20.   Josie purchased shares of a load mutual fund for $22.96 a share. The net asset
        value of the fund was $20.18. During the year, Josie received dividends and
        capital gains distributions of $1.36 a share. At the end of the year, the net asset
        value of the fund was $25.15. Josie's one-period rate of return was

        a.   27.6%.
        b.   31.4%.
        c.   21.6%.
    *   d.   15.5%.
        e.   none of the above.

II.   SHORT ANSWER QUESTIONS

1.   Jake invested $5,000 in a mutual fund that had a 4% load. The net asset value of
        the fund was $22.10, and the purchase price was $23.04. His brother, Marshall,
        also invested $5,000 in a mutual fund. Marshall's fund was a no load fund with at
        net asset value of $22.10, but the fund had a redemption fee of 1% when he sold
        his shares one year later. Both funds distributed $0.90 in dividends and capital
        gains at the end of the year, and both had a net asset value of $26.42 at the end of
        the year. Calculate each brother's rate of return.

2.   Paul Stevenson manages a midcap mutual fund with a current value of $15,000,000 and has decided to use a futures contract on the S&P Midcap 400 Index to execute an imperfect hedge for his portfolio. The futures contract is valued at $500 times the index. Paul enters a short position in 65 contracts for December delivery at 407.90. The S&P Midcap 400 Index was trading at 403.32. The initial margin requirement was 3%. By the December delivery date, the S&P 400 Midcap Index was at 363, and his portfolio's value had decreased by 10%.

a.   Had Paul not executed the hedge, what would his profit or loss have been?

b.   What is his profit or loss on the hedged position?

3.   Discuss the advantages of investing in a SPDR over investing in a traditional S&P 500 Index fund.

4.   Describe the three types of investment companies that are defined by the Investment Company Act of 1940. What are the differences among them?

5.   Describe two different techniques that can be used by a manager of an indexed fund to hedge against a decrease in the value of the fund.

CHAPTER TWELVE: SOLUTION GUIDELINES

Multiple Choice

1. **c**: Closed-end investment company shares may also sell at a price that is below their net asset value. There is a fixed number of shares and the shares are bought and sold on exchange floors.

2. **d**: Income from both closed-end and open-end investment companies is taxable at the investor level only. Shares of open-end investment companies are bought and sold directly through the company while closed-end investment company shares are traded on exchange floors. Open-end investment companies do not have termination dates. If an open-end investment company is a load fund, the purchase price will be greater than the net asset value per share; if it is a no load fund, the purchase price will be equal to the net asset value per share. Closed-end investment company shares may sell for a price that is less than the net asset value per share.

3. **e**: Index mutual funds are typically more fully invested than actively managed funds, and because they are passively managed, they are more tax-efficient investments than actively managed funds. The passive management style results in a lower, not higher, turnover ratio. Index funds are usually no load funds.

4. **c**: A unit investment trust has a fixed number of shares and, thus, is a special type of closed-end investment company.

5. **e**: Tracking errors result when the indexed fund's returns are different from that of the underlying index. The after-tax return to the investor is not a factor in this.

6. **c**: SPDRs are unit investment trusts, which are special types of closed-end investment companies, that are continuously traded on the AMEX. They have a fixed number of shares and are not, therefore, mutual funds.

7. **d**: SPDRs may not use derivatives. They may be sold short, even on a downtick. They can be bought and sold throughout the trading day at market prices that are continuously updated, and investors who execute 50,000 share transactions have the option of receiving a basket of the underlying stock rather than cash.

8. **a**: iShares are open-end investment companies that have no fixed number of shares. New shares may be created so long as there are investors wishing to buy the shares. Because they are passively managed, they have relatively low turnover rates. iShares are shares in a mutual fund that is indexed to a stock market index from a non-U.S. country.

9. **d**: Investors in S&P 500 Index futures contracts do not receive any cash dividend payments. There is only a cash settlement on the delivery date. Long positions will profit if the S&P 500 Index increases in value. The minimum initial margin requirement is 3%.

10.   **d**:   There is only a cash settlement when an investor chooses to exercise an option on the S&P 500 Index. An investor who purchases a put option will profit from a decline in the value of the index. The intrinsic value of a put option is equal to MAX(0, exercise price - market price). Therefore, before the owner of a put option will earn profits, the difference between the exercise price on the option and the market price of the underlying must be greater than the price the investor paid for the option.

11.   **e**:   If the S&P 500 Index decreases in value, the manager of an indexed fund will offset the losses to her portfolio by having a short position in an S&P 500 futures contract. She can also use a protective put to hedge her portfolio.

12.   **b**:   High-yield bonds are the high risk junk bonds. Bonds issued by blue-chip corporations are investments made by high-grade bond funds. Some municipal bonds may be classified as junk bonds, but because of their tax-exempt feature, they will not offer as high a yield as junk bonds issued by corporations. Long-term government bonds are considered default risk-free and will not offer high yields.

13.   **b**:   Net asset value per share =

$$\frac{\text{current market value of the fund's total assets - total liabilities}}{\text{total number of shares outstanding}} = \frac{\$620 \text{ million } - \$150 \text{ million}}{10 \text{ million}} = \$47.$$

14.   **a**:   Penny's one-period rate of return $= \dfrac{\$0.12 + \$0.10 + (\$12 - \$9.66)}{\$9.66} = 26.5\%.$

15.   **b**:   The turnover rate =
$$\frac{\text{MIN(annual sales, annual purchases)}}{\text{average value of portfolio's assets}} = \frac{\text{MIN}(\$75,167,243, \$66,180,868)}{\$96,263,492} = 0.687 = 68.7\%.$$

16.   **c**:   Sue will need to deposit 0.05(1351)($250) = $16,887.50 to enter this position.

17.   **b**:   Sue will have gained with her long position since the S&P 500 Index increased in value. Her gain is [1370 - 1351]($250) = $4,750.

18.   **e**:   Since the exercise price on the put option is less than the value of the S&P 500 Index at expiration, the intrinsic value of the put is zero. Mark will, therefore, let his option expire. His loss is equal to the premium paid for the put, $39.25.

19.   **b**:   A protective put protects against loss if the value of the S&P 500 Index falls below the exercise price of the put since the value of the put increases as the value of the index decreases. While the put will *reduce* potential profits by the premium paid for the put if the S&P 500 Index increases in value, it does not *limit* the portfolio's profit potential. A writer of a call will also profit if the value of the S&P 500 Index falls, but the call writer's profits are limited to the premium received for writing the option.

20.   **d**:   Josie's one-period rate of return is $\dfrac{\$1.36 + (\$25.15 - \$22.96)}{\$22.96} = 15.5\%$.

Short Answer

1.   Since Jake's fund was a load fund, he purchased only $5,000/$23.04 = 217.01 shares with his $5,000 investment. His return was

$$\frac{\$0.90(217.01) + (\$26.42 - \$23.04)(217.01)}{\$5,000} = 18.6\%.$$

Marshall purchased $5,000/$22.10 = 226.24 shares of his fund at its net asset value. However, when he sold the shares, he received only $26.42(1 - 0.01) = $26.16 a share. His return was

$$\frac{\$0.90(226.24) + (\$26.16 - \$22.10)(226.24)}{\$5,000} = 22.4\%.$$

2a.   If Paul had not hedged the portfolio, his loss would be 10% of his portfolio's value or 0.10($15,000,000) = $1,500,000.

b.   Paul's gain on the futures position offsets part of the 10% decrease in the value of his portfolio. His net loss is only $40,750.

Decrease in portfolio value	($1,500,000)
Gain on futures position = $500(407.90)(65) - $500(363)(65)	$1,459,250
Net loss	($ 40,750)

3.   Unlike the traditional S&P 500 Index funds, SPDRs are traded continuously on AMEX. Investors can buy and sell SPDRs at continuously updated market prices rather than at market-close only prices. Investors may also sell SPDRs short, even on a downtick. Because SPDR Trust managers may not use derivatives, no counterparty risks are involved. Traditional index funds may trade derivatives, which exposes investors to counterparty risk. Additionally, if the manager of a traditional index fund misuses the derivatives, large tracking errors may result.

   In addition to the market order, investors may also use other types of orders when purchasing or selling SPDRs; this option is not available to investors in traditional indexed mutual funds. Finally, if an investor executes a 50,000 share transaction, he can choose to receive a basket of the underlying stocks rather than the cash settlement. This is a tax efficient way to execute the transaction since any price gains that might have occurred while the SPDRs were held are not realized for tax purposes in a payment-in-kind transaction.

4. The Investment Company Act of 1940 defines the following three different types of investment companies:

    (1) Open-end investment companies, also known as mutual funds, have no fixed number of shares. The fund can create new shares so long as investors wish to buy shares of the fund. Shares are bought and sold directly through the fund.

    (2) Closed-end investment companies have a fixed number of shares. The shares are bought and sold on exchange floors.

    (3) Unit investment trusts (UITs) are rigidly defined closed-end investment companies. In addition to having a fixed number of shares, a UIT has a termination date that is specified when it is created. Furthermore, unlike other closed-end investment companies, securities held by the UIT may not be actively traded by the portfolio manager.

5. A manager of an indexed fund can enter a short position in a futures contract on the index to hedge against a decrease in the value of the fund. If the value of the index decreases, the loss on the fund's portfolio will be offset by a gain on the futures position. Alternatively, a manager of an indexed fund can buy a put option on the index. If the value of the index decreases, the value of the put option increases and offsets the losses to his portfolio.

CHAPTER THIRTEEN: ASSET ALLOCATION

I.   MULTIPLE CHOICE QUESTIONS

1.   A defined benefit pension plan

      a.   is a profit-sharing plan.

      b.   entitles the pensioners to nothing if the portfolio is badly managed and
goes bankrupt.

*   c.   is more difficult to manage than a defined contribution plan.

      d.   Both a and b are true statements.

      e.   All of the above are true statements.

2.   Gary estimates that he will have accumulated $800,000 when he retires in ten
years, and he expects inflation to average 3.5% a year over this period. To the
nearest dollar, the purchasing power of his $800,000 in ten years will be
equivalent to how much today?

      a. $1,128,479

*   b. $567,135

      c. $772,947

      d. $828,000

      e.   none of the above

3.   Analysts who study historical market data in hopes of finding patterns that will
repeat themselves in the future are known as

      a.   risk-return analysts.

      b.   fundamental analysts.

      c.   graphic analysts.

*   d.   technical analysts.

      e.   pattern analysts.

4.   An asset allocation strategy that is used to derive long-run asset allocation weights
that are not changed when capital market conditions experience temporary
changes is known as

      a.   insured asset allocation.

      b.   dynamic asset allocation.

      c.   tactical asset allocation.

      d.   integrated asset allocation.

*   e.   strategic asset allocation.

5.   An asset allocation strategy that gives simultaneous consideration to the investor's goals and policies and capital market conditions and uses these data as inputs to an optimizer is known as

     a.   insured asset allocation.
     b.   dynamic asset allocation.
     c.   tactical asset allocation.
*   d.   integrated asset allocation.
     e.   strategic asset allocation.

6.   The asset allocation decision

*   a.   involves selecting the classes of assets in which funds will be invested.
     b.   should focus on selecting assets that are expected to offer the highest return over the investment horizon.
     c.   refers to the decision on what specific securities the funds should be used to purchase.
     d.   should be strictly adhered to throughout the investment horizon in order to maintain a well-diversified portfolio.
     e.   Both "b" and "c" are true statements.

7.   Stacey reported the following income on her tax return:

Short-term capital gains $8,000   Short-term capital losses $10,800
Long-term capital gains $15,000   Long-term capital losses $7,000

Stacey pays taxes on long-term capital gains at a rate of 20%, and her ordinary income is taxed at a rate of 28%. Stacey's tax liability on her investment income is

*   a. $1,040.
     b. $2,160.
     c. $816.
     d. $5,240.
     e.   none of the above.

8.	Which of the following statements about the asset allocation process is (are) *true*?

    a.	One hundred percent of an investor's funds should be invested in an IRA, if possible.

    b.	Tax consequences should not be a concern of the asset allocator; the investor must be solely responsible for tax management.

    c.	A good investment policy statement should be as restrictive as possible to insure that the money manager behaves in the client's best interest.

*	d.	The risk-return preferences of the client should be clearly stated in the investment policy statement.

    e.	Selections "c" and "d" are both true.

9.	A client should expect her asset allocator to

    a.	invest only in securities expected to outperform the market.

    b.	perform technical analysis in order to time the market.

*	c.	study current conditions, analyze alternatives, and forecast likely outcomes.

    d.	examine the financial data of individual companies closely to find underpriced securities.

    e.	all of the above

The following information is provided for four clients and is to be used to answer Questions 10, 11, 12, and 13:

Tom is a single, twenty-six year old and is employed by one of the nation's largest software producers in Boston. His annual salary is $68,000, and he takes advantage of a discount stock purchase plan offered by his employer. He is in good health, has health insurance provided by his employer, and his income more than meets his current needs. He enjoys going on gambling junkets to Atlantic City and studying the stock market in his spare time. In addition to saving for retirement, he wants to save for a down payment on a home that he hopes to be able to buy in the next five years.

Rich is forty years old and is married with two sons, ages nine and eleven. He works as an independent contractor, laying carpet, and earns $35,000 a year. His wife, Jean, works part-time at a daycare center and earns $10,000 a year. Rich and Jean barely make ends meet although they live conservatively. The only retirement plan they have at this time is social security. Jean recently received, however, an inheritance of $160,000, and Rich and Jean would like to invest it in hopes that they can both retire when Rich turns sixty. The inheritance also included an educational endowment for their children, so they no longer have to worry about funding their sons' college education. They are concerned with liquidity as well, since they have only catastrophic health insurance. They claim total ignorance when it comes to the investment vehicles available.

Mary is a sixty-two year old homemaker and a recent widow. As her husband's sole beneficiary, she received $50,000 from his life insurance company, and she receives benefits from his retirement plan as well as social security benefits, but this income falls about $250 short of covering all her monthly expenses. Upon the death of her husband, Mary sold their lavish home and purchased a condominium, netting $275,000. She is in good health and expects to live for another twenty-five years, at least. Her husband had handled all their financial affairs, and Mary is just learning how to balance her checkbook.

Bob and Regina are in their early thirties and married to each other. They have no children and do not plan to start a family at any point in the future. They both work in the health care industry and have a combined annual income of $142,000. They have no immediate money problems and live a fairly conservative life style. They have learned that they can each contribute to a tax-sheltered annuity plan offered by their employers and have been given several families of mutual funds into which they can designate their contributions to go. Neither has any knowledge regarding what types of funds they should select, however. They are willing to assume only moderate levels of risk.

10.   Which of the clients could be expected to have the *greatest* percentage of funds allocated to an aggressive growth mutual fund?

*   a.   Tom
        b.   Rich and Jean
        c.   Mary
        d.   Bob and Regina
        e.   None of the clients should have any funds directed to an aggressive growth mutual fund.

11.   A good candidate for a large percentage of Bob and Regina's tax-sheltered annuity funds would be a

        a.   municipal bond fund.
        b.   long-term government bond fund.
*   c.   S&P 500 Index fund.
        d.   money market fund.
        e.   Either a or b would be good candidates.

12.   Which of the clients is most likely to have municipal bonds as part of their asset allocation?

*   a.   Tom
        b.   Rich and Jean
        c.   Mary
        d.   Bob and Regina
        e.   None of the clients should have any funds invested in municipal bonds since they offer lower yields than similar risk investments.

13. Which of the clients will need to have a large percentage of their assets in a money market mutual fund?

        I.   Tom
        II.   Rich and Jean
        III.   Mary
        IV.   Bob and Regina

    a.   I and II
*   b.   II and III
    c.   III only
    d.   IV only
    e.   II and IV

14. The following are three model portfolios:

    I.   Cash/money market fund: 30%; high-grade bonds: 20%; blue-chip stocks: 20%; income stocks: 10%; aggressive growth stocks: 10%; foreign stocks: 10%.
    II.   Cash/money market fund: 10%; high-grade bonds: 10%; foreign stocks: 25%; blue-chip stocks: 25%; income stocks: 5%; aggressive growth stocks: 25%.
    III.   Cash/money market fund: 20%; high-grade bonds: 20%; foreign stocks: 15%; blue-chip stocks: 25%; income stocks: 10%; aggressive growth stocks: 10%.

Which portfolio best represents the asset allocation for a low risk investor?

*   a.   I
    b.   II
    c.   III
    d.   either II or III
    e.   None of the above; a low risk investor should be entirely invested in government securities and/or money market funds.

15.   Arrange the following steps of the asset allocation process in the order in which they should take place:

I.   The asset allocator uses market index data to educate the client.
II.   The asset allocator allocates the portfolio's funds to categories of assets.
III.   The client and asset allocator work up a written policy statement.
IV.   The asset allocator learns about the client's financial position, goals, constraints, and the risk-return preferences of the investor.

   a.   I, II, III, IV
   b.   III, I, II, IV
   c.   IV, III, I, III
   d.   I, IV, III, II
* e.   IV, I, III, II

16.   Greg has estimated that he will have $750,000 accumulated at retirement. He expects to be able to earn a nominal after-tax return of 8% on his money at that point. If he expects to live for forty years after he retires, how much can he spend each year after he retires without running out of money?

   a. $18,750
* b. $62,895
   c. $60,000
   d. $24,982
   e. $41,776

17.   Which of the following statements about the Unified Transfer Tax is (are) *true*?

   a.   The estate-tax exclusions available are indexed for inflation and, therefore, change every year.
   b.   Only those with estates in excess of $1 million need to be concerned about the Unified Transfer Tax.
* c.   The Unified Transfer Tax levies a tax on gifts given during one's lifetime as well as on estates.
   d.   A payment made by a donor to a hospital to cover the medical expenses of the recipient will be counted as part of the annual gift tax exclusion amount in determining the gift tax that must be paid.
   e.   Both c and d are true statements.

18.   Which of the following portfolios could *not* lie on the efficient frontier defined by Markowitz?

		Expected return	Standard deviation
a.	Portfolio A	12.5%	18.2%
b.	Portfolio B	18.0%	32.3%
* c.	Portfolio C	10.0%	20.4%
d.	Portfolio D	15.1%	22.2%
e.	Portfolio E	5.0%	3.1%

19.   A Markowitz efficient portfolio

   a.   has the maximum expected return for its level of risk.
   b.   has the minimum level of risk for its level of expected return.
   c.   has all risk diversified away, so its standard deviation will equal zero.
   d.   will contain all risky assets.
* e.   both "a" and "b" are true statements.

20.   One of the first measures an asset allocator must take is to

   a.   liquidate all of the client's non-discretionary assets in order to have more control over the client's portfolio.
   b.   convince the client to accept more risk than he is comfortable in assuming in order to maximize the portfolio's returns.
* c.   determine the client's financial position, goals, constraints, and risk-return preferences.
   d.   decide how to allocate the client's assets in order to obtain the maximum possible real returns.
   e.   convince the client that his funds are best managed by a professional money manager with little interference from the client.

II.   SHORT ANSWER QUESTIONS

1.   Bonnie, a thirty-six year old single woman, is a new client, and in your initial meetings with her, you have been impressed. Bonnie has been working and earning a substantial income since her graduation from college fourteen years ago and is in the 28% tax bracket. She has wisely contributed the maximum allowed to her employer's tax sheltered annuity plans each year, and you have ascertained that she will have no difficulty meeting her retirement goals by the time she is sixty. She is in good health and has an exceptional health care plan through her employer. She has been accumulating her savings in a money market fund, however, and has been disappointed with the 5% annual return that she has been receiving on her current balance of $120,000. While she has no formal training in investments, she realizes that she could allocate her funds to receive a higher return. She is willing to take on a moderate level of risk in order to do so. She does plan to use $20,000 of the money she has saved for a down payment on a small condo, but wants you to help her decide on how best to invest the remaining

$100,000, as well as her future savings, which she expects to be about $12,000 a year. Her goals are to use this money to travel and to have money available for periodic purchases, such as new cars and new furniture as the necessity arises. Which of the following asset allocations would best meet her needs? Explain.

I.   Cash/money market fund: 30%; high-grade bonds: 20%; blue-chip stocks: 20%; income stocks: 10%; aggressive growth stocks: 10%; foreign stocks: 10%.

II. Cash/money market fund: 10%; high-grade municipal bonds: 5%; foreign stocks: 25%; blue-chip stocks: 25%; income stocks: 25%; aggressive growth stocks: 10%.

III. Cash/money market fund: 10%; high-grade municipal bonds: 25%; foreign stocks: 15%; blue-chip stocks: 15%; growth stocks: 25%; aggressive growth stocks: 10%.

2.   Fielding and Associates is a financial planning firm. The CEO and founder, Bob Fielding, was trained in economics and develops three or four possible economic scenarios every quarter. He establishes a probability distribution for the scenarios, forecasts the quarterly returns for domestic stocks and bonds (both corporate and long-term government bonds) under each scenario and uses the input to calculate expected returns and standard deviations for each of the three categories of assets. Mr. Fielding then uses historical covariances to forecast the expected returns and standard deviations for various combinations of these assets. The financial planners use this information to change the allocation weights of each of their client's portfolios every quarter to duplicate the combination that is expected to offer the highest return for the least risk. Comment on this strategy.

3.   Jeremy is 28 years old and is single. He is a buyer for a large sporting goods retail chain and has a 401K plan with his employer. Jeremy took an investments course when he was in college and learned all about the benefits of a passively managed portfolio. He decided to follow that strategy and, as a result, is directing 100% of his 401K monies into an S&P 500 Index fund. Additionally, Jeremy has been investing all of his discretionary funds into the same S&P 500 Index fund. His goal is to retire when he is 55 years old. Comment on Jeremy's strategy.

4.   Catherine O'Leary is in the 28% marginal tax bracket. She is trying to decide between two bond funds. One is a high-grade municipal bond fund that is yielding 6.8%, and the other is a high-grade corporate bond fund that is yielding 9%. (Assume that the entire yield for both funds comes from interest income.)

a.   Which is the better choice for Catherine?

b.   If the rate of inflation is 3.1%, what will Catherine's real return be on this investment?

5.   Cliff Caldwell is sixty-two years old and has recently retired and received a $650,000 lump sum distribution from his retirement plan, which he has deposited in a savings

account that pays 5% a year in interest. He reasons that this will give him $32,500 a year in income, which is about what is expenses are. He is comfortable with this since he also receives social security payments of $800 a month, which he feels he can spend on splurges. Construct a table to illustrate the purchasing power of Cliff's $650,000 principal and his real annual interest income in 5, 10, 15, and 20 years if the inflation rate averages 3.5% a year over the next 20 years.

CHAPTER THIRTEEN: SOLUTION GUIDELINES

Multiple Choice

1. **c**: A defined benefit pension plan stipulates the benefits that the employee will receive upon retirement whereas a defined contribution pension plan does not. Therefore, the defined benefit plan manager must earn an average rate of return on the portfolio that will meet the cash outflow requirements as the plan members retire. Defined contribution plan members are not guaranteed anything.

2. **b**: The purchasing power of Gary's retirement money ten years from now is $\$800,000/(1.035)^{10} = \$567,135$.

3. **d**: This is the definition of a technical analyst.

4. **e**: This is the definition of strategic asset allocation.

5. **d**: This is the definition of integrated asset allocation.

6. **a**: The asset allocation decision involves selecting the classes of assets, rather than the specific securities, in which to invest. It needs to be based on the objectives and constraints of the investor, which may not be investing to offer the highest expected return. It must be revisited regularly to insure that the objectives and constraints are still being met and to make any necessary changes if the objectives and constraints are modified due to changes in the investor's circumstances.

7. **a**: Stacey's net short-term losses are netted against her net long-term gains to determine her taxable income.

$ 8,000	short-term gains	$15,000	long-term gains
$10,500	short-term losses	$ 7,000	long-term losses
$ 2,800	net short-term losses	$ 8,000	net long-term gains

Net taxable long-term gain = $8,000 - $2,800 = $5,200. Her tax liability is, therefore, 0.2($5,200) = $1,040.

8. **d**: Because of withdrawal penalties associated with an IRA, it would be unwise for all of an investor's funds to be invested in an IRA; liquidity needs must be considered. The asset allocator should consider the investor's tax situation when constructing the portfolio in order to try to minimize the investor's taxes. The allocator also needs the consider the risk-return preferences of the client, and these need to be clearly stated in the investment policy statement. The statement should not be so restrictive, however, as to prevent the asset allocator from taking advantage of some opportunities that may arise that would increase the client's return without affecting his risk.

9.   **c**:   Typically, the only way to outperform the market is to invest in assets that are riskier than average, which may not conform to the investor's risk-return preferences. Furthermore, it is unlikely that technical analysis will allow an asset allocator to time the market or that fundamental analysis will allow the allocator to find underpriced securities. Therefore, the best that a client can hope for is that the allocator studies current conditions, analyzes alternatives, and forecasts likely outcomes in order to allocate the funds wisely and in accordance with the client's investment objectives and constraints.

10.   **a**:   Of the four clients listed, Tom appears to have the least risk aversion. He also is able to accept more risk since he is young, and one of his investment goals is saving for retirement. Bob and Regina may have some small portion of their funds invested in aggressive growth stocks, but they have stipulated that they want to be exposed to only moderate risk. Rich and Jean may also have a small portion of their funds invested in aggressive growth stocks in order to earn a return that will allow them to reach their retirement goal. However, they are not in a situation to allow them to be exposed to as much risk as Tom. They have a need for liquidity, and they also have a shorter investment horizon than Tom. Mary is older and one of her primary needs is preservation of principal; she also needs to supplement her current income. None of her portfolio should be invested in aggressive growth funds, which offer high risk and no current income.

11.   **c**:   Bob and Regina do not seem to have need for much liquidity, so very little of their funds should be allocated to a money market mutual fund. A municipal bond fund is not a good alternative for a tax-sheltered annuity since the tax-exempt feature of the municipal bond interest is of no value in a TSA, but the bonds still offer a lower yield than similar risk investments because of it. A long-term government bond fund also offers lower yields due to their lower risk, and, thus, lower real returns. Bob and Regina need to invest more in assets that offer higher real returns if they wish to maintain their present lifestyle after they retire. An S&P 500 Index fund will offer them higher expected real returns and expose them to only moderate risk levels, which is one of their criteria.

12.   **a**:   Both Tom and Bob and Regina are in marginal tax brackets that would make municipal bonds a likely investment. However, Bob and Regina are interested in a fund in which to direct their tax-sheltered annuity funds. Municipal bonds would not be a good investment vehicle for a TSA since the tax-exempt feature of the municipal bond interest is of no value, but the bonds still offer a lower yield than similar risk investments because of this feature. An allocation in municipal bonds for Tom would allow him to accumulate tax-free income with which to save for a downpayment on a home.

13.   **b**:   Both Rich and Jean and Mary have greater liquidity needs than do Tom or Bob and Regina; thus these two clients would have more of their funds allocated to a money market mutual fund.

14.   **a**:   A low risk investor will have the greatest percentage of his funds invested in a money market fund. He will also have the bulk of the remainder of his funds invested in

high-grade bonds and blue-chip stocks. Portfolio I has 70% of the funds divided among these three asset classes. Portfolio II, with 50% allocated to foreign stocks and aggressive growth stocks, is a high risk portfolio, while Portfolio III is structured for a more moderate risk investor.

15. **e**: The first step of the asset allocation process is for the client and the asset allocator to become familiar with each other. The asset allocator then needs to educate his clients regarding realistic risk-return expectations. A written policy statement is then developed, after which the asset allocator allocates the funds in accordance with the objectives and constraints outlined in the policy statement.

16. **b**: Greg will have $62,895 a year to spend.

$$\$750,000 = \text{pmt} \sum_{t=1}^{40} \frac{1}{(1.08)^t}$$
$$\text{pmt} = \$62,895$$

17. **c**: Estate-tax exclusions are not indexed for inflation. The Unified Transfer Tax also affects gifts given during one's lifetime, not only estates; however, payments made to cover medical expenses of the recipient are not considered part of the gifted amount so long as the payments are made directly to the institution that provided the services.

18. **c**: The efficient frontier is comprised of those portfolios that offer the highest return for each level of risk and the lowest risk for each level of return. Portfolio C could not lie on the efficient frontier since it offers a lower return, but has a higher level of risk, than portfolio A.

19. **e**: A Markowitz efficient portfolio is one that has the highest return for each level of risk and the lowest risk for each level of return. The portfolio does not necessarily contain all risky assets, nor is all the risk diversified away.

20. **c**: The very first step that an asset allocator must take is to get to know his client.

Short Answer

1. Portfolio III would be the best choice for Bonnie. She has little need for liquidity, so only 10% is allocated to a money market fund. Another 40% is invested in high-grade municipal bonds and blue-chip stocks, with only 25% in the riskier foreign stocks and aggressive growth stocks. Of the three portfolios listed, this would meet her requirement for moderate risk. Bonnie is also in need of some tax-preferenced investments. The 25% allocation to municipal bonds and 35% in growth stocks and aggressive growth stocks, which offer most, if not all, of their return as capital gain income, provides this benefit.

2. While Mr. Fielding has the right idea in attempting to forecast returns, there are several weaknesses associated with his methods. First, Mr. Fielding should be using expected covariances, rather than historical covariances, as inputs. A second problem is in the

frequency in which his client's portfolios are adjusted. The quarterly adjustments result in tax consequences to the clients, and their annual after-tax returns may end up being less than what they would have been otherwise. Third, all the clients' portfolios are adjusted without consideration of each individual client's objectives and constraints. The allocations should differ based on each investor's risk-return preferences as well as other unique needs of the individual investor.

3. A passively managed portfolio has the advantage of lower transactions costs and is more tax-efficient than actively managed portfolios. However, Jeremy's portfolio is not as well diversified as it should be with 100% of his funds directed into the same S&P 500 Index mutual fund. First of all, the S&P 500 is comprised of only large, domestic stocks. Jeremy should also allocate part of his funds to foreign stocks, growth stocks, and aggressive growth stocks, particularly if he wishes to meet his goal of retiring at the age of 55. While these investments are riskier, they also have higher expected returns. He could do this by investing in passively managed funds that are indexed to a small cap index, a mid cap index, and a foreign stock index (such as the EAFE Index). He should also consider diversifying across fund managers and not putting all of the funds that he wants to keep invested in and S&P 500 Index fund in the same S&P 500 Index fund.

4a. Catherine's after-tax return on the corporate bond fund would be 9%(1 - 0.28) = 6.48%. Since the municipal bond fund is yielding 6.8%, it is the better investment for her.

b. Catherine's real return would be 6.8% - 3.1% = 3.7%.

5. Cliff's purchasing power is eroded over the years.

	Purchasing power of $650,000 @ 3.5% inflation rate	Interest rate	Real annual interest income
Today	$650,000	5%	$32,500
5 years	$547,283	5%	$27,364
10 years	$460,797	5%	$23,040
15 years	$387,979	5%	$19,399
20 years	$326,668	5%	$16,333

CHAPTER FOURTEEN: PORTFOLIO ANALYSIS

I. MULTIPLE CHOICE QUESTIONS

1. Diversifiable risk includes which one of the following sources?

    a. systematic purchasing power risk
  * b. unsystematic default risk
    c. bull and bear market risk
    d. inflation-induced interest rate risk
    e. "b," "c," and "d" only

2. Which of the following statements accurately describes undiversifiable risk?

  * a. It is caused by changes in the political, economic or sociological environment that affects all assets at the same time.
    b. It leads to default and, frequently, even bankruptcy.
    c. It can be reduced to zero by diversifying an investment portfolio across enough different assets.
    d. It is caused by the factors that affect only low-quality market assets.
    e. Both "a" and "c" describe undiversifiable risk.

3. Dominant assets have which of the following characteristics?

    a. the highest rate of return
    b. the lowest risk
  * c. the highest return in their risk class
    d. a negative correlation with all other assets
    e. both "a" and "b"

4. Simple (or naïve) diversification is best described by which of the following statements?

  * a. It is as effective as diversifying across industries as a way to reduce risk.
    b. It is almost completely futile as a means of reducing risk.
    c. It is the most effective risk-reduction technique available.
    d. It is effective as a way to reduce systematic risk.
    e. Both "a" and "d" describe simple diversification.

5. Markowitz diversification is best described by which of the following statements?

    a. It maximizes the portfolio's return.
    b. It selects the minimum risk assets with which to construct portfolios.
  * c. The correlation coefficient of the assets' returns is the key delineating the efficient frontier.
    d. All of the above describe Markowitz diversification.
    e. Only "a" and "b" describe Markowitz diversification.

6.   Stocks A, B, and C each have the same expected return and standard deviation. Given the following correlation matrix, which portfolio constructed from these stocks has the lowest risk?

Correlation Matrix

Stock	A	B	C
A	+1.0		
B	+0.8	+1.0	
C	+0.1	- 0.3	+1.0

       a.   a portfolio equally invested in stocks A and B
       b.   a portfolio equally invested in stocks A and C
*   c.   a portfolio equally invested in stocks B and C
       d.   a portfolio totally invested in stock C
       e.   Selections "a" and "b" would result in equally risky portfolios.

7.   Which of the following statements about portfolio diversification is (are) *true*?

       a.   Proper diversification can reduce or eliminate systematic risk.
       b.   The risk-reducing benefits of diversification do not occur until at least 10 to 15 individual securities have been purchased.
       c.   Because diversification reduces a portfolio's total risk, it necessarily reduces the portfolio's expected return.
*   d.   Typically, as more securities are added to a portfolio, total risk would be expected to fall at a decreasing rate.
       e.   All of the above are true statements.

8.   Which of the following statements regarding superfluous diversification is (are) *true*?

       a.   It will reduce risk in the same way as simple diversification, but it has accompanying disadvantages.
       b.   The administrative costs of tracking a large number of investments can be prohibitive.
       c.   It will minimize total risk.
       d.   All of the above are true statements.
*   e.   Only "a" and "b" are true statements.

9.   Which of the following is the most important factor in determining the risk of a well-diversified portfolio?

       a.   the expected returns of the securities in the portfolio
       b.   the weights invested in each security in the portfolio
       c.   the variance of the returns of each security in the portfolio
*   d.   the covariances of the returns of each pair of securities in the portfolio
       e.   all of the above

10. The slope of the Capital Allocation Line (CAL) represents

    a.   the total risk of an asset
    b.   the expected return of an asset
    c.   the systematic risk of an asset
*   d.   the risk premium received for each additional unit of risk
    e.   none of the above

The following information is supplied for use in Questions 11, 12, and 13:

$$RFR = 6\%$$
$$E(r_R) = 14\%$$
$$\sigma_R = 18\%$$

where $E(r_R)$ is the expected return on risky asset, R, and σ_R is the standard deviation of the returns on risky asset, R.

11. Determine the expected return and standard deviation of a portfolio that consists of investing 30% in the risk-free asset and 70% in risky asset, R.

    a. $E(r_p) = 11.6\%$, $\sigma_p = 25.6\%$
*   b. $E(r_p) = 11.6\%$, $\sigma_p = 12.6\%$
    c. $E(r_p) = 14.4\%$, $\sigma_p = 9.8\%$
    d. $E(r_p) = 9.8\%$, $\sigma_p = 12.6\%$
    e.   cannot be determined without knowing the covariance of the returns on the risk-free asset and the risky asset, R

12. What is the reward-to-variability ratio of the Asset Allocation Line defined by the given parameters?

    a.   0.78
    b.   2.33
*   c.   0.44
    d.   1.11
    e.   none of the above

13. Determine the expected return and standard deviation of a portfolio that consists of borrowing 30% of the investment funds at the risk-free rate and investing all the funds in risky asset, R.

*   a. $E(r_p) = 16.4\%$, $\sigma_p = 23.4\%$

        b. $E(r_p) = 12.2\%$, $\sigma_p = 18\%$

        c. $E(r_p) = 20.0\%$, $\sigma_p = 23.4\%$

        d. $E(r_p) = 20.0\%$, $\sigma_p = 44.4\%$

        e.   cannot be determined without knowing the covariance of the returns on the risk-free asset and the risky asset, R

14. Which of the following statements about indifference curves is (are) *true*?

        a.   The indifference curves of risk-averse investors will always slope downward.

        b.   The indifference curves of risk-loving investors will consist of parallel horizontal lines.

        c.   Given a single indifference curve, an investor will prefer to invest in an asset that plots on the furthest point to the right.

*   d.   Given a set of indifference curves, an investor will prefer to invest in an asset that plots on the highest curve.

        e.   Both "c" and "d" are true.

15. Which of the following statements about correlation coefficients is true?

        a.   Even if the correlation coefficient for the returns of two securities is +1.0, some risk reduction can take place if appropriate weights are chosen.

*   b.   If the returns of two securities are perfectly negatively correlated, it is possible to determine weights such that all risk is eliminated.

        c.   Investing in two securities for which the correlation coefficient of the returns is -1.0 will always offer a lower expected return than investing in two securities for which the returns are uncorrelated.

        d.   In order to reduce the amount of risk on a portfolio, securities selected must have negatively-correlated returns. Positive correlations result only in risk averaging.

        e.   While it is a good theory, in reality it is impossible to find assets with uncorrelated returns.

16.   Consider the following two assets:

Asset	Stock price	Expected return	Standard deviation
M	$30.00	18%	23%
N	$55.00	14%	19%

$\rho_{M,N} = 0.4$

Calculate the expected return and standard deviation of a portfolio that consists of 150 shares of M and 100 shares of N.

    a. $E(r_p) = 16.4\%$, $\sigma_p = 18.2\%$

    b. $E(r_p) = 16.4\%$, $\sigma_p = 0$

    c. $E(r_p) = 15.8\%$, $\sigma_p = 16.9\%$

*   d. $E(r_p) = 15.8\%$, $\sigma_p = 17.4\%$

    e.   none of the above

17.   A negative weight

    a.   is not permissible in Markowitz portfolio analysis.
    b.   is used to represent a short sale.
    c.   is used to represent a margined position.
*   d.   both "b" and "c"
    e.   none of the above

18.   Security A has an expected return of 8% with a standard deviation of 1.5%. Security B has an expected return of 12% with a standard deviation of 2.4%. The two securities have a correlation coefficient of 0.20. If you invest 40% of your funds in Security A and 60% in security B, the standard deviation of the portfolio will be

    a.   11.84%.
    b.   3.44%.
    c.   2.61%.
*   d.   1.67%.
    e.   none of the above.

19. Which of the following statements is *false*?

    a. If two securities' returns have a covariance of zero, their correlation coefficient will also be equal to zero.

*   b. As the number of assets in a portfolio increases, the risk of the portfolio increases.

    c. The risk of a portfolio declines as assets that are not perfectly correlated with the assets already contained in the portfolio are added.

    d. If the assets in a portfolio are perfectly positively correlated, no risk diversification takes place.

    e. All of the above statements are true.

20. Which of the following is an example of undiversifiable risk?

*   a. the risk that a nation will enter a war

    b. the risk that a certain airline company will file for bankruptcy

    c. the risk that a company will win a lawsuit it has filed against a competitor for patent infringement

    d. the risk that the CEO of a company will leave the company for a similar position with a competitor

    e. only a, b, and c

II. SHORT ANSWER QUESTIONS

1. Olaf has invested his money in 500 shares of Stock X, which is selling for $30 a share and has an expected return of 15% with a standard deviation of 6%, and 400 shares of Stock Y, which is selling for $12.50 a share and has an expected return of 20% with a standard deviation of 9%. The returns of the two stocks have a correlation coefficient of +1.0.

    a. What is the expected return on Olaf's portfolio?

    b. What is the risk of Olaf's investment, as measured by the standard deviation?

    c. Is Olaf any better off investing in this portfolio of two securities than if he had invested all of his money in Stock X or all of it in Stock Y? Explain.

2. Abdul currently holds a portfolio of securities that has an expected return of 13.5% with a standard deviation of 5.2%. He is considering adding one of the following three securities to his portfolio:

Security	Expected return	Standard deviation	Correlation of returns with Abdul's existing portfolio returns
1	15.0%	5.78%	+0.9
2	12.0%	4.62%	-0.2
3	11.8%	4.55%	0

Which security would be Abdul's best choice? Why?

3. Consider the following information about a bond issued by the Gengis Corporation, an Asian company, and a stock issued by the Bosnic Corporation, an American company:

Security	Expected return	Standard deviation of returns
Gengis bond	8%	5%
Bosnic stock	13%	18%

$\rho_{G,B} = -1.0$

What weights must be invested in each to construct a zero-risk portfolio?

4. Anita recently attended a seminar and learned about the benefits of diversification. She had been considering investing all of her available funds in the All American Tech Stock Fund, but has now decided to allocate her funds evenly among four funds that are offered by All American--the All American Tech Stock Fund, the All American Tech Leaders Fund, the All American Tech Innovators Fund, and the All American E-Commerce Fund. Comment on Anita's strategy.

5. Consider an N-asset portfolio that is constructed such that equal weights are invested in each of the assets ($w_1 = w_2 = w_3 = \ldots = w_N$). Also assume that all of the assets have the same expected return and variances and that the returns of all pairs of the assets are uncorrelated. Demonstrate mathematically how the risk of this portfolio will approach zero as the number of assets, N, increases.

CHAPTER FOURTEEN: SOLUTION GUIDELINES

Multiple Choice

1. **b**: Diversifiable risk is unsystematic risk. Systematic risk affects all firms to some extent. Systematic purchasing power risk, bear and bull market risk, and inflation-induced interest rate risk are all non-diversifiable.

2. **a**: Undiversifiable risk affects all firms and is caused by changes in the political, economic or sociological environment. Risk that affects only one firm or a small number of firms is diversifiable.

3. **c**: Dominant assets offer the highest return for their level of risk and the minimum risk for their level of return.

4. **a**: Nothing can diversify away systematic risk, but simple diversification has been proven just as effective as diversifying across industries in reducing the risk. It is not, however, the most effective risk-reduction technique available.

5. **c**: The efficient frontier contains those portfolios that offer the highest return for each level of risk and the minimum risk for each level of return. It is the correlation coefficients of each pair of assets in the portfolio that will determine the amount of risk that can be diversified away, without affecting expected returns.

6. **c**: The lowest risk portfolio would be comprised of stocks for which the returns are negatively correlated.

7. **d**: No amount of diversification can reduce systematic risk, since it is undiversifiable. Holding even two assets for which the returns are not perfectly positively correlated will reduce some of the risk of the portfolio. Expected returns are not affected. Once a number of securities has been added to a portfolio, the total risk reduction potential declines since most of the unsystematic (diversifiable) risk will have already been diversified away.

8. **e**: Total risk can be minimized without superfluous diversification, which has several disadvantages, including high search costs, poorer portfolio management and the inclusion of lackluster performers.

9. **d**: In a well-diversified portfolio, the funds are assumed to be spread evenly across the assets. Individual variances become less and less important as the number of assets increases. It is the covariances of the returns of each pair of assets that cannot be diversified away.

10. **d**: The slope of the Capital Allocation Line is equal to $\dfrac{E(r_i) - RFR}{\sigma_i}$. It, therefore, indicates the risk premium received for each additional unit of risk.

11.	**b**:	$E(r_p) = 0.3(6\%) + 0.7(14\%) = 11.6\%$

$\sigma_p = 0.7(18\%) = 12.6\%$

12.	**c**:	$S_{AAL} = \dfrac{E(r_R) - RFR}{s_R} = \dfrac{14\% - 6\%}{18\%} = 0.44$

13.	**a**:	$E(r_p) = -0.3(6\%) + 1.30(14\%) = 16.4\%$

$\sigma_p = 1.30(18\%) = 23.4\%$

14.	**d**:	The indifference curves of risk-averse investors will always slope upward and those of risk-lovers will slope downwards. Investors will be indifferent among investments that plot at any point along an individual indifference curve, however they will prefer to be on the highest indifference curve possible since these assets offer the highest return for each unit of risk.

15.	**b**:	If the correlation coefficient is anything less than +1.0, some diversification will take place. If there is a perfect negative correlation, all risk can be eliminated if the appropriate amounts are invested in each security. There are numerous investments for which the returns are uncorrelated; one good example is any investment and the risk-free asset. Correlations have no effect on expected returns, thus selection c is incorrect.

16.	**d**:	The total investment in each stock is calculated as follows:

Stock M:	150($30) = $ 4,500

Stock N:	100($55) = $ 5,500

Total			$10,000

Thus, 45% is invested in M and 55% is invested in N.

$E(r_p) = 0.45(18\%) + 0.55(14\%) = 15.8\%$

$\sigma_p = \sqrt{(0.45)^2(23)^2 + (0.55)^2(19)^2 + 2(0.45)(0.55)(0.4)(23)(19)} = \sqrt{302.851} = 17.4\%$

17.	**d**:	Negative weights can be interpreted as either a short sale or a margined position since a borrowing position is indicated.

18.	**d**:	$\sigma_p = \sqrt{(0.4)^2(1.5)^2 + (0.6)^2(2.4)^2 + 2(0.4)(0.6)(0.2)(1.5)(2.4)} = 1.67\%$

19.	**b**:	As the number of assets for which the returns are not perfectly positively correlated increases, the risk of the portfolio decreases. This is the concept underlying naïve diversification. Returns for which the covariance is zero will also have a zero correlation coefficient since the correlation coefficient is equal to the covariance divided by the product of the standard deviations of the two securities. If returns are perfectly positively correlated, no risk diversification can take place.

20.   **a:**   Undiversifable risk is risk that is associated with the system--systematic risk. It is a risk that all firms face. Diversifiable, or unsystematic risk, is risk that affects only a single firm or subset of firms.

Short Answer

1a.   The proportion invested in each stock is calculated as follows:

Stock X: $30(500) = $15,000
Stock Y: $12.50(400) = $ 5,000
Total $20,000

Thus, Olaf has invested 75% of his funds in Stock X and 25% in Stock Y. The expected return on his portfolio is $E(r_p) = 0.75(15\%) + 0.25(20\%) = 16.25\%$.

b.   The risk of Olaf's portfolio is calculated as follows:

$$\sigma_p = \sqrt{(0.75)^2(6)^2 + (0.25)^2(9)^2 + 2(0.75)(0.25)(+1.0)(6)(9)} = \sqrt{45.5625} = 6.75\%.$$

c.   No. Since the correlation coefficient is +1.0, no risk diversification has taken place. Olaf has only averaged his risk as can be seen by calculating the weighted average standard deviation of the two securities: $0.75(6) + (0.25)(9) = 6.75\%$.

2.   Abdul should choose Security 2 since its returns are negatively correlated with the returns on Abdul's existing portfolio, thereby providing the greatest diversification benefits.

3.   Since the correlation coefficient for the returns of the two securities is -1.0, we can use the equation for the variance of a two-security portfolio to solve for the weights that will make the variance equal to zero.

$0 = x^2(5)^2 + (1 - x)^2(18)^2 + 2(x)(1 - x)(-1.0)(5)(18)$
$0 = 25x^2 + (1 - 2x + x^2)(324) - 180(x - x^2)$
$0 = 25x^2 + 324 - 648x + 324x^2 - 180x + 180x^2$
$0 = 529x^2 - 828x + 324$

Using the quadratic equation to solve for x, we get the following:

$$x = \frac{-b \pm \sqrt{b^2 - 4ac}}{2a} = \frac{828 \pm \sqrt{685{,}584 - 685{,}584}}{936} = \frac{828}{936} = 0.88$$

Therefore, 88% of the funds must be invested in the Gengis Corporation bond and 12% in the Bosnic Corporation stock to construct a zero-risk portfolio.

4.   While Anita has the right idea, and she will achieve some amount of diversification by using this strategy since she will be invested in a large number of stocks, all of the stocks are technological stocks, and their returns will have a high positive correlation. It is also

likely that there will be some overlapping of stocks selected by each of the four funds. A better strategy would be for Anita to invest some of her investment money in other types of funds, such as an S&P 500 Index fund or a fund that invests internationally. These types of funds are likely to have a smaller positive correlation (and in the case of the international fund, perhaps even a negative correlation) with the returns of the All American Tech Stock Fund, which will provide her with greater diversification benefits.

5. To begin, consider the formula for the variance of a 2-asset portfolio under the conditions described:

$$\sigma_p^2 = (1/2)^2 \sigma^2 + (1/2)^2 \sigma^2 = 2(1/2)^2 \sigma^2$$

since $\sigma_1^2 = \sigma_2^2$ and $Cov(r_1, r_2) = 0$.

For a three-security portfolio, the formula becomes

$$\sigma_p^2 = (1/3)^2 \sigma^2 + (1/3)^2 \sigma^2 + (1/3)^2 \sigma^2 = 3(1/3)^2 \sigma^2$$

since $\sigma_1^2 = \sigma_2^2 = \sigma_3^2$ and all the covariance terms are zero.

Generalizing, then,

$$\sigma_p^2 = N(1/N)^2 \sigma^2 = (1/N)\sigma^2$$

and it can be seen that as N approaches infinity, $(1/N)\sigma^2$ will approach zero.

CHAPTER FIFTEEN: CAPM AND APT

I.   MULTIPLE CHOICE QUESTIONS

1.   Which of the following statements about the curved efficient frontier defined by Markowitz is (are) true?

    a.   The portfolios lying on the Markowitz efficient frontier contain only systematic risk.

    b.   The portfolios lying on the Markowitz efficient frontier are all perfectly positively correlated with one another.

    c.   The portfolios lying on the Markowitz efficient frontier are all highly positively correlated with one another, but they are not all perfectly positively correlated.

    d.   No risk-free asset exists on the Markowitz efficient frontier.

*   e.   "a," "c," and "d" are all true.

2.   The slope of the security market line (SML) is

    a.   the asset's beta.

*   b.   the risk premium for the market portfolio.

    c.   the risk-free rate.

    d.   the total risk of the asset.

    e.   the asset's systematic risk.

3.   Which of the following is NOT an assumption underlying the capital market line?

    a.   There are no taxes or transactions costs.

    b.   Fractional shares may be purchased in any portfolio or individual asset.

    c.   Everyone can borrow or lend at the risk-free rate.

    d.   All investors face the same one-period investment horizon.

*   e.   All of the above are assumptions underlying the capital market line.

The following information is supplied for Questions 4 and 5:

	Expected return	**Standard deviation**
Bikemor stock	18%	28%
Market portfolio	15%	22%
Risk-free rate	6%	0%

$\rho_{B,M} = 0.2$

4.   Calculate the beta for Bikemor stock.

        a.   0.04
    *   b.   0.25
        c.   0.16
        d.   0.56
        e.   none of the above

5.   What is the expected *equilibrium* rate of return for Bikemor's stock?

    *   a.   8.25%
        b.   3.75%
        c.   9.75%
        d.   18.0%
        e.   none of the above

6.   If borrowing and lending rates differ

        a.   the SML is not a continuous line.
        b.   there is a different tangency portfolio depending on whether an investor is
                a borrower or a lender.
        c.   the SML is blurred.
        d.   the SML becomes a dotted line.
    *   e.   Both "b" and "c" are true statements.

7.   Which of the following statements is (are) true regarding the capital market line (CML)
        and the security market line (SML)?

        a.   The SML depicts the expected equilibrium returns on an asset or a portfolio of
                assets as a function of its total risk.
    *   b.   Only efficient portfolios will plot on the CML, but the SML can be used to
                evaluate individual securities and inefficient portfolios.
        c.   The CML plots expected returns against the covariance of the returns of a security
                with the market portfolio.
        d.   The CML depicts the expected equilibrium returns on a portfolio of assets as a
                function of its systematic risk.
        e.   Both "b" and "c" are true statements.

8.   The capital asset pricing model asserts that the expected return on an asset is a function of
        its

    *   a.   systematic risk.
        b.   diversifiable risk.
        c.   non-diversifiable risk plus a liquidity premium.
        d.   total risk.
        e.   both "a" and "b" since these are equivalent terms.

9.   A 1997 study by Dongcheol Kim found that

    a.   firm size was a better predictor of the expected return on an asset than its beta.
    b.   the most powerful predictor of the expected return on a stock was its market-to-book ratio.
    c.   the most powerful predictor of the expected return on a stock was the earnings-price ratio.
*   d.   individual stocks' betas had a significant positive relation with average returns.
    e.   individual stocks' betas had a significant positive relation with average returns for large firms, but not for small firms.

10.   The assumption of homogeneous expectations means that

    a.   all investors are investing for the same single-period time horizon.
    b.   all assets have the same expected return and risk.
*   c.   all investors have the same expected return and risk expectations for a specific asset.
    d.   everyone can borrow or lend at the risk-free rate.
    e.   all of the above.

11.   The separation theorem states that

    a.   investors should invest their retirement funds in accounts that are separate from other investments.
*   b.   an investor should invest in the optimal portfolio and then decide whether to borrow or lend at the risk-free rate.
    c.   in making an investment decision, the risk and return statistics of an asset should be considered separately.
    d.   the security market line is a distinct and separate tool from the capital market line in security evaluation.
    e.   none of the above

12.   Assuming that there is a single optimal portfolio of risky assets in which every investor should invest that offers the highest return for its level of risk, then

    a.   no investor can expect to earn a higher return than the expected return on the optimal portfolio of risky assets.
    b.   an investor can only increase her expected return by lending a portion of her investment funds at the risk-free rate.
*   c.   an investor can only increase her expected return by borrowing a portion of her investment funds at the risk-free rate.
    d.   an investor can only increase her expected return by investing future funds in IPOs.
    e.   either "c" or "d"

140

13. The following information is provided for the common stock of the Deshnick Corporation and the market portfolio:

	Expected return	Standard deviation
Deshnick Corporation	15%	21%
Market portfolio	13%	18%

$COV(r_D, r_M) = 126.50$
$RFR = 5.5\%$

The expected equilibrium return for the stock of Deshnick Corporation is

    a.   16.6%.
*   b.   8.4%.
    c.   9.7%.
    d.   7.7%.
    e.   15.2%.

14. The capital asset pricing model asserts that, all else equal, securities that have a high covariance with the market

*   a.   have a high level of systematic risk.
    b.   will be in high demand.
    c.   will have relatively high prices and high expected returns.
    d.   have a low level of systematic risk.
    e.   both "b" and "c"

15. All else equal, an increase in the expected rate of inflation will

*   a.   cause a parallel upward shift in the SML.
    b.   cause the SML to be more steeply sloped.
    c.   have no effect on the SML.
    d.   result in a decrease in the expected equilibrium returns of all securities.
    e.   increase the betas of all securities.

16. Which of the following statements is a CORRECT comparison of the original CAPM and Fischer Black's zero-beta model?

*   a.   The original CAPM has only one unknown variable, the return on the market portfolio, whereas the Black model has two--the return on the market portfolio and the return on a zero-beta asset.
       b.   The Black model includes a liquidity premium while the original model does not.
       c.   Unlike the original CAPM, the Black model is a multi-factor model that incorporates a firm's size, book-to-market ratio, and earnings-price ratio as variables that determine a firm's expected return.
       d.   Unlike the original CAPM, the Black model does not assume that a single optimal portfolio exists in which all investors should invest.
       e.   none of the above

17. Calculate the expected return on the following portfolio of stocks assuming that the expected return on the market portfolio is 16% and the risk-free rate is 9%.

Stock	Price per share	Shares held	Estimated beta
Quad	$15	4,000	1.25
Delphi	$10	1,000	1.05
Triad	$ 8	5,000	1.15

       a.   17.26%
       b.   6.28%
*   c.   17.37%
       d.   15.25%
       e.   cannot be determined without knowing the covariance of the returns of each stock with the market portfolio

18. The expected return on the market portfolio is 14%, with a standard deviation of 10% and the risk-free rate is 8%. Calculate the expected return and standard deviation of a portfolio in which an investor invests $16,000 in the market portfolio, borrowing $6,000 of the investment funds at the risk-free rate.

       a. $E(r_p) = 18.8\%; \sigma_p = 16\%$

*   b. $E(r_p) = 17.6\%; \sigma_p = 16\%$

       c. $E(r_p) = 10.25\%; \sigma_p = 3.75\%$

       d. $E(r_p) = 27.2\%; \sigma_p = 10\%$

       e.   none of the above

19. The security market line (SML) has which of the following asset pricing implications?

   a. Assets with beta coefficients of less than +1.0 are underpriced.
* b. Assets that plot above the SML are underpriced.
   c. Assets that plot below the SML are underpriced.
   d. Stocks issued by large firms are usually overpriced.
   e. Stocks with returns that are negatively correlated with the market are underpriced.

20. The security market line can be used to evaluate which of the following?

   I.   efficient portfolios
   II. inefficient portfolios
   III. individual securities

   a. I only
   b. I and II only
   c. II and III only
   d. III only
* e. I, II, and III

21. Empirical research by Professors Chen, Roll, and Ross isolated what risk factors that significantly influenced all securities' returns in the APT?

   I.   unanticipated changes in inflation
   II. unanticipated changes in the index of industrial production
   III. unanticipated changes in the slope of the yield curve for Treasury securities
   IV. unanticipated changes in the level of unemployment
   V.   unanticipated changes in the yield spread between high-grade and low-grade corporate bonds

   a. I only
   b. I and II only
   c. I, II, and III only
   d. I, II, III and IV only
* e. I, II, III, and V only

22. Compare and contrast the beta coefficient from the characteristic regression line, denoted **B** in this question, with the factor betas(s) in the APT, denoted **b**.

   a. The **B** and **b** are elasticities with respect to the market.
   b. The **B** and **b** are elasticities with respect to different risk factors.
   c. The only time **B** and **b** are the same is when a single-factor APT uses the market portfolio as its risk factor.
   d. Both "a" and "c" are true.
* e. Both "b" and "c" are true.

23. How is the arbitrage pricing theory (APT) similar to Capital Market Theory?

   a. Both theories assume that undiversifiable risk is priced.
   b. Both theories assume that diversifiable risk is priced.
   c. Both theories assume investors will hold a well-diversified portfolio.
   d. Both "a" and "b" are true.
* e. Both "a" and "c" are true.

24. An APT risk factor must always be related to

   a. the inflation rate.
   b. interest rates and yield curves.
   c. the market portfolio.
   d. the growth rate of the economy.
* e. An APT risk factor can be any random variable that fluctuates through time and has a significant effect on security prices.

25. Arbitrage Pricing Theory (APT) defines an arbitrage opportunity as

   I.   a perfectly hedged portfolio.
   II.   one that requires no initial cash flow.
   III. one that exposes the investor to no risk.
   IV.   one that has a positive expected return, with a 90% probability.

   a. I and II only.
   b. I and III only.
   c. II and III only.
* d. I, II, and III only.
   e. I, II, III, and IV.

26.   Proponents of the Arbitrage Pricing Theory (APT) suggest that it is superior to the capital market theory because of which of the following reasons?

      a.   The derivation of the APT requires fewer simplifying assumptions that the capital asset pricing model (CAPM).
      b.   The APT is a more general model than the CAPM because it incorporates more factors.
      c.   The factor analytic statistical techniques sometimes used to estimate the APT model are superior to the regression analysis used to test the CAPM.
      d.   all of the above
*   e.   "a" and "b" only

27.   The Arbitrage Pricing Theory (APT) is based on which of the following simplifying assumptions?

      a.   Everyone can borrow and lend at the risk-free rate of interest.
      b.   There exists an optimal portfolio, the market portfolio, that contains every risky asset in the world.
*   c.   Arbitrage portfolios can be constructed with zero invested wealth.
      d.   The returns of all assets are generated by different market models that are all driven by the same common factor.
      e.   all of the above

Use the following information to answer Questions 28 and 29:

Assume three well-diversified portfolios exist, such that all diversifiable risk has been eliminated. A one-factor model has been developed. The market price of risk for the single factor has been determined to be 5%. Below are the estimated beta coefficients for each portfolio and the expected returns on each portfolio:

Portfolio	b_{i1}	Expected return
A	1.5	11.5%
B	1.0	12.0%
C	0.5	6.5%

28.   What is the equilibrium rate of return on each security if the zero-beta return is 4%?

      a. $E(r_A) = 7.5\%$, $E(r_B) = 5\%$, $E(r_C) = 2.5\%$
      b. $E(r_A) = 11\%$, $E(r_B) = 9\%$, $E(r_C) = 7\%$
      c. $E(r_A) = 6\%$, $E(r_B) = 4\%$, $E(r_C) = 2\%$
*   d. $E(r_A) = 11.5\%$, $E(r_B) = 9\%$, $E(r_C) = 6.5\%$
      e.   none of the above

29.   An arbitrage profit could be obtained by

       a.   short selling portfolio B and investing the proceeds equally in portfolios A and C.
       b.   short selling portfolio A and investing the proceeds equally in portfolios B and C.
*   c.   short selling equal amounts of portfolios A and C and investing the
             proceeds in portfolio B.
       d.   short selling equal amounts of portfolios B and C and investing the proceeds in
             portfolio A.
       e.   No arbitrage opportunity exists.

30.   The following information is provided for two well-diversified portfolios, M and N:

Portfolio	b_{i1}	b_{i2}	$E(r_i)$
M	0.4	0.8	11%
N	0.8	0.5	9.8%

       What are the correct proportions to invest in M and N such that the combination results in
       zero risk for factor 1?

       a.   Buy $4 shares of M and $6 shares of N.
       b.   Buy $2 shares of M and sell $4 shares of N.
       c.   Buy $6 shares of M and $4 shares of N.
*   d.   Buy $10 shares of M and sell $5 shares of N.
       e.   none of the above

Use the following information to answer Questions 31 and 32:

       Assume you have three stocks, none of which pays a dividend. Each stock is currently
       selling for $10 a share and has an expected price of $12 a share. You have estimated the
       following model to explain security returns:

       $R_i = 2\% + b_{i1}F_1 + b_{i2}F_2 + b_{i3}F_3 + b_{i4}F_4 + b_{i5}F_5$

       The expected values of each of the factors are as follows:

       $E(F_1) = 4\%, E(F_2) = 2\%, E(F_3) = 1\%, E(F_4) = 0\%, E(F_5) = 0\%$

The factor sensitivities for each of the three stocks has been estimated as follows:

Stock	b_{i1}	b_{i2}	b_{i3}	b_{i4}	b_{i5}
R	3.0	1.0	0.5	1.0	0.0
S	6.0	2.0	1.0	2.0	0.0
T	3.0	0.0	6.0	0.0	1.0

146

31.	Which of the stocks are overpriced, underpriced, and correctly priced in the market according to your estimates?

	Overpriced	Underpriced	Correctly priced
a.	R	S	T
* b.	S	R	T
c.	S	T	R
d.	T	R	S
e.	T	S	R

32.	The data provided seem to indicate that the "common factors" are

a.	F_1
b.	F_4 and F_5
c.	F_1 and F_2
*	d.	F_1, F_2, and F_3
e.	F_1, F_2, F_3, and F_4

33.	A *disadvantage* of Arbitrage Pricing Theory (APT) is that

a.	it does not assume the existence of an optimal market portfolio.
*	b.	the priced factors are unknown.
c.	it is based on the assumption of a non-linear relationship between risk and return.
d.	it is based on utility theory, which is hard to define.
e.	all of the above

34.	In his empirical tests of the APT, Nai-Fu Chen concluded which of the following?

a.	The security market line (SML) was able to explain part of the error terms in the APT model.
b.	The first risk factor in the APT resembles the market portfolio.
c.	There exists more than one risk factor.
d.	The SML appeared to be econometrically misspecified in most cases.
*	e.	Selections "b," "c," and "d" are all conclusions made by Nai-Fu Chen.

35.	In the estimation of the APT factor risk premiums, a factor is said to be priced if

a.	the lambda risk premium is equal to zero.
b.	the lambda risk premium is equal to one.
*	c.	the lambda risk premium is significantly different from zero.
d.	the lambda risk premium represents a macro-economic risk factor.
e.	the lambda risk premium is highly correlated with all the other factor risk premiums.

36. Which of the following statements regarding the arbitrage pricing theory (APT) model and the capital asset pricing model (CAPM) is (are) *true*?

    a. Although they are based on completely different logical developments, the APT model and the CAPM will always lead to the same investment implications.
    b. The law of one price is the principle underlying both the APT model and the CAPM.
    c. The CAPM describes a linear relationship while the APT model is an exponential function.
    d. All of the above are true statements.
*   e. None of the above is a true statement.

37. Which of the following statements regarding the principles underlying the arbitrage pricing theory (APT) model is (are) *true*?

    a. The APT model assumes that no short selling is permitted.
    b. The law of one price says that two perfect substitutes must sell for the same price or arbitrage profits will be available.
    c. The APT model assumes that security-unique risk can be eliminated by holding a well-diversified portfolio.
    d. All of the above are true statements.
*   e. Only "b" and "c" are true statements.

38. Which of the following is *not* an assumption underlying the APT model?

*   a. Rates of return conform to a normal probability distribution.
    b. Investors are able to create self-financing portfolios.
    c. Investors are able to conduct short sales.
    d. Neither a nor b are assumptions underlying the APT model.
    e. All of the above are assumptions underlying the APT model.

II. SHORT ANSWER QUESTIONS

1. The chairman of the Federal Reserve has stated that he believes the stock market is overpriced. His statement has caused concern for investors. Explain, in the context of the CAPM, how this will affect security prices. Specifically, what factor(s) in the CAPM are affected by this statement, and how does this relate to security prices?

2. You have determined that the correlation of the returns of the stock of the Roberts Corporation and the market is 0.8. You have estimated the expected return on the stock of the Roberts Corporation to be 22%, with a standard deviation of 26.32%, and the market portfolio has an expected return of 18% with a standard deviation of 20%. The risk-free rate is 5%.

    a. Calculate a beta for the Roberts Corporation.

b. What is the expected return for Roberts Corporation if the markets are in equilibrium?

c. Based on your estimates, is Roberts' stock underpriced, correctly priced, or overpriced? Explain.

3. Based on extensive financial analysis, you expect the stock of the Wilson Electronics Corporation to return 21% over the next year. The stock has a beta of 1.4. The relevant risk-free rate is 4.5%, and the market risk premium has averaged 9.2% in recent years. Based on what you know of the capital asset pricing model and your expectations for Wilson Electronics, is it a good investment? Explain.

4. The stock of the Xenon Corporation has a beta of 0.60 and you have estimated its expected return to be 14%, with a standard deviation of 5%. The stock of the Yoshimo Corporation has a beta of 1.2, and it is estimated to have an expected return of 18%, with a standard deviation of 7.3%. The correlation coefficient of the returns of the two stocks is 0.6. You have decided to invest in 300 shares of Xenon, at a price of $40 a share, and 200 shares of Yoshimo, at a price of $40 a share.

a. What is the expected return on your portfolio?

b. What is the standard deviation of the portfolio's returns?

c. What is the beta of the portfolio?

d. If the relevant risk-free rate is 6% and the expected return on the market is 15%, is this portfolio a good investment? Explain.

5. The stock of the Misner Corporation has a beta of 0.90. The risk-free rate is 5.5%, and the market risk premium has averaged 8% in recent years. Misner pays a dividend of $2.00 a share, and this is expected to grow at the rate of 10% indefinitely. If Misner is selling for $85 a share, should you buy it? Explain.

6. What is meant by a priced factor, in the context of the APT model? What statistical characteristic do priced factors have in common?

7. Assume you have developed a two-factor APT model and have determined that Securities I and II have the following sensitivites to the two factors:

Security	Sensitivity to Factor 1	Sensitivity to Factor 2
I	0.20	0.80
II	0.80	0.20

Explain how you can construct a portfolio that will be sensitive only to Factor 1 and be totally unsensitive to Factor 2.

8. The TriValley Distribution Corporation has a two-factor return generating function. TriValley's stock is expected to earn a 5% rate of return if the economy is stagnant (i.e., $E(r_{TV}) = \sigma_{TV} = 5\%$.) In addition, TriValley has a sensitivity coefficient for the inflation rate of 4.0, and its sensitivity coefficient for the percentage change in the unemployment rate is 1.0. Based on your financial analysis of the firm, you expect the stock to offer a

return of 15% this year. You also expect that the rate of inflation will be 3.5% and that unemployment will increase by 2%. Based on your analysis, is TriValley underpriced, overpriced, or correctly priced?

9.   Assume that the following two-factor model is descriptive of reality:

$E(r_i) = 5\% + 3.0b_{i1} + 2.0b_{i2}$.

You have determined the following sensitivity factors for securities R and S:

Security	b_{i1}	b_{i2}
R	2.0	1.0
S	1.5	2.0

A third security, T, also exists that has the following characteristics:

$E(r_T) = 12\%$, $b_{T1} = 1.8$, $b_{T2} = 1.4$

What arbitrage opportunities are available?

10.   The Charter Aviation Corporation (CAC) paid a dividend of $0.50 a share this year. This dividend is expected to grow at a rate of 10% for the foreseeable future. The following two-factor model is assumed to be appropriate for CAC:

$$E(r_{CAC}) = 4\% + b_{i1}(2\%) + b_{i2}(8\%)$$

The factor betas for Charter Aviation are $b_{i1} = 2.5$ and $b_{i2} = 1.2$. Based on this information, calculate the fair market value of a share of Charter Aviation's stock.

CHAPTER FIFTEEN: SOLUTION GUIDELINES

Multiple Choice

1. **e**: The portfolios lying on the Markowitz efficient frontier are highly positively correlated with one another because they all move together systematically, but they are not perfectly positively correlated because they do not lie on a straight line. All of the portfolios on the efficient frontier have had all diversifiable risk eliminated and contain only systematic risk. The curved Markowitz efficient frontier does not intersect the y-axis, thus, no risk-free asset exists.

2. **b**: The slope of the security market line is $E(r_m)$ - RFR, or the market risk premium.

3. **e**: All of the selections are assumptions on which the capital market line is based.

4. **b**: $\text{beta} = \dfrac{\rho_{B,M}\sigma_B\sigma_M}{VAR(r_M)} = \dfrac{(0.2)(28\%)(22\%)}{(22\%)^2} = \dfrac{123.2}{484} = 0.25$

5. **a**: Using the beta calculated in Question 4 of 0.25, the expected equilibrium rate of return for Bikemor is $E(r_B) = 6\% + (15\% - 6\%)(0.25) = 8.25\%$.

6. **e**: If different borrowing and lending rates are assumed, the security market line is not continuous, and the optimal portfolio for investors will differ depending on whether they choose to borrow or lend.

7. **b**: The capital market line represents combinations of the optimal risky portfolio and the risk-free rate, which are efficient portfolios. All diversifiable risk is eliminated for these portfolios. The capital market line depicts the expected returns on these efficient portfolios as a function of their total risk, while the security market line depicts the expected equilibrium returns on individual assets, inefficient portfolios, and efficient portfolios as a function of their systematic risk levels. The systematic risk is determined by the covariance of the returns of a security or portfolio of securities with the optimal market portfolio.

8. **a**: The equation of the security market line depicts the expected equilibrium return on an asset as a function of its beta, which is a measure of the systematic, or undiversifiable, risk of the asset.

9. **d**: Kim found that previous research that had concluded that factors such as firm size, market-to-book ratios, and earnings-price ratios were more powerful predictors of a security's returns than was beta was subject to the errors-in-variables problem and a selection bias inherent in the database used. After overcoming these biases, he found a statistically positive relationship existed between an individual stock's average returns and its beta value.

10. **c:** This is the definition of homogenous expectations as used in capital market theory.

11. **b:** This is the body of the separation theorem.

12. **c:** An investor can increase her expected return on the optimal portfolio by leveraging her investment and borrowing at the risk-free rate. This will offer a higher expected return (and more risk) than simply investing in the optimal portfolio. Since the optimal portfolio includes all risky assets, IPOs are included in this theoretical construct.

13. **b:** The beta for Deshnick Corporation is calculated first:

$$\text{beta} = \frac{COV(r_D, r_M)}{VAR(r_M)} = \frac{126.5}{(18)^2} = 0.39$$

The expected return for Deshnick stock is then calculated using the equation of the security market line:

$E(r_D) = 5.5\% + (13\% - 5.5\%)(0.39) = 8.4\%$

14. **a:** Since the systematic risk of a security is calculated by dividing its covariance with the market portfolio by the variance of the market, securities with a high covariance with the market will have a high level of systematic risk. It does not follow that these securities will be in particularly high demand or sell at relatively high prices although, if fairly priced, they will have relatively high expected returns to compensate investors for their higher levels of systematic risk.

15. **b:** An increase in the expected rate of inflation will increase the nominal risk-free rate. All else equal, this will increase the y-intercept of the security market line, resulting in an upward parallel shift.

16. **a:** The zero-beta model is often referred to as a two-factor model since there are two unknowns--the return on the market and the return on a zero-beta asset. The Black model does not include a liquidity premium, nor does it include fundamental variables such as firm size, book-to-market, or earning-price ratios. It does, however, assume that an optimal portfolio in which all investors should invest exists.

17.   **c:**   First the weights invested in each security are calculated:

Stock	Price per share	Shares held	Total investment	Weight
Quad	$15	4,000	$ 60,000	0.55
Delphi	$10	1,000	$ 10,000	0.09
Triad	$ 8	5,000	$ 40,000	0.36
		Total investment	$110,000	1.00

The portfolio beta is calculated as the weighted average of the individual security betas:

$$beta_p = 0.55(1.25) + 0.09(1.05) + 0.36(1.15) = 1.196$$

The beta is then used in the equation of the security market line to determine the expected equilibrium rate of return for the portfolio:

$$E(r_p) = 9\% + 1.196(16\% - 9\%) = 17.37\%$$

18.   **b:**   Since $6,000 is being borrowed, this represents 60% of the cash available, $10,000, so 160% is being invested in the market portfolio.

$$E(r_p) = 1.60(14\%) + (-0.60)(8\%) = 17.6\%$$
$$\sigma_p = 1.60(10\%) = 16\%$$

19.   **b:**   The equation of the security market line calculates the expected return on a security or a portfolio of securities if the security is fairly priced. If the security's expected return plots above the SML, it is offering a return that is greater than what is needed to compensate the investor for the systematic risk of the investment. It is, therefore, an underpriced security.

20.   **e:**   The security market line plots expected return against the systematic risk (beta) of an investment. It can be used to evaluate individual securities as well as both efficient and inefficient portfolios.

21.   **e:**   Chen, Roll, and Ross isolated four factors that significantly influenced securities' returns: unanticipated changes in the rate of inflation, unanticipated changes in the index of industrial production, unanticipated changes in the yield spread between high-grade and low-grade corporate bonds, and unanticipated changes in the slope of the term structure of interest rates, as measured by the difference between the yield on long-term government bonds and Treasury bills.

22.   **e:**   The beta coefficient, **B**, in the regression line equation and the factor betas, **b**, in the APT model represent elasticities with respect to different risk factors. When a single-factor APT uses the market portfolio as its risk factor, the two are identical in that they both represent the elasticity with respect to the market portfolio.

23. **e**: Both the APT and Capital Market Theory assume that investors hold well-diversified portfolios such that all diversifiable risk is eliminated. Therefore, both theories assume that only undiversifiable risk is priced.

24. **e**: An APT risk factor can be any random variable that fluctuates through time and has a significant effect on security prices.

25. **d**: The APT defines an arbitrage opportunity to be a perfectly hedged portfolio that can be acquired at zero cost, generates zero cash flows before the position is terminated, and will have a positive value with *certainty* at the end of the investment.

26. **e**: The APT model is based on fewer simplifying assumptions than the CAPM and is a more general model than the CAPM because it incorporates more factors. The factor analytic statistical techniques are basically the same as those used to test the CAPM. In fact, the security market line of CAPM is identical to a one-factor APT model if the single risk factor happens to be the market portfolio.

27. **c**: The APT model does not depend on the existence of a risk-free return; nor does it assert the existence of an optimal market portfolio. It does assume that arbitrage portfolios can be constructed with zero invested wealth and that the returns on all assets are driven by a number of common factors.

28. **d**: The expected equilibrium rates of return are calculated using the following equation: $E(r_i) = 4\% + b_{i1}(5\%)$.

$E(r_A) = 4\% + 1.5(5\%) = 11.5\%$

$E(r_B) = 4\% + 1.0(5\%) = 9\%$

$E(r_c) = 4\% + 0.5(5\%) = 6.5\%$

29. **c**: According to the APT model, Portfolio B is underpriced. A portfolio composed of equal amounts of Portfolios A and C will have the same factor sensitivity as that of Portfolio B: $0.5(1.5) + (0.5)(0.5) = 1.0$. The resultant portfolio will, however, have a lower expected return than Portfolio B; therefore the new portfolio should be sold short and the proceeds invested in Portfolio B.

30. **d**: The sensitivity of Portfolio M to factor 1 is 0.4, and the sensitivity of Portfolio N to factor 1 is 0.8. Therefore, if you sell $5 shares of N and use the proceeds to purchase $10 shares of N, the resultant beta for factor 1 will be $10(0.4) + (-5)(0.8) = 4 + (-4) = 0$.

31. **b**: The equilibrium rates of return for each stock are as follows:

$E(r_R) = 2\% + 3.0(4\%) + 1.0(2\%) + 0.5(1\%) + 1.0(0\%) + 0.0(0\%) = 16.5\%$

$E(r_S) = 2\% + 6.0(4\%) + 2.0(2\%) + 1.0(1\%) + 2.0(0\%) + 0.0(0\%) = 31\%$

$E(r_T) = 2\% + 4.0(4\%) + 1.0(0\%) + 2.0(1\%) + 0.0(0\%) + 1.0(0\%) = 20\%$

The expected returns based on the dividend and price information provided are the same for each stock: ($12 - $10)/$10 = 20%. Therefore, S is overpriced, R is underpriced, and T is correctly priced.

32. **d**: The three stocks all have betas for factors 1, 2, and 3, but only two of them, R and S, have beta coefficients for factor 4 and only one, T, has a sensitivity to factor 5. Therefore, factors 4 and 5 are not "common factors."

33. **b**: The APT is based on the "law of one price" rather than utility theory. However, like CAPM, it describes a linear relationship between expected returns and risk. Unlike CAPM, it does not assume the existence of an optimal market portfolio. A disadvantage, however, is that the factors that should be priced are not known.

34. **e**: Nai-Fu Chen concluded that the first risk factor in the APT resembles the market portfolio, but that more than one risk factor exists. The APT was able to explain some of the SML's unexplained residual returns, but the SML was unable to explain anything about the error terms in the APT model. The SML appeared to be econometrically misspecified in most cases.

35. **c**: If the lambda risk premium is significantly different from zero, the factor is said to be priced.

36. **e**: The law of one price is the principle underlying the APT model while CAPM is based on utility theory. Both are linear models; however, they will not always lead to the same investment implications unless a one-factor APT model that is identical to the CAPM is used.

37. **e**: The APT model is based on the law of one price that says that two perfect substitutes must sell for the same price or arbitrage profits will be available. The model assumes that security-unique risk can be eliminated by holding a well-diversified portfolio and that investors can use the proceeds from short sales of overpriced securities to enter long positions in underpriced securities, thus earning arbitrage profits with a zero initial cash flow.

38. **a**: The APT model assumes that investors are able to create self-financing portfolios by using the proceeds from short sales to enter long positions. Unlike the CAPM, the APT does not assume that rates of return conform to a normal probability distribution.

Short Answer

1. The equation of the security market line is $E(r_i) = RFR + (E(r_M) - RFR)(beta)$. It states that the return on a security or portfolio, i, is a function of the risk-free rate, the systematic risk of the security or portfolio, and a market risk premium. The latter is a measure of the risk aversion of investors. The greater the risk aversion, the greater will be the market risk premium. If the statement of the chairman of the Federal Reserve causes investors to be concerned about investing in stocks, this risk premium will increase. This will cause the slope of the security market line to increase and, therefore,

the required return on all securities to increase. An increase in the required returns will cause the prices of securities to fall.

2a. $\text{beta}_{\text{Roberts}} = \dfrac{\rho_{R,M}\sigma_R\sigma_M}{VAR(r_M)} = \dfrac{0.8(26.32)(20)}{(20)^2} = 1.0528$

b. Using the beta calculated in part (a) and the equation of the security market line, we determine the expected equilibrium rate of return for Roberts Corporation to be 18.69%:

$$E(r_{\text{Roberts}}) = 5\% + 1.0528(18\% - 5\%) = 18.69\%.$$

c. Since you have estimated the expected return on Roberts Corporation to be 22% and the CAPM indicates that it needs only to offer a return of 18.69% based on its risk, the stock is underpriced.

3. The expected equilibrium rate of return for the Wilson Corporation is found by using the equation of the security market line:

$$E(r_{\text{Wilson}}) = 4.5\% + 1.4(9.2\%) = 17.4\%$$

Based on your expectations, Wilson is a good investment since you expect it to return 21%, which is more than the CAPM indicates it needs to return to compensate you for your risk.

4a. $E(r_p) = 0.6(14\%) + 0.4(18\%) = 15.6\%$

b. $\sigma_p = \sqrt{(0.6)^2(5)^2 + (0.4)^2(7.3)^2 + 2(0.6)(0.4)(0.6)(5)(7.3)} = \sqrt{28.0384} = 5.3\%$

c. $\text{Beta}_p = 0.6(0.6) + 0.4(1.2) = 0.84$

d. The capital asset pricing model indicates that the portfolio should offer a 13.6% return to compensate an investor for its risk:

$$E(r_p) = 6\% + 0.84(15\% - 6\%) = 13.6\%$$

Based on part (a), you expect it to return 15.6%, so yes, it is a good investment.

5. According to CAPM, if Misner's stock is fairly priced, it should offer a return of 12.7%:

$$E(r_{\text{Misner}}) = 5.5\% + 0.9(*\%) = 12.7\%$$

Applying this rate to the constant growth model presented in Chapter 2 of this book, we obtain a fair market price of $81.48 for the Misner Corporation:

$\text{Price} = \dfrac{\$2(1.10)}{0.127 - 0.10} = \$81.48$. Therefore, at a price of $85, it is overpriced, and you should not buy it.

6. A priced factor is one that is valued by the market in the determination of security prices. A factor is considered to be priced if the lambda risk premium associated with it, generated by a second-pass regression, is significantly different from zero.

7. Since $0.2X_1 + 0.8(1 - X_1)$ must equal 1.0, X_1 must equal -0.33 and $(1 - X_1) = 1.33$. You would short sell $0.33 of Security I and use the proceeds plus $1 of your own money to invest in Security II.

8. According to the two-factor model, the expected equilibrium return for TriValley Distribution Corporation is $E(r_{TV}) = 5\% + 4.0(3.5\%) + 1.0(2\%) = 21\%$. Since you expect it to return only 15% this year, it is overpriced.

9. An arbitrage portfolio that duplicates the risk factors of Security T can be formed by investing 60% in Security R and 40% in Security S.

    $b_{p1} = 0.6(2.0) + 0.4(1.5) = 1.8$

    $b_{p2} = 0.6(1.0) + 0.4(2) = 1.4$
    $E(r_p) = 5\% + 1.8(3\%) + 1.4(2\%) = 13.2\%$

    Security T is, therefore, overpriced since it offers an expected return of only 12%. Arbitrage profits can be earned by selling Security T short and investing the proceeds in a portfolio, denoted p, consisting of 60% in Security R and 40% in Security S.

Investment	Initial cash flow	Ending cash flow	b_{i1}	b_{i2}
Sell T short	+$100	- $112.00	- 1.8	- 1.4
Buy portfolio p	-$100	+$113.20	+1.8	+1.4
	0	+$ 1.20	0	0

10. According to the two-factor model presented, the stock of Charter Aviation should offer a return of 18.6%:

    $E(r_{CA}) = 4\% + 2.5(2\%) + 1.2(8\%) = 18.6\%$

    Applying this required return to the constant growth model, the fair market price of Charter Aviation is $6.40:

    $$Price = \frac{Dividend_1}{Required\ return - growth\ rate} = \frac{\$0.50(1.10)}{0.186 - 0.10} = \frac{\$0.55}{0.086} = \$6.40$$

CHAPTER SIXTEEN: PORTFOLIO PERFORMANCE EVALUTION

I. MULTIPLE CHOICE QUESTIONS

1. A mutual fund that invests in glamorous common stocks that typically have high price-earnings ratios and higher than average growth is called a(n)

    a. value fund.
    b. income fund.
    c. balanced fund.
 * d. growth fund.
    e. liquid assets fund.

2. Which of the following statements regarding mutual funds is (are) true?

    a. They are all, by definition, open-end funds.
    b. They may be either open-end or closed-end funds.
    c. They are all required by the Investment Company Act of 1940 to be no-load funds.
    d. They may be either load or no-load funds.
 * e. Both "a" and "d" are true statements.

3. Which of the following statements regarding closed-end funds is (are) true?

    a. Shares are bought and sold at their net asset value per share.
    b. The income earned by the fund is subject to double taxation, unlike that of an open-end fund.
    c. The price per share will always be greater than or equal to the net asset value per share.
 * d. The number of shares remains fixed after its initial public offering.
    e. Statements "b," "c," and "d" are all true.

4. If a portfolio manager has an uncanny ability to buy at the market's low points and sell short at the market's peak levels, then the second beta coefficient (i.e., the beta for the squared market return) of the Treynor-Mazuy characteristic line for this manager's portfolio will be

    a. a large negative number.
    b. an insignificant negative number.
    c. not statistically different from zero.
    d. an insignificant positive number.
 * e. a large positive number.

5. The Sharpe (SHARPE) and Treynor (TREYNOR) investment performance measures are best described by which of the following statements?

      a. They are both single parameter performance measures.

      b. They are both based on the assumption that money can be borrowed and lent at a single risk-free rate.

      c. They render performance rankings that are highly positively correlated with each other.

*   d. All of the above are true.

      e. Only "b" and "c" are true.

6. Which of the following statements regarding the SHARPE index and the TREYNOR index is (are) true?

      a. The TREYNOR index measures the risk premium per unit of total risk while the SHARPE index measures the risk premium per unit of systematic risk.

*   b. The TREYNOR performance measure has the disadvantage that it can be sensitive to the market index that is used to estimate the investment's betas.

      c. The SHARPE index has the advantage that it can be used to compare both individual assets and portfolios while the TREYNOR index can be used only to evaluate portfolios.

      d. All of the above are true.

      e. Only "a" and "c" are true statements.

7. Jensen's alpha

      a. is superior to both the SHARPE index and the TREYNOR index in ranking the performance of different assets in that it adjusts for the relative risk of the assets.

      b. is identical to the alpha intercept term of the original characteristic line introduced in Capital Market Theory.

*   c. has no meaning if a regression's beta is not statistically significant.

      d. will be negative if the asset earned returns that were appropriate for its level of systematic risk.

      e. will be positive if the asset earned returns that were appropriate for its level of systematic risk.

8. The Investment Company Act of 1940

      a. limits sales commissions on the sale of new shares of mutual funds to 10%.

      b. mandates that the income earned by a mutual fund is tax-exempt to the fund.

*   c. limits mutual funds' use of margin.

      d. all of the above

      e. "a" and "b" only

9.   A study of closed-end funds by Barclay, Holderness, and Pontiff concluded that

      a.   most closed-end funds sell at a premium from their net asset values.
*   b.   the price per share of the fund will sell at a larger discount from net asset
            value the greater the percentage of managerial stock ownership in the fund.

      c.   the price per share of the fund will sell at a larger discount from net asset if hired
            managers are used rather than owner/managers.
      d.   most closed-end funds sell for their net asset values per share.
      e.   closed-end funds are usually underpriced and are, therefore, good investments to
            consider adding to one's portfolio.

10.   A no-load fund is one that

*   a.   does not deduct an initial sales commission from the amount invested.
      b.   charges no redemption fee when an investor sells shares.
      c.   has no 12b-1 (distribution) fees.
      d.   charges no management fees.
      e.   "a," "b," and "c" only

11.   Donald Farrar's study of mutual funds as well as more recent studies have concluded that

      a.   most mutual funds tend to be efficient portfolios.
      b.   the published investment objectives of funds provides a reliable measure of the
            quantitative risk and average return statistics.
*   c.   the funds that accepted higher risk levels also tended to have higher
            returns.
      d.   the risk levels of the funds tended to be inversely related to their average returns.
      e.   both "a" and "c".

12.   In the factor analysis technique developed by William Sharpe to analyze a portfolio's
      management style, the twelve beta coefficients, $b_{i,k}$ can be interpreted as

*   a.   the weights that fund i invests in asset category k.
      b.   the residual return of the mutual fund during the time period.
      c.   the sensitivity of the fund's returns to twelve different macro-economic
            variables.
      d.   the sensitivity of the fund's returns to the various fees associated with a mutual
            fund, such as loads, 12b-1 fees, commissions, etc.
      e.   none of the above.

13. Which of the following statements regarding quantitative management style analysis is (are) true?

    a. It is a useful tool that can be used to rank mutual funds by their performances.

    b. It provides more accurate forecasts regarding mutual funds risk and return statistics than do the more subjective comments published by popular financial services, such as Morningstar.

    c. It provides a way to anticipate and avoid moral hazards, such as misleading or false investment objectives provided by fund managers.

    d. all of the above

*   e. "b" and "c" only

14. Consider the following information regarding two funds:

Fund	SHARPE index	TREYNOR index
Millennium Growth Fund	0.586	0.734
Planet Growth Fund	0.595	0.644

Which of the following statements is true?

    a. The Millennium Fund must be riskier than the Planet Fund.

    b. The Planet Fund offered a greater return for each unit of systematic risk than did the Millennium Fund.

*   c. The Planet Fund is better diversified than the Millennium Fund.

    d. The Millennium Fund is better diversified than the Planet Fund.

    e. Both "a" and "b" are true statements.

15. You have applied Jensen's model to the historical excess returns of the Select Value Fund and have obtained the following equation:

$$(r_{SV,t} - RFR_t) = +0.0365 + 0.978(r_{M,t} - RFR)$$
If these results are statistically significant, you can conclude that

    a.   the fund earned a return that was greater than that of the market.
    b.   the fund earned a return that was not adequate to compensate investors for its systematic risk.
*   c.   the fund earned a return that was greater than what was adequate to compensate investors for its systematic risk.
    d.   the fund earned a return that was less than that of the market.
    e.   the fund did not perform as well as a passive buy and hold strategy.

Use the following information to answer Questions 16 and 17:

Portfolio	Average annual return	Standard deviation	Beta
H	10%	6%	0.7
I	16%	12%	1.0
J	20%	14%	2.0
K	25%	20%	1.8

RFR = 5%

16. Rank the portfolios from *best* to *worst*, using the Sharpe performance measure.

    a.   H, I, J, K
    b.   I, J, H, K
*   c.   J, K, I, H
    d.   K, I, J, H
    e.   K, J, I, H

17. Rank the portfolios from *best* to *worst*, using the Treynor performance measure.

    a.   H, I, J, K
    b.   I, J, H, K
    c.   J, K, I, H
*   d.   K, I, J, H
    e.   K, J, I, H

18.   Which of the following statements regarding the Sharpe, Treynor, and Jensen performance measures is *true*?

      a.   The three measures will always yield identical performance rankings.
      b.   The alpha term in Jensen's model reflects the portfolios' returns that are unrelated to the market returns.
      c.   Jensen's alpha is the best of the three measures to use in ranking portfolios.
*   d.   If all portfolios being evaluated are perfectly positively correlated with the market, the rankings using the Sharpe index will be identical to the rankings using the Treynor index.
      e.   none of the above

19.   An excess return regression was performed on the historical quarterly returns of the First Fund, yielding the following result:

$$(r_{FF,t} - RFR_t) = 0.037 + 0.784(r_{M,t} - RFR_t)$$

Which of the following statements is *true*?

*   a.   The systematic risk of First Fund could be passively duplicated by investing 78.4% in the market portfolio and 21.6% in Treasury bills.
      b.   The fund underperformed the market by 3.7%.
      c.   The fund underperformed the market by 78.4%.
      d.   The fund had more systematic risk than the market.
      e.   none of the above

20.   An excess return regression was performed on the historical returns of four funds over the same time period with the following results:

Fund	Regression equation	Standard error of Estimate [SE(u)]
A	$(r_{A,t} - RFR_t) = 0.112 + 0.634(r_{M,t} - RFR_t)$	1.534
B	$(r_{B,t} - RFR_t) = 0.021 + 1.781(r_{M,t} - RFR_t)$	2.687
C	$(r_{C,t} - RFR_t) = 0.049 + 0.889(r_{M,t} - RFR_t)$	0.950
D	$(r_{D,t} - RFR_t) = 0.117 + 0.559(r_{M,t} - RFR_t)$	1.877

Rank the funds from the *best* to the *worst* performer based on the information provided.

      a.   A, B, C, D
*   b.   A, D, C, B
      c.   D, A, C, B
      d.   B, C, D, A
      e.   D, C, B, A

II.   SHORT ANSWER QUESTIONS

1.   True, False, or Uncertain: If the portfolios being evaluated are perfectly diversified (that is, $\rho_{p,M} = 1.0$ for each portfolio), then the Sharpe and Treynor performance measures will provide identical rankings. Justify your answer mathematically.

2.   Discuss the interpretation of Jensen's alpha.

3.   Assume an excess return regression is performed on the historical monthly returns of the Premier Fund, with the following resultant equation:

$$(r_{P,t} - RFR_t) = -0.0434 + 1.253(r_{M,t} - RFR_t)$$

Based on this equation, how could the systematic risk of the Premier Fund be duplicated by some combination of investing in the market portfolio and the risk-free asset?

4.   The following monthly data is provided for the Pinnacle Group Portfolio:

Month	Value per share	Dividend
December	$22.50	
January	$21.75	
February	$23.50	
March	$23.50	$0.25
April	$24.00	
May	$23.75	
June	$24.25	$0.25
July	$25.75	
August	$26.00	
September	$26.50	$0.25
October	$26.25	
November	$27.00	
December	$28.25	$0.28

During the same period, the S&P 500 Index earned an average monthly return of 1.58%, with a standard deviation of 1.78%. The monthly risk-free rate was 0.375%, and the beta of the Pinnacle Group portfolio was 1.84. Calculate the Sharpe and Treynor performance measures and discuss the performance of the Pinnacle Group portfolio relative to that of the S&P 500 Index.

5.   "When selecting a mutual fund, it is a waste of time to compare the historical performances of various funds since past performance is not indicative of future performance." Comment on this statement, citing studies in your answer.

CHAPTER SIXTEEN: SOLUTION GUIDELINES

Multiple Choice

1. **d**: These are distinguishing characteristics of a growth fund.

2. **e**: A mutual fund, by definition, is an open-end fund. It may be either a load fund or a no-load fund.

3. **d**: Shares of closed-end funds trade on securities' exchanges, and prices are set by supply and demand. The price of a closed-end fund may, therefore, be greater than, less than, or equal to its net asset value per share. Income is taxed at the investor level, so closed-end investment company income is not subject to double taxation. The number of shares must remain fixed after its initial public offering, hence the name "closed-end fund."

4. **e**: The ability of a portfolio manager to time the market is reflected in the second beta coefficient of the Treynor-Mazuy characteristic line. If a manager is exceptionally skilled, the coefficient will be a statistically significant positive number.

5. **d**: Both the Sharpe and the Treynor performance measures are single parameter measures and are based on the assumption that money can be borrowed and lent at a single risk-free rate since both are based on the assumptions of the CAPM. They render performance rankings that are highly positively correlated with each other, but not perfectly positively correlated. Any differences in rankings is due to differences in the diversification of the portfolios.

6. **b**: The TREYNOR index measures the risk premium per unit of systematic risk; the SHARPE index measures the risk premium per unit of total risk. The SHARPE index is best used to compare the performance of diversified portfolios since it is based on the capital market line while the TREYNOR index, based on the security market line, can be used to compare both individual assets and portfolios. Because it is based on the security market line, the TREYNOR index is sensitive to the market index that is used to estimate the investment's beta.

7. **c**: Jensen's alpha is somewhat different from the alpha intercept term of the original characteristic line introduced in Capital Market Theory. It is based on a regression of excess returns. If the alpha value is negative, the asset earned returns that were not enough to compensate an investor for the level of systematic risk assumed; if positive, the asset earned returns that were greater than what was necessary to compensate an investor for the level of systematic risk assumed. It is not appropriate to rank the performance of different assets on the basis of Jensen's alpha without first adjusting for risk by translating Jensen's alpha to an appraisal ratio. Jensen's alpha also has no meaning if a regression's beta is not statistically significant.

8. **c**: The Investment Company Act of 1940 limits sales commissions on the sale of new shares of mutual funds to 8 1/2%, not 10%. It is the Internal Revenue Service which allows for the tax-exempt treatment of the income earned by a mutual, not the Investment

Company Act of 1940. The act does, however, limit the ability of mutual fund managers to use margin.

9. **b**: The Barclay, Holderness, and Pontiff study indicated that the greater the managerial stock ownership in closed-end funds, the larger the discounts to net asset value. The three researchers argue that owner/managers receive private benefits that are not available to other shareholders and that the owner/managers will veto open-ended proposals to preserve these benefits.

10. **a**: By definition, a no-load fund is one that charges no initial sales commission. No-load funds may, however, charge redemption fees, 12b-1 fees, and management fees.

11. **c**: Donald Farrar's study of the performance of 23 mutual funds indicated that none of them were efficient portfolios. He also found that in some cases, a fund's stated investment objectives differed from its performance and was not a reliable measure of the quantitative risk and average return statistics. The empirical evidence did indicate that the funds that accepted higher risk levels also tended to have higher average returns.

12. **a**: Sharpe used price indexes for twelve asset classes as the explanatory variables in his factor analysis. The twelve beta coefficients can be interpreted as the weights that fund i invests in asset category k. Macro-economic variables and fund fees play no role in his analysis.

13. **e**: Quantitative management style analysis cannot be used to rank mutual funds by their performances. However, it does provide a way to anticipate and avoid moral hazards, such as misleading or false investment objective statements. It also provides more accurate forecasts about mutual funds' risk and return statistics than do the more subjective comments published by some of the popular financial services firms.

14. **c**: The SHARPE and TREYNOR indexes rank the funds based on the risk and return statistics, not risk alone. According to the information provided, the Millennium Growth Fund provided the higher return for each unit of systematic risk, as indicated by the higher TREYNOR ranking. However, the SHARPE index provides a conflicting ranking; therefore, the Planet Growth Fund must be better diversified than the Millennium Growth fund. Note that the TREYNOR index can be restated as TREYNOR

$= \text{SHARPE}(\frac{\sigma_M}{\rho_{p,M}})$. If the portfolios being ranked are perfectly diversified, such that

their correlation with the market is 1.0, the rankings will be identical. If, however, the investments aren't perfectly diversified ($\rho_{p,M} < 1.0$), the rankings may differ, and the portfolio with the lesser correlation with the market will have a lower SHARPE index.

15. **c**: Since the alpha value of the excess return regression is positive, the Select Value Fund earned a return that was greater than what was adequate to compensate an investor for the level of systematic risk assumed.

16. **c**: The SHARPE indexes for the four funds are calculated below:

$$\text{SHARPE}_H = \frac{10-5}{6} = 0.833 \text{ (Fourth)}$$

$$\text{SHARPE}_I = \frac{16-5}{12} = 0.917 \text{ (Third)}$$

$$\text{SHARPE}_J = \frac{20-5}{14} = 1.071 \text{ (First)}$$

$$\text{SHARPE}_K = \frac{24-5}{20} = 1.000 \text{ (Second)}$$

17.   **d**:   The TREYNOR indexes for the four funds are calculated below:

$$\text{TREYNOR}_H = \frac{10-5}{0.7} = 7.143 \text{ (Fourth)}$$

$$\text{TREYNOR}_I = \frac{16-5}{1.0} = 11.000 \text{ (Second)}$$

$$\text{TREYNOR}_J = \frac{20-5}{2.0} = 7.500 \text{ (Third)}$$

$$\text{TREYNOR}_K = \frac{25-5}{1.8} = 11.111 \text{ (First)}$$

18.   **d**:   Note that the TREYNOR index can be restated as TREYNOR =
SHARPE($\frac{\sigma_M}{\rho_{p,M}}$). If the portfolios being ranked are perfectly diversified, such that their
correlation with the market is 1.0, the rankings will be identical since the TREYNOR will
simply be the SHARPE times the standard deviation of the market, which is a constant at
a given point in time.

19.   **a**:   The beta of Jensen's model has the same interpretation as the beta of the security
market line. Since the beta of First Fund is 0.784, the systematic risk of First Fund could
be passively duplicated by investing 78.4% in the market portfolio, which has a beta of
1.0, and 21.6% in Treasury bills, which has a beta of 0.0.

20.   **b**:   In order to rank the portfolios, an appraisal ratio must be calculated for each.
These ratios are as follows:

$$\text{Appraisal ratio}_A = \frac{0.112}{1.534} = 0.073 \text{ (First)}$$

$$\text{Appraisal ratio}_B = \frac{0.021}{2.687} = 0.008 \text{ (Fourth)}$$

$$\text{Appraisal ratio}_C = \frac{0.049}{0.950} = 0.052 \text{ (Third)}$$

$$\text{Appraisal ratio}_D = \frac{0.117}{1.877} = 0.062 \text{ (Second)}$$

Short Answer

1. True. Recall that beta $= \dfrac{\sigma_p \rho_{p,M}}{\sigma_M}$. Therefore, the Treynor index can be restated as

    $\text{TREYNOR} = \text{SHARPE}\left(\dfrac{\sigma_M}{\rho_{p,M}}\right)$. If all the portfolios being evaluated are perfectly

    diversified, their correlation with the market portfolio will be 1.0, and the TREYNOR will equal the SHARPE times the standard deviation of the market portfolio, which is a constant over the evaluation period, regardless of the portfolio being evaluated.

2. The alpha intercept from the characteristic line in risk premium form can be interpreted as a measure of the excess returns from the asset. If an asset is fairly priced, then it should not offer returns in excess of or less than the appropriate risk premium, and its alpha value will be zero. If the asset is underpriced, it will offer a rate of return that is greater than its appropriate risk premium, and its alpha value will be positive. If it is overpriced, it will offer a rate of return that is less than its appropriate risk premium, and its alpha value will be negative.

3. The systematic risk of the Premier Fund is indicated by the beta coefficient of the regression model, 1.253. Since this beta has the same interpretation as the beta of the security market line, the systematic risk of the Premier Fund can be duplicated by borrowing 25.3% of the investment funds at the risk-free rate (beta = 0) and investing 125.3% in the market portfolio (beta = 1.0). The beta, or systematic risk, of the resultant portfolio will be 1.253(1.0) + (-0.253)(0) = 1.253.

4. The first step is to calculate the monthly returns for the portfolio of the Pinnacle Group. Only then can an average monthly return and standard deviation be calculated.

Month	Value per share	Dividend	Return
December	$22.50		not applicable
January	$21.75		- 3.33%
February	$23.50		+8.05%
March	$23.50	$0.25	+1.06%
April	$24.00		+2.13%
May	$23.75		- 1.04%
June	$24.25	$0.25	+3.16%
July	$25.75		+6.19%
August	$26.00		+0.97%
September	$26.50	$0.25	+2.88%
October	$26.25		- 0.94%
November	$27.00		+2.86%
December	$28.25	$0.28	+5.67%
		Average	+2.31%
		Standard deviation	3.27%

The Sharpe measure for both the portfolio and the S&P 500 Index are as follows:

$$\text{SHARPE}_{pg} = \frac{2.31 - 0.375}{3.27} = 0.592$$

$$\text{SHARPE}_{S\&P} = \frac{2.10 - 0.375}{1.78} = 0.969$$

The Treynor measures are as follows:

$$\text{TREYNOR}_{PG} = \frac{2.31 - 0.375}{1.84} = 1.052$$

$$\text{TREYNOR}_{S\&P} = \frac{2.10 - 0.375}{1.00} = 1.725$$

Regardless of which index is considered, the S&P 500 Index performed better than the Pinnacle Group Portfolio over the time period evaluated.

5. Studies on the repeat-performance of mutual fund winners have provided us with conflicting results. A study by Goetzmann and Ibbotson indicated that there was a tendency for winners to repeat their good performances, although there is no guarantee that this will be the case. Goetzmann and Ibbotson duplicated their study using risk-adjusted returns and using subsamples spanning different time periods with the same results. A study by Mark Carhart concluded that funds with high returns for a year tended to have higher-than-average expected returns the following year, but not in years thereafter. Carhart also found that there was a strong tendency for losers to remain

losers. Burton Malkiel argues against the repeat-winners theory on the basis that he found repeat-winners observable in the 1970s, but not in the 1980s. In light of the conflicting results, it may not be a total waste of time to consider historical returns when selecting a mutual fund, particularly given Carhart's conclusion that losers persist in being losers. At the very least, an investor would be wise to avoid funds that rank at the bottom, given their investment objectives.

CHAPTER SEVENTEEN: FOREIGN EXCHANGE

I.   MULTIPLE CHOICE QUESTIONS

1.   Which of the following statements about "dirty float" is (are) correct?

*   a.   It is a system in which governments are free to intervene with the free
             market system of determining exchange rates in an attempt to slow the speed at
             which exchange rate adjustments take place.
      b.   It is a system that is no longer allowed except in the case of the
             governments of third world countries.
      c.   Under a dirty float system, short-term fluctuations in foreign exchange
             rates are very predictable.
      d.   Both "a" and "b" are correct.
      e.   All of the above are correct.

2.   Which of the following are potential problems that may exist in the future of the European
      Monetary Union (EMU)?

      a.   The cost of foreign exchange transactions might be less than the
             administrative costs associated with operating the EMU.
      b.   Cultural differences between some EMU member nations will continue to exist.
      c.   Member countries will still be free to pursue individual monetary policies, which
             may be conflicting.
      d.   The member nations may resent having to give up their national political
             identities.
*   e.   both "a" and "b"

3.   Which of the following statements about the forward market for currency exchanges is
      (are) *true*?

      a.   Any currency that trades in the spot market will also trade in the forward
             market.
      b.   The forward price will always be greater than the spot price of a currency.
      c.   The forward market is also referred to as the physicals market.
*   d.   Only the few currencies that enjoy a large volume of transactions trade in
             the forward market.
      e.   both "a" and "b"

4.   If a Japanese investor and an American investor both use yen to purchase the stock of a Japanese company and, subsequently, the value of the U.S. dollar depreciates relative to the value of the yen, then

      a.   the Japanese investor will have earned the higher total return on this investment.

*   b.   the American investor will have earned the higher total return on this investment.

      c.   the two investors will have earned the same total return on this investment.

      d.   the American investor would have been better off hedging his investment in yen by entering a forward contract to sell yen.

      e.   the American investor would have been better off hedging his investment in yen by purchasing a put option on yen.

5.   If the expectations hypothesis for foreign exchange is correct, then

      a.   the best estimate of the foreign exchange spot rate that will exist between two currencies in three months is the current spot rate.

      b.   a currency's forward premium or discount should equal the expected percentage change in the exchange rate.

      c.   the best estimate of the foreign exchange spot rte that will exist between two currencies in three months is the current 3-month forward rate for the two countries.

      d.   both "a" and "b"

*   e.   both "b" and "c"

6.   An American investor wishes to purchase 100 shares of a Pakistani stock that is selling for 1200 rupees per share. The spot price is 55.95 rupees per U.S. dollar. This investment will cost the American investor

      a.   6,714,000 rupees.

*   b.   2,148 U.S. dollars.

      c.   2,145 rupees.

      d.   6,714 rupees.

      e.   6,714 U.S. dollars.

7.   Calley Williamson invested in some shares of a Japanese stock on the Tokyo exchange when the exchange rate between the U.S. dollar and the Japanese yen was 108.30 yen per dollar. When Calley sold the stock one year later, the exchange rate was 112.80 yen per dollar. What was Calley's gain or loss on her investment in yen?

      a.   4.16% gain

      b.   3.26% gain

      c.   4.16% loss

*   d.   3.26% loss

      e.   It cannot be determined without knowing the beginning and ending prices of the Japanese stock.

8.   The following risk estimates for U.S. and German investors are provided:

Standard deviation of returns on the MSCI German
stock market index: 22.92%

Standard deviation of returns on the U.S.
stock market index: 15.98%

Correlation coefficient for the MSCI German Index
returns and the returns on the German currency: 0.45

Standard deviation of the returns earned by an
American investor on an investment in
German deutschemarks: 9.64%

Calculate the total risk, as measured by the standard deviation, assumed by an American
investor who invests in the MSCI German stock index.

*   a.   26.79%
      b.   717.68%
      c.   31.19%
      d.   55.23%
      e.   25.62%

9.   Which of the following results might occur after a country's money supply is
        increased?

        a.   The rate of inflation in that country will immediately increase.
        b.   The rate of inflation in that country will immediately decrease.
*   c.   The rate of inflation could increase, but only after a lag of one to three
               years.
        d.   The rate of inflation could decrease, but only after a lag of one to three years.
        e.   The country's currency will experience an immediate revaluation.

10.   Which of the following is (are) criticism(s) of the theory of purchasing power parity?

        a.   Purchasing power parity is based on the "law of one price," which has
               been proven invalid.
        b.   The items in the basket of goods used to calculate a country's price index changes
               continuously over time.
        c.   Different baskets of goods are appropriate for each different country.
        d.   Inflation measurements are based on historical data that does not reflect expected
               future price changes.
*   e.   "b," "c," and "d"

11.　　　　　If the current exchange rate between the U.S. dollar and the German deutschemark is $0.5567 per deutschemark, then an investor will receive

　　　a.　　0.5567 deutschemarks per U.S. dollar.
*　　b.　　1.7963 deutschemarks per U.S. dollar.
　　　c.　　0.4433 deutschemarks per U.S. dollar.
　　　d.　　1.7963 U.S. dollars per deutschemark.
　　　e.　　0.7963 U.S. dollars per deutschemark.

12.　　　　　An American investor invested 1,000 deutschemarks in a German firm that was selling for DM40 a share when the deutschemark was trading at $0.6200 per deutschemark. After one year, the German firm was selling for DM52 a share and the exchange rate between the U.S. dollar and the German mark was $0.6310 per deutschemark. The German firm paid no dividends. What was the American investor's total return on this investment?

　　　a.　　30.00%
　　　b.　　16.87%
　　　c.　　17.52%
*　　d.　　32.30%
　　　e.　　22.10%

13.　　　　　The exchange rate between the U.S. dollar and the British pound is currently £1.7210 per U.S. dollar. Nancy Daubenmeyer, an American, exchanged her dollars for British pounds and invested in 100 shares of a British corporation at a price of £33.50 per share. One year later, she received dividends of £0.51 a share from the firm. At that time, the price per share was £37.20 and the exchange rate was £1.6990 per U.S. dollar. Nancy's total return on this investment was

*　　a.　　11.16%.
　　　b.　　-4.81%.
　　　c.　　13.89%.
　　　d.　　 9.76%.
　　　e.　　12.33%.

14. Purchasing power parity implies that if inflation in France is 8% and inflation in Brazil is 24%, then the French franc should

* a. appreciate by 14.8% relative to the Brazilian real to maintain economic equilibrium.
  b. depreciate by 14.8% relative to the Brazilian real to maintain economic equilibrium.
  c. appreciate by 8.71% relative to the Brazilian real to maintain economic equilibrium.
  d. depreciate by 8.71% relative to the Brazilian real to maintain economic equilibrium.
  e. appreciate by 0.87% relative to the Brazilian real to maintain economic equilibrium.

15. The current spot exchange rate between the U.S. dollar and the German deutschemark is $0.5990. The inflation rate in Germany is expected to be 8% over the next year while the inflation rate in the U.S. is expected to be 3% over the same period. Assuming purchasing power parity, this would imply that a futures contract on deutschemarks with a delivery date one year from today would be priced at

  a. $0.5713 per deutschemark.
  b. $1.7505 per deutschemark.
* c. $0.6281 per deutschemark.
  d. $1.5922 per deutschemark.
  e. none of the above.

16. The exchange rate between the Japanese yen and the U.S. dollar is currently $0.9574 per yen while the 30-day forward exchange rate if $0.9443. This means that

  a. a forward premium of 1.37% exists.
* b. a forward discount of 1.37% exists.
  c. the spot exchange rate in 30 days will be $0.9705 per yen.
  d. the expected spot exchange rate in 30 days will be $0.9705.
  e. both "b" and "d"

17. Assume that the nominal risk-free rate in the U.S. is 5.2% and the nominal risk-free rate in Britain is 7%. Assume, also, that the current exchange rate between U.S. dollars and British pounds is £0.6154 per dollar. Covered interest rate parity suggests that the exchange rate between the U.S. dollar and the British pound for delivery in one year should be

* a. $1.5977 per pound.
  b. $1.6528 per pound.
  c. $0.6259 per pound.
  d. $0.6050 per pound.
  e. none of the above.

18. If a government decides to expand its money supply rapidly by printing money, which of the following is likely to occur?

  *   a.   A period of high inflation will follow.

          b.   Interest rates in that country will be lower since the government will be able to pay its debts using the newly printed currency.

          c.   The prices of the country's exports will decrease.

          d.   all of the above

          e.   "a" and "b" only

19. Which of the following would **not** affect the total risk faced by an American who invests in a Japanese stock on the Tokyo exchange?

          a.   the uncertainty of the returns on the Japanese stock

  *   b.   the covariance of the American dollar with the U.S. stock market returns

          c.   the covariance of the Japanese yen/U.S. dollar exchange rate with the returns on the Japanese stock

          d.   the foreign exchange risk

          e.   All of the above will have an effect on the total risk faced by the American investor who in a Japanese stock.

20. The foreign exchange parity model that asserts that the differences in nominal interest rates between two countries can be explained by differences in the countries' real interest rates and differences in their inflation rates is the

          a.   relative purchasing power parity model.

          b.   Fisher closed model.

  *   c.   Fisher open model.

          d.   uncovered interest rate parity model.

          e.   covered interest rate parity model.

II.   SHORT ANSWER QUESTIONS

1.   Currently, the German deutschemark is trading at DM1.8342 per dollar. A year ago, it was trading for DM1.6224 per dollar. If the return on the German stocks had been 17% in the last year, what would have been the net return earned by a U.S. investor?

2.   Assume the expected rate of return and standard deviation of returns from investing German deutschemarks in the common stock of Lufthansa, which is headquartered in Germany, are 14% and 20% respectively. Assume also that the deutschemark has been appreciating relative to the dollar at a rate of 0.5% a year with a standard deviation of 5% and that the correlation coefficient between the returns from Lufthansa stock and the deutschemark is 0.8. How much return and total risk should an American investor who pays deutschemarks for the stock of Lufthansa expect?

3.   Assume that the spot rate between the U.S. dollar and the Australian dollar is A$1.8993 per U.S.$ and that the one-year forward exchange rate is A$1.9234 per U.S.$. If American investors can earn 11% on their investments in Australian dollars, what does covered interest rate parity suggest the interest rate for domestic U.S. borrowers must be?

4.   What is meant by a "common market"? What benefits are associated with such an organization, and why are these benefits expected to occur?

5.   Discuss the role that the correlation between the returns on a foreign currency and the risk associated with a foreign security's returns plays in determining the total risk faced by a foreign investor relative to a domestic investor.

CHAPTER SEVENTEEN: SOLUTION GUIDELINES

Multiple Choice

1. **a**: This is the definition of dirty float.

2. **e**: The European Monetary Union does not require that member
nations give up their national political identities; however, member countries will no
longer be able to pursue individual monetary policies. The administrative costs
associated with the EMU may be greater than the cost of foreign exchange transactions,
and cultural differences between some of the EMU member nations will continue to exist,
and may cause conflict.

3. **d**: Only the currencies that enjoy a large volume of transactions trade in the
forward market; it is not profitable to create forward contracts on
currencies that have relatively few transactions.

4. **b**: Unlike the Japanese investor, the American investor has two investment
positions—one in the stock of the Japanese company and one in yen. If the value of the
dollar depreciates relative to the yen, the American investor will receive more dollars for
each yen and his return on his investment in yen will cause his total return to be higher
than that of the Japanese investor.

5. **d**: The expectations hypothesis for foreign exchange states that the best estimate of
the foreign exchange rate that will exist between two countries in three months is the 3-
month forward rate for the two currencies. If the forward rate equals the expected future
spot rate, an arbitrage profit opportunity would exist unless the currency's forward
premium or discount is equal to the expected percentage change in the exchange rate.

6. **b**: The American investor would have to pay $1/55.95 = \$0.0179$ per rupee. The total
investment would cost him $\$0.0179 \times 1200 \times 100 = \$2,148.00$.

7. **d**: When Calley invested in the Japanese stock, she paid $1/108.30 = \$0.0092$ per yen.
When she sold the stock, she received $1/112.80 = \$0.0089$ per yen. The return on her
investment in yen is

$$r_c = \frac{SP_t - SP_{t-1}}{SP_{t-1}} = \frac{0.0089 - 0.0092}{0.0092} = -3.26\%.$$

8. **a**: $VAR(r_f) = VAR(r_c) + VAR(r_d) + \rho_{cd}\sqrt{VAR(r_c)}\sqrt{VAR(r_d)}$
$$= (9.64)^2 + (22.92)^2 + 0.45(9.64)(22.92) = 717.68296$$

$\sigma_f = \sqrt{717.68296} = 26.79\%$.

9. **c**: An increase in a country's money supply by more than a few percent per year for several years can result in inflation. However, there is a lag of one to three years before the country's rate of inflation responds with the increase.

10. **e**: Purchasing power parity is based on the "law of one price," but this is not an invalid theory. Criticisms of the theory of purchasing power parity are as follows: (1) The items in the basket of goods used to calculate a country's price index changes continuously over time, making it difficult for government researchers to alter appropriately the basket of goods that they use in their calculations. (2) The items in the basket of goods used to calculate one country's price index is not the same as the items used in the calculation of another country's price index. (3) Although most inflation measurements are based on historical data and, therefore, do not take expected price changes into account, people base their decisions on expected inflation, not historical inflation rates.

11. **b**: $1/\$0.5567 = 1.7963$ deutschemarks per dollar

12. **d**: The American investor was able to purchase $DM1{,}000/DM40 = 25$ shares of the German firm. The return earned on the investment in the German firm is calculated as follows: $r_d = \dfrac{25(DM52) - 25(DM40)}{DM1{,}000} = 30\%$. The return that the investor earned on the foreign currency is $r_c = \dfrac{\$0.6310 - \$0.6200}{\$0.6200} = 1.77\%$. The total return is $r_f = r_d + r_c + r_d r_c$ $= (30\%) + (1.77\%) + (0.531\%) = 32.30\%$.

13. **a**: Nancy's return on her investment in the British Corporation is calculated as follows: $(£37.20 - £33.50 + £0.51)/£33.50 = 12.6\%$. Her return on her investment in British pounds was $(£1.6990 - £1.7210)/£1.7210 = -1.28\%$. Her total return was $r_f = 12.6\% + (-1.28\%) + (12.6\%)(-1.28\%) = 11.16\%$.

14. **a**: The ratio of the future spot exchange rate to the current spot exchange rate is equal to $\dfrac{1 + INF_f}{1 + INF_d}$, according to purchasing power parity. Therefore, the percentage difference is $\dfrac{1.24}{1.08} - 1 = 14.8\%$. This means that the French franc should appreciate by 14.8% relative to the Brazilian real in order to maintain economic equilibrium.

15. **c**: According to purchasing power parity,

$$\frac{SP_1}{SP_0} = \frac{1 + INF_f}{1 + INF_d}. \text{ So, } SP_1 = SP_0 \frac{1 + INF_f}{1 + INF_d} = \$0.599\left(\frac{1.08}{1.03}\right) = \$0.6281 \text{ per deutschemark.}$$

16. **b**: The percentage discount or premium is calculated as $FP_1/SP_0 - 1.0$. $\$0.9443/\$0.9574 - 1.0 = -1.37\%$. Since the sign is negative, a forward *discount* of 1.37% exists.

17.   **c**:   Covered interest rate parity states that $\dfrac{1+r_f}{1+r_d}=\dfrac{FP_1}{SP_0}$. Therefore, FP_1

$$=0.6154\left(\frac{1.07}{1.052}\right)=0.6259 \text{ pounds per dollar, or } 1/0.6259 = \$1.5977 \text{ per pound.}$$

18.   **a**:   If a government decides to expand its money supply rapidly by printing money, high inflation can result. The higher rate of inflation would result in higher, not lower, interest rates in that country, according to the Fisher closed model. Furthermore, the increase in prices will cause the prices of that country's exports to increase as well.

19.   **b**:   The total risk faced by a foreign investor is dependent on the uncertainty of the returns of the foreign stock, the uncertainty of the foreign exchange rate, and the covariance of the foreign exchange rate with the returns on the foreign stock. The covariance of that investor's domestic currency exchange rate with the stock returns in his domestic market plays no role.

20.   **c**:   Relative purchasing power parity states that a basket of identical goods should sell at the same price around the world if no barriers to trade exist and if the goods are priced in a common currency The model suggests a relationship between exchange rates and inflation rates in two countries. Uncovered interest rate parity depicts the relationship between the nominal interest rates of two countries and the current and expected future spot rates of those countries. Covered interest rate parity is similar to uncovered interest rate parity, but it is more useful since it uses forward exchange rates instead of expected future spot rates in depicting the relationship. The Fisher closed model deals with only one country's interest rates. It is the Fisher open model that depicts the differences in nominal interest rates between two countries as a function of the differences in the countries' real interest rates and the differences in their inflation rates.

Short Answer

1.   Last year, an American dollar would purchase 1.6224 deustchemarks , or \$0.61637 = 1DM. This year it will buy 1.8342 deustchemarks, or \$0.54520 = 1DM. Therefore, the loss on the German currency was $\dfrac{0.54520-0.61637}{0.61637}=-11.5\%$. The total gain is calculated as (1 + return on stocks)(1 + return on currency) - 1 = (1.17)(1 + -0.115) - 1 = 3.5%.

2.   The return that a foreign investor will earn is calculated as follows:

$r_f = (1 + r_d)(1 + r_c) - 1 = (1.14)(1.005) -1 = 14.57\%$

The risk that a foreign investor will earn is calculated as follows:

$$VAR(r_f) = Var(r_c) + Var(r_d) + \rho_{cd}\sqrt{Var(r_c)}\sqrt{Var(r_d)}$$
$$= (5)^2 + (20)^2 + (0.8)(5)(20) = 505$$

The risk as measured by the standard deviation is $\sqrt{505} = 22.47\%$.

3. The covered interest rate parity model suggests that the interest rate for domestic U.S. borrowers must be 9.6%:

$$\frac{1+r_f}{1+r_d} = \frac{FP_1}{SP_0}$$

$$\frac{1.11}{1+r_d} = \frac{1.9234}{1.8993}$$

$$1.9234(1+r_d) = 2.1082$$

$$1.9234 + 1.9234r_d = 2.1082$$

$$1.9234r_d = 0.1848$$

$$r_d = 9.6\%$$

4. A common market is a voluntary organization of nations that adopts a single common currency and establishes policies to foster a cross-border trade. Nations that enter this type of organization believe it will spur business activity. Increased sales are expected, which will, in turn, facilitate specialized manufacturing, promote technological advances, and increase the flow of foreign capital such that the common market member nations prosper. These benefits are expected to occur for three reasons: (1) When the member nations adopt one common currency, it reduces the number of foreign exchange transactions in their common market. (2) A common currency is expected to spur business competition by facilitating price comparisons within the common market. (3) The adoption of a common currency may bond the members of the common market together more closely.

5. A foreign investor faces two types of risk--foreign exchange risk due to her investment in the foreign currency and the risk associated with investment in the foreign security. If the return on the foreign exchange is positively correlated with the investments returns, the foreign investor's risk will be greater than that of a domestic investor in the same security. This can be seen clearly by examining the mathematical formula for the risk of a two-asset portfolio, the assets in this case being the foreign currency and the foreign security:

$$VAR(r_f) = VAR(r_c) + VAR(r_d) + (\rho_{cd})\sqrt{VAR(r_c)}\sqrt{VAR(r_d)}$$

The $VAR(r_d)$ term is the risk that the domestic investor faces by investing in the security. Note that if the correlation coefficient is greater than or equal to zero, the risk of the foreign investor will necessarily be greater than that of the domestic investor. If the correlation coefficient is negative, it is possible that the risk faced by the foreign investor would be less than that of the domestic investor. As an example, assume that the currency risk, as measured by the variance is 9 and the risk associated with the investment in the security is 16. Assume also that the correlation coefficient for the returns of the two investments is -0.8. Then,

$VAR(r_f) = 9 + 16 + (-0.8)(3)(4) = 15.4\%$, which is less than the domestic investor's risk of $VAR(r_d) = 16$.

CHAPTER EIGHTEEN: GLOBAL INVESTING

I.   MULTIPLE CHOICE QUESTIONS

1.   Multinational diversification provides greater benefits when

      a.   the economic activity of all countries is highly positively correlated.
      b.   there are no government restrictions on foreign ownership.
      c.   insider trading is not allowed in the security markets of the countries.
*   d.   barriers to entry that hinder and frustrate international investors exist.
      e.   "a," "b," and "c" only

2.   All else equal, as the correlation between the returns from two countries declines from +1 to −1, the risk of the two-country portfolio will

      a.   increase.
*   b.   decrease.
      c.   increase or decrease, depending on the individual foreign exchange risks involved.
      d.   remain unaffected.
      e.   decrease, as will the returns on the portfolio.

3.   Which of the following statements regarding the historical inter-country correlations between stock market indexes is *true*?

      a.   The correlations between all pairs of emerging market countries are positive, as are the correlations between developed nations.
      b.   The correlations between all countries are negative, but the correlations are less negative between developed nations.
*   c.   The correlations between all pairs of developed nations are positive, but some negative correlations exist between emerging market countries.
      d.   Regardless of whether the pair of countries are developed or whether they are emerging market nations, the correlations are all positive, although the correlations for the emerging market nations are close to zero.
      e.   none of the above

4. International investing is perennially a valuable investment opportunity because of which of the following advantages?

    a. Different technological advantages are possessed by foreign companies than exist in the U.S.
*   b. Returns from U.S. investments have lower correlations with foreign investments than with most other U.S. investments.
    c. High growth rates in the lesser-developed countries can cause firms in those countries to earn some of the highest rates of return in the world.
    d. There are tax benefits that are not enjoyed when investing in American corporations.
    e. all of the above

5. The empirically derived international efficient frontier of investment opportunities that was derived in this chapter obtained the most dominant set of investment opportunities by using which of the following groups of countries?

    a. emerging market countries
    b. developed market countries
    c. U.S. markets
*   d. as many different countries as possible
    e. Each country had roughly equal opportunities if the international correlation coefficients are ignored.

6. Differences between inter-country rate of return correlations results from which of the following?

    a. different currencies and foreign exchange regulations
    b. different languages, accounting systems, and trade restrictions
    c. different political systems and different political and military alliances
*   d. all of the above
    e. "a" and "b" only

7. Solnik's empirical study of simple international diversification suggests which of the following conclusions?

    a. Simple diversification within the borders of any country in the world appears to result in substantial risk reduction.
    b. Every country in the world appears to have some level of systematic or undiversifiable risk below which simple diversification cannot reduce the total risk of a portfolio.
    c. Multinational investing tends to reduce risk below domestic diversification for the countries studied by Solnik.
*   d. all of the above
    e. "b" and "c" only

8.   The abbreviation "ADR" stands for

    a.   Automated Document Representation.
    b.   Association of Domestic Representatives.
*   c.   American Depository Receipts
    d.   Allied Despots and Representatives.
    e.   American Dividend Restatements.

9.   An investor in an ADR receives which of the following?

    a.   a claim on a bankrupt corporation's assets that is prior to the claim of the
          corporation's common stockholders.
    b.   a single share of a foreign company's stock per ADR, which entitles them to the
          dividends or interest paid by the firm; these payments to the investor will be made
          in the currency of the home country of the firm.
*   c.   one or more shares of a foreign company's stock, depending on the ADR,
          which entitles them to receive dividends and interest income paid by the
          firm; the investor will receive these payments in dollars since they will
          have been converted from the foreign currency to dollars by the parent
          bank that created the ADR.
    d.   one or more shares of a foreign company's stock, depending on the ADR,
          which entitles them to the dividends or interest paid by the firm; these
          payments to the investor will, however, be made in the home country of
          the firm, and the investor will have to pay a fee to have the income
          converted to dollars.
    e.   shares of a fully-owned foreign subsidiary of an American corporation, which
          entitles them to receive dividends and interest income paid by the American
          corporation. These payments will, however, be received in the foreign currency
          rather than in dollars.

10.   The greater the degree of integration between two financial markets and the more
      interaction between the two nations' economies

    a.   the lower will be the correlation between their financial markets.
*   b.   the greater will be the correlation between their financial markets.
    c.   the more unstable will be the correlation between their financial markets.
    d.   the greater will be the diversification benefits for investors.
    e.   both "a" and "d"

11. Which of the following is a conclusion of the research conducted by Solnik, Boucrelle, and Le Fur that was discussed in this chapter?

    a.   Correlations between countries tend to be relatively stable over time.

*   b.   Correlations between countries tend to increase during periods when the financial markets are most volatile.

    c.   Correlations between countries tend to decrease during periods when the financial markets are the most volatile.

    d.   As the world's financial markets become more integrated, the correlations between countries seems to be trending toward zero.

    e.   both "a" and "b"

12. Which of the following statements about international diversification is (are) true?

    a.   The greater the volatility of the financial markets, the lower the correlation of the returns between two markets is, and, therefore, the greater the diversification potential for investors.

    b.   Because the correlation between two country's financial markets is relatively stable over time, investors do not have to worry about rebalancing their portfolio's assets unless their investment objectives change.

    c.   Investors can achieve the same level of international diversification more cheaply and easily by investing in stocks of multinational corporations.

    d.   all of the above

*   e.   none of the above

13. Which of the following is (are) problems that may be encountered by investors in ADRs?

    a.   Dividends and interest are paid directly to the investors in a foreign currency; the investors must then pay exchange rate fees if they wish to convert the foreign currency to dollars.

    b.   ADR commissions are typically much higher than the commissions that a small investor would have to pay if he invested directly in a foreign security.

*   c.   Some ADRs may not provide a complete set of financial statements that have been translated into English.

    d.   all of the above

    e.   "a" and "b" only

14. Which of the following statements about Global Depository Receipts (GDRs) is (are) true?

    a. GDRs can be denominated in any currency.
    b. GDRs can be issued in the U.S. without the long and costly registration procedure required for a U.S. corporation.
    c. GDRs, unlike ADRs, eliminate the foreign exchange risk faced by investors.
    d. all of the above
*   e. "a" and "b" only

15. Which of the following types of investments can be used to eliminate exposure to foreign exchange rate risk?

    a. American Depository Receipts
    b. Global Depository Receipts
    c. iShares
    d. International funds
*   e. none of the above

16. A problem inherent in applying the international security market line (ISML) is that

    a. no index exists that can be reasonably used as a proxy for the world's market portfolio in calculation an asset's international beta.
    b. international risk premiums differ for each country.
    c. the world's financial markets are not fully integrated.
    d. all of the above
*   e. "b" and "c" only

17. The international arbitrage pricing theory (IAPT) model has which of the following advantages over the international security market line (ISML)?

    a. It is simpler to formulate.
    b. It can account for country to country violations in purchasing power parity by incorporating this as a priced risk factor.
    c. It can account for the home bias of each country by incorporating this as a priced risk factor.
*   d. all of the above
    e. "b" and "c" only

18.   A mutual fund that invests in both foreign and domestic securities is referred to as a(n)

    a.   international fund.
*   b.   global fund.
    c.   country fund.
    d.   iShares.
    e.   foreign fund.

19.   Based on his research, with which of the following statements might Bruno Solnik agree?

    a.   The risk-reducing value of multinational diversification can be achieved only if the international portfolios are hedged against foreign exchange losses.
    b.   International portfolios that are hedged against foreign exchange losses have significantly lower risk than unhedged portfolios and offer the same high returns.
*   c.   International portfolios that are hedged against foreign exchange losses have only slightly less risk than unhedged portfolios and, on average, the rate of return on the hedged portfolio is less due to the transactions costs involved and due to the elimination of potential gains enjoyed by an unhedged portfolio.
    d.   Diversification across industries provides a reduction in risk that is similar to diversifying across countries.
    e.   both "a" and "b"

20.   Homogeneous markets

    a.   would increase the diversification benefits of multinational investing.
*   b.   exist only when there are no barriers to investing or trade between countries and when the economic activity of all countries is highly positively correlated.
    c.   exist only when there are no barriers to investing or trade between countries and when the economic activity of all countries is uncorrelated.
    d.   are the cause of international market segmentation.
    e.   both "a" and "b"

II.   SHORT ANSWER QUESTIONS

1.   Discuss the similarites and differences between American Depository Receipts (ADRs) and Global Depository Receipts (GDRs).

Use the following information for the securities' market returns for two countries to answer Problems 2 and 3:

Year	Country A	Country B
2001	22.5%	15.1%
2002	39.4%	12.0%
2003	8.2%	18.3%
2004	10.0%	8.4%
2005	12.8%	20.6%

2. Calculate the correlation coefficient for the returns of the two countries for the five-year period.

3. Assume that the historical means, standard deviations, and the correlation coefficient for the returns of the two countries are reasonable estimates of expected values. Determine the expected return and risk of a portfolio that is composed of equal investments in each country.

4. True, false, or uncertain: "When world financial markets become more volatile, the diversification benefits of international investing is reduced." Explain.

5. Summarize Bruno Solnik's findings when he researched the diversification benefits of international investing.

Multiple Choice

1. **d**:   Multinational diversification provides the greatest diversification potential when there are not homogeneous markets; i.e., when there are barriers to entry and when the economic activity of all countries is not highly positively correlated.

2. **b**:   As the returns between two countries' become less and less correlated, the diversification potential is greater. This will not affect the expected returns on the portfolio, however.

3. **c**:   An examination of the historical inter-country correlations reveals that the correlations between all pairs of developed nations are positive, but some negative correlations are found between the countries with emerging markets.

4. **b**:   International investing provides a valuable investment opportunity due to the diversification benefits, which result from the fact that U.S. investments have lower correlations with foreign investments than with most other investments to be had in the U.S.

5. **d**:   The most dominant set of investment opportunities was the portfolio that contained investments in as many different countries as possible since this portfolio offered the greatest return per unit of risk. It was computed using 50 stock market indexes.

6. **d**:   Different currencies and foreign exchange regulations, different languages, different accounting systems, different trade restrictions, different political systems, and different political and military alliances all contribute to the differences between inter-country correlations.

7. **d**:   Solnick's study concluded that multinational investing provides more risk-reducing benefits than domestic diversification. However, even simple diversification within the borders of any one country was found to have substantial risk-reducing benefits. Even with multinational investing, the risk is not eliminated, due to the fact that every country seems to have some level of systematic risk.

8. **c**:   An ADR is an American Depository Receipt.

9. **c**:   An investor in an ADR receives one or more shares of a foreign company's stock, depending on the stipulation of the ADR. The investor is entitled to any dividend or interest income paid by the foreign firm. The foreign firm makes the payments in its home currency, but the parent bank that created the ADR converts the foreign currency to dollars prior to making the payment to the investor.

10. **b**:   The tendency for the correlation coefficients between two countries to increase over time is probably a result of the increasing integration of their financial markets and greater interaction between the two nations' economies.

11. **b**:   The Solnik, Boucrelle, and Le Fur study concluded that correlations between countries are not stable through time and tend to increase during periods when the financial markets are most volatile. As the financial markets become more integrated, the correlations between countries exhibit an upward trend.

12. **e**:   The greater the volatility of the financial markets, the higher the correlation of the returns between two markets is, lessening the diversification potential for investors. Correlations between two countries' financial markets are not stable through time, so rebalancing of portfolios is necessary, even if an investor's investment objectives remain unchanged. Investing through multinational corporations does not appear to provide much, if any international diversification benefits since the variability in the MNC's stock returns are largely determined by variations in the MNC's domestic stock market.

13. **c**:   ADR commissions are typically much lower than those that a small investor would face if investing directly in a foreign security. Dividends and interest income are forwarded to the parent bank of the ADR, which then converts the foreign currency to cash prior to paying the investors the income due them. Unsponsored ADRs may not provide a complete set of financial statements that have been translated into English.

14. **e**:   GDRs can be denominated in any currency and can be issued in the U.S. without the long and costly registration procedure required for a U.S. corporation, under Rule 144A of the Securities Exchange Commission. However, they do not eliminate foreign exchange risk; they only disguise it.

15. **e**:   Regardless of whether they invest using ADRs, GDRs, iShares, or international mutual funds, investors are exposed to foreign exchange rate risk, but because these investments make their payments to investors in dollars rather than in a foreign currency, the foreign exchange rate risk is hidden.

16. **e**:   While there are several global market indexes that can be used to calculate an asset's international beta, international risk premiums may differ among countries, and the world's financial markets are not fully integrated. Some emerging markets also violate the ISML's idealized assumptions much more than those of more developed nations, such as the U.S. and Canada, and their economies are poorly integrated with the rest of the world.

17. **d**:   The IAPT model is easier to use than the ISML because it can be used to analyze either a few or many assets. It can incorporate numerous risk factors, such as those involving purchasing power parity and a home bias.

18. **b**:   Global funds invest in both foreign and domestic securities; international funds or foreign funds invest primarily in foreign securities, and country funds confine their investments to a single country.

19.   **c**:   Solnik found that international portfolios that are hedged against foreign exchange losses have only slightly less risk than unhedged portfolios and, on average, the rate of return on the hedged portfolio is less due to the transactions costs involved and due to the elimination of potential gains that an unhedged portfolio could achieve. He also found that diversification across countries and across both countries and industries are superior strategies to diversification onlly across industries.

20.   **b**:   Multinational diversification would not be beneficial if the world's capital markets were perfectly homogeneous. However, homogeneous markets exist if there are no barriers to investing or trade between countries and when the economic activity of all countries is highly positively correlated. When barriers to investing or trade exist, the result is international market segmentation, which makes international diversification more beneficial.

Short Answer

1.   Both American Depository Receipts (ADRs) and Global Depository Receipts (GDRs) are special certificates representing ownership interests in foreign securities, which are created to minimize investors' foreign exchange transactions. However, ADRs are denominated in dollars; most GDRs are not. ADRs are traded in the U.S. markets, and most are created by American commercial banks that have large international departments. GDRs can be issued in the United States, Europe, Asia, or any other country and can be denominated in any currency. Neither ADRs nor GDRs eliminate foreign exchange rate risk; the risk is merely hidden.

2.   The average returns, standard deviations, and the covariance of the returns must be calculated first:

The average return for the five-year period for Country A is 18.6% and the average return for the five-year period for Country B is 14.9%.

The standard deviations are calculated below:

$$\sigma_A = \sqrt{\frac{(22.5-18.6)^2+(39.4-18.6)^2+(8.2-18.6)^2+(10.0-18.6)^2+(12.8-18.6)^2}{4}}$$

$$= \sqrt{165.9025} = 12.88\%$$

$$\sigma_B = \sqrt{\frac{(15.1-14.9)^2+(12.0-14.9)^2+(18.3-14.9)^2+(8.4-14.9)^2+(20.6-14.9)^2}{4}}$$

$$= \sqrt{23.6875} = 4.87\%$$

The covariance of the returns is -18.015:

$$\text{COV}(r_A, r_B) = \frac{\begin{array}{l}(22.5-18.6)(15.1-14.9)+(39.4-18.6)(12-14.9)+(8.2-18.6)(18.3-14.9)\\+(10-18.6)(8.4-14.9)+(12.8-18.6)(20.6-14.9)\end{array}}{4}$$

$$= -18.015$$

The correlation coefficient is -0.29:

$$\rho_{A,B} = \frac{-18.015}{(12.88)(4.87)} = -0.29$$

3. The arithmetic averages calculated in the previous problem are proxies for the expected returns of each country. If equal amounts are invested in each country, the expected return of the portfolio is (0.5)(18.6%) + (0.5)(14.9%) = 16.75%.

    The risk of the investment, as measured by the standard deviation is 6.92%:

    $$\sigma_p = \sqrt{(0.5)^2 (165.9025) + (0.5)^2 (23.6875) + 2(0.5)(0.5)} = 6.92\%$$

4. True. The results of a study by Solnik, Boucrelle, and Le Fur indicated that correlations between countries tend to increase during periods when the financial markets are most volatile. The greater the correlation, the lower is the risk-reduction possibility.

5. Bruno Solnik used stock returns from eight different countries over a five-year period to study the benefits of diversification across different countries. He assumed only U.S. dollars were invested in the stocks from every country, so his results combine foreign exchange risk with the risk of investing in foreign securities. Stocks were randomly selected (1) across countries, (2) across industries, (3) across both countries and industries, and (4) across countries with and without currency hedging to reduce foreign exchange risk.

    Solnik found that selection across countries is superior to diversifying domestically within the United States. He also concluded that selection across countries and across both countries and industries are superior strategies to diversifying across industries. His experiments used random diversification and suggest that a portfolio need not contain much more than two or three dozen common stocks to achieve substantial benefits from either domestic or international diversification. His results using hedged versus unhedged portfolios suggest that a substantial portion of the risk-reducing value of multinational diversification occurs whether or not international portfolios are hedged against foreign exchange losses. Furthermore, the portfolios that were hedged against foreign exchange losses had only slightly less risk than the unhedged portfolio, and hedging is costly. The rate of return on hedged portfolios is reduced by transactions costs and the elimination of the potential gains that an unhedged position can offer.

CHAPTER NINETEEN: GLOBAL BOND MARKETS

I.   MULTIPLE CHOICE QUESTIONS

1.   Bonds issued by the German government are called

*   a.   Bunds.
       b.   OATs.
       c.   Gilts.
       d.   Deutschebonds.
       e.   GGBs.

2.   The NYSE-operated Automated Bond System (ABS) provides

       a.   bond prices that are market prices determined by the natural forces of
              supply and demand.
       b.   a liquid market for bonds.
*   c.   only estimated bond prices that are based on quotations from
              bonds that have similar coupon rates, maturities, quality ratings, and call
              provisions.
       d.   a market that is free from internal arbitrage opportunities.
       e.   "a" and "b" only

3.   A bond that is issued in one country and currency by a foreign entity and that is traded in
       the country of issuance is called a(n)

       a.   domestic bond.
*   b.   foreign bond.
       c.   Eurobond.
       d.   Eurodollar bond.
       e.   FNMA bond.

4.   A bond that is denominated in British pound sterling and is issued by a foreign entity and
       traded in the United Kingdom is called a(n)

       a.   Yankee bond.
       b.   Shogun bond.
*   c.   Bulldog bond.
       d.   Matador bond.
       e.   Carvela bond.

5.   In which of the following ways do Yankee bonds differ from Eurodollar bonds?

    a.   Eurodollar bonds are underwritten by an international investment banking syndicate, whereas Yankee bonds are underwritten by a U.S. investment banker.

    b.   Yankee bonds are taxed and regulated by the U.S. government; Eurodollar bonds are not.

    c.   Eurodollar bonds are denominated in dollars, whereas Yankee bonds are denominated in the currency of the foreign issuer.

    d.   all of the above

*   e.   "a" and "b" only

6.   A Discount Brady Bond is

    a.   a type of Brady bond for which the face value equals the par value of the defaulted debts.

    b.   a zero-coupon bond that is sold at an original issue discount from its face value.

    c.   a fixed-rate bond for which principal and interest payments are amortized progressively over 20 to 25 years.

*   d.   a bond that is issued at a deep discount from the par value of the defaulted debts that it replaces.

    e.   "b" and "c" only.

7.   An investor who deposits his coupon payments from a bond investment that offered a yield-to-maturity of 10.2% when purchased into a savings account that pays 5%

    a.   will earn an average annual rate of return of 10.2% so long as the issuer does not default on the timing or the amount of the promised payments.

    b.   will earn an average annual rate of 10.2% so long as the bond is held to maturity.

*   c.   will necessarily earn less than an average annual rate of return of 10.2%.

    d.   may earn either more or less than 10.2% if the bond is held to maturity.

    e.   both "a" and "b"

8.   Which of the following statements about the bond markets of Japan, Germany, and the U.S. is (are) *true*?

    *   a.   While both Japan and the U.S. have a corporate bond market, there is no real corporate bond sector in Germany.

           b.   Of the three nations, only the U.S. has federal government agency bonds.

           c.   The Japanese corporate bond market represents a larger proportion of the nation's aggregate bond market than that of the other two nations.

           d.   The German federal government is second only to the U.S. government in terms of the amount of borrowing.

           e.   both "a" and "b"

9.   Which of the following statements *best* describes the "gray market" for Eurobonds?

           a.   The bonds are sold for one-half of whatever is eventually established as the bond issue's final offering price.

    *   b.   The "gray market" is essentially a forward market for bonds that do not yet exist.

           c.   Members of the selling group experience large losses due to the existence of the "gray market."

           d.   The "gray market" refers to the sale of Eurobonds by dealers who are not member of the IPO's selling group.

           e.   both "c" and "d"

10.   Which of the following statements about Eurobonds is (are) *true*?

           a.   Eurobonds are all corporate bonds.

           b.   Eurobonds are all government bonds.

    *   c.   Eurobond IPOs require significantly less time to complete than do new issues of U.S. bonds.

           d.   The Eurobond market is the largest bond market in the world.

           e.   "a," "c," and "d" only

11.   A bond's yield-to-maturity will be equal to its current yield if

           a.   the bond is selling at a premium.

           b.   the bond is selling at a discount.

    *   c.   the bond is selling at par.

           d.   it pays a fixed coupon rather than a floating-rate coupon.

           e.   "a," "b," and "c"

12. Which of the following statements about the Brady plan is (are) *true*?

    a.   It provided for the full payment of defaulted bank loans of emerging countries.

    b.   It provided for the issue of bonds that come with a 100% guarantee of the U.S. government.

*   c.   It provided a way to finance defaulted bank loans until they could eventually be paid off.

    d.   It has been a failure due to the illiquid market for the resulting Brady bonds.

    e.   both "a" and "b"

13. Which of the following types of analysis is based on the assumption that interest rate forecasting should be the focal point of bond analysis since market interest rates are the primary determinant of bond prices?

    a.   political analysis

    b.   macroeconomic analysis

*   c.   monetary economics

    d.   industry analysis

    e.   security analysis

14. A certain bond has a $1,000 face value, a 10% coupon, and makes semiannual interest payments. The last coupon payment was made 60 days ago, and the next coupon payment is due in 120 days. To the nearest cent, the accrued interest is

*   a. $16.67.

    b. $33.33.

    c. $25.00.

    d. $50.00.

    e.   none of the above.

15. A bond's clean price is affected by

    a.   the length of the compounding period.

    b.   the day count convention used.

    c.   the coupon rate on the bond.

    d.   all of the above.

*   e.   "a" and "c" only.

16. A certain bond has a $1,000 face value, pays a 9% coupon, with interest paid semiannually, and has six years to maturity. The bond is currently selling for a price of $1,090. Its bond equivalent yield is

     a.   3.565%.
*   b.   7.130%.
     c.   7.257%.
     d.   14.211%.
     e.   none of the above.

17. Which of the following statements about the relationship between a bond equivalent yield (BEY) and the effective yield-to-maturity (EYTM) on a bond is *true*?

     a.   If a bond makes interest payments more than once a year, the BEY will be greater than the EYTM.
*   b.   If a bond makes interest payments more than once a year, the BEY will be less than the EYTM.
     c.   Regardless of the number of compounding periods per year, if a bond is selling for its par value, the BEY will equal the EYTM.
     d.   In the U.S., the number quoted as the yield-to-maturity for a bond is usually its effective yield-to-maturity (EYTM).
     e.   The bond equivalent yield assumes the reinvestment of all coupon payments; the effective yield-to-maturity does not.

18. John Malis purchased a newly issued $1,000 Eurodollar bond that matured in ten years and had a coupon rate of 8% for its face value. The bond made annual interest payments. One year later, having received his interest payment, John sold the bond for $910. His holding period return was

     a.   17.0%.
     b.   18.7%.
*   c.   -1.0%.
     d.   -5.5%.
     e.   none of the above.

19. A certain bond has a $1,000 face value, a 12% coupon, with semiannual payments, and twelve years to maturity. It currently sells for $1,150 and is callable in three years at $1,112. Its yield-to-call is

     a.   4.73%.
     b.   6.73%.
     c.   13.46%.
*   d.   9.46%.
     e.   6.12%.

20.   A 7% coupon bond with a $1,000 face value was just purchased for $870. Interest payments are made semiannually, and the bond has nine years to maturity. Its current yield is

      a.   7.00%.
      b.   9.15%.
*   c.   8.05%.
      d.   4.02%.
      e.   none of the above.

II.   SHORT ANSWER QUESTIONS

1.   A $1,000 bond pays an 8% coupon, with interest paid annually, and matures in fifteen years. It is callable in five years at $1,080. Assume that, in five years, interest rates have fallen to 6% and remain stable for the remaining ten years. Calculate the average annual rate of return for an investor who purchases the bond at its face value, assuming that it is called in five years and that the investor must reinvest the proceeds at the lower rate of 6%.

2.   A $1,000 bond pays an 8.2% coupon and matures in ten years. Interest is paid semiannually.

      a.   Calculate the bond's price if its yield-to-maturity is 10%.

      b.   Given your answer to part (a), what is the current yield for this bond?

3.   What is meant by the "gray market" for Eurobonds? Explain how the gray market operates.

4.   Explain, in words, how a bond equivalent yield differs from the effective yield-to-maturity on a bond.

5.   An American investor invested in two bonds. One bond was issued by a Japanese company and the other was issued by a German firm. Each bond's payments were denominated in the currency of the issuer. The coupon rates and time to maturity were identical for the two bonds, and both bonds were selling for their face values when the investment was made. Assuming that each bond was held to maturity and that neither issuer defaulted or made untimely payments, will the total return earned on each bond by the American investor be the same? Why or why not?

CHAPTER NINETEEN: SOLUTION GUIDELINES

Multiple Choice

1.   **a**:   Bunds are the bonds issued by the German government.

2.   **c**:   The ABS provides only estimated bond prices that are based on quotations from bonds that have similar coupon rates, maturities, quality ratings, and call provisions. They are not market prices, which have been determined by the natural forces of supply and demand. It is not a liquid market nor is it a market that is free from internal arbitrage opportunities. If an investor gave the NYSE a large order to buy or sell a particular bond, he would probably find that he would not be able to buy or sell more than a few of the bonds at the posted prices.

3.   **b**:   This is the definition of a foreign bond.

4.   **c**:   This is the definition of a Bulldog bond.

5.   **e**:   Both Yankee bonds and Eurodollar bonds are denominated in U.S. dollars, but Eurodollar bonds are underwritten by an international investment banking syndicate, while Yankee bonds are underwritten by a U.S. investment banker. Yankee bonds are taxed and regulated by the U.S. government. Like other Eurobonds, Eurodollar bonds are not regulated by the U.S. government.

6.   **d**:   This is the definition of a Discount Brady Bond.

7.   **c**:   Because the reinvestment rate for the investor is less than the yield-to-maturity, he will necessarily earn less than the 10.2%. The yield-to-maturity calculation assumes that the cash flows from the investment will be reinvested at that same yield--in this case, 10.2%.

8.   **a**:   Both Japan and the U.S. have federal government agency bonds and both have corporate bond markets. The U.S. corporate bond market, however, represents a larger proportion of the nation's aggregate bond market than does Japan's. There is no real corporate bond sector in Germany. The Japanese government, not the German government, is second only to the U.S. government in terms of the amount of borrowing.

9.   **b**:   The "gray market" refers to the pre-selling of IPO Eurobonds by members of the selling group at a discounted price. This price, however, would not be one-half of the eventual final offering price. The members of the selling group must pay for the bond, and as long as the discounted gray market price exceeds what the member has to pay, the selling member will profit from the gray market sale.

10.   **c:**   Eurobonds may be either corporate or government bonds. Because they are not subject to the regulation to which new issues of U.S. bonds are subjected (such as the registration requirement of the SEC), Eurobonds can be issued in significantly less time. Although it is the most sophisticated bond market in the world, the Eurobond market is not the largest.

11.   **c:**   A bond's yield-to-maturity will be equal to its current yield if the bond is selling at par since all the bond's return will be comprised of interest income.

12.   **c:**   The Brady bonds are liquid instruments. They do not provide for the payment of defaulted bank loans, but only serve as a method to finance defaulted bank loans until they can be eventually paid off. They are not guaranteed by the U.S. government, however.

13.   **c:**   Monetary economists believe that, because market interest rates are the primary determinant of bond prices, interest rate forecasting should be the focal point of bond analysis. Political analysts believe that the analysis of sovereign risk should be the focal point. Macroeconomic analysts focus on the economic strength of the nations. Industry analysts argue that industry analysis is most important in order to ascertain which industries are producing profitable products and which are not. Security analysts conduct a bottom-up analysis and focus initially on the bond issuer's financial condition and protective covenants associated with the bond.

14.   **a:**   The accrued interest is $50(60/180) = $16.67.

15.   **e:**   The day count convention does not affect the clean price of a bond since it does not take accrued interest into account.

16.   **b:**   The semiannual yield is determined first:

$$\$1,090 = \$45 \sum_{t=1}^{12} \frac{1}{(1+YTM/2)^t} + \$1,000 \left[\frac{1}{(1+YTM/2)^{12}} \right]$$

A financial calculator can be used to determine that YTM/2 = 3.565%; The bond equivalent yield is 2 x 3.565% = 7.130%.

17.   **b:**   The bond equivalent yield does not consider the interest earned on the interest paid at the half year while the effective yield-to-maturity does. Therefore, if interest is paid more than once a year, the BEY will be less than the EYTM. In the U.S., the bond equivalent yield is used when quoting the yield-to-maturity on a bond.

18.   **c:**   John's return is $r = \dfrac{P_1 - P_0 + CF}{P_0} = \dfrac{\$910 - \$1,000 + \$80}{\$1,000} = -1.0\%.$

19. **d**: The semiannual yield-to-call is calculated first. Since the bond is callable in three years, n = 6. The final cash flow is the call price of $1,112.

$$\$1,150 = \$60 \sum_{t=1}^{6} \frac{1}{(1+YTC/2)^t} + \frac{\$1,112}{(1+YTC/2)^6}$$

A financial calculator can be used to determine that YTC/2 = 4.728%. The annual yield-to-call is 2 x 4.728% = 9.46%.

20. **c**: The current yield is equal to the annual coupon divided by the bond's price. $70/$870 = 8.05%.

Short Answer

1. Since interest rates have fallen, the bond will be called in five years. For the five-year holding period prior to the call, an investor will earn the following:

Total annual interest payments	$ 400.00
Interest earned on interest	$ 106.87
Call price	$1,080.00
Total	$1,586.87

This is an average rate of return of 9.68% a year:

$$\$1,586.87 = \$1,000(1 + r)^5$$
$$r = \sqrt[5]{\frac{\$1,586.87}{\$1,000}} - 1$$
$$r = 9.68\%$$

Since the investor will have to invest the proceeds for the next 10 years, his average annual rate of return will be:

$$r = \sqrt[15]{(1.0968)^5 (1.06)^{10}} - 1 = 7.21\%$$

2a. The semiannual coupon on the bond is $41, and there are 20 periods to maturity. The semiannual discount rate is 5%.

$$\text{Price} = \$41 \sum_{t=1}^{20} \frac{1}{(1.05)^t} + \$1,000 \frac{1}{(1.05)^{20}} = \$887.46$$

b. The current yield is the annual coupon divided by the price, or $82/$887.46 = 9.2%.

3. The gray market for Eurobonds begins before the final offering price of the bond is established. Members of the selling group sell the bonds at conditional prices that are discounted from whatever is established as the bond's final offering price. It is a forward

market for bonds that do not yet exist. As long as the discounted gray market price exceeds what the member of the selling group must pay for the bond, the selling member will earn a profit on the sale.

4.   The bond equivalent yield is calculated by taking the semiannual yield and multiplying by two. Therefore, it does not take into account the interest earned on any mid-year interest payments. The effective yield-to-maturity does consider the interest earned on any mid-year interest payments.

5.   It is highly unlikely that the total return earned on each bond will be the same. The return on an investment in a foreign bond is comprised of three factors: coupon income, capital appreciation, and a foreign exchange component. It is this last component that would cause the total returns of the two bonds to differ since they each pay the same coupon, have the same maturity, and sell for their face values. The differences between the exchange rate for the American dollar versus the Japanese yen and the American dollar versus the German deutschemark, both at the time of the investment and at the times when the American receives cash flows from the investment, will cause the American's total return on the two bonds to be different.

CHAPTER TWENTY: MARKET INTEREST RATES

I.   MULTIPLE CHOICE QUESTIONS

1.   You observe that a 12-month Treasury bill is yielding 5.4%. The real risk-free rate has averaged 2.2% in recent history. According to the Fisher effect, the expected rate of inflation over the next twelve months is

       a.   7.6%.
*   b.   3.2%.
       c.   2.45%.
       d.   4.07%.
       e.   none of the above.

2.   The realized real risk-free rate

       a.   will always be positive.
       b.   will always be greater than the rate of inflation for the same period.
       c.   will always be negative.
*   d.   may be positive or negative.
       e.   is the holding period return that an investor earned on a Treasury security.

3.   Which of the following does not influence the general level of market interest rates?

       a.   the business cycle
       b.   borrowing by the federal government
       c.   the monetary policy of the Federal Reserve
*   d.   the length of time to maturity on a bond.
       e.   All of the above influence the general level of market interest rates.

4.   All else constant, which of the following is *not* a characteristic associated with economic expansion?

*   a.   lower interest rates
       b.   increased borrowing by businesses
       c.   lower unemployment rates
       d.   higher interest rates
       e.   Neither "a" nor "c" are associated with economic expansion.

5.   A quality spread represents the difference between the yields on

       a.   a U.S. Treasury bill and a U.S. Treasury bond.
*   b.   a U.S. Treasury bond and a risky bond with a similar maturity.
       c.   a U.S. Treasury bond and the S&P 500 Index.
       d.   large and small company stocks.
       e.   Either "b" or "c" may be used to calculate a quality spread.

6.   Which of the following statements about quality spreads is (are) *true*?

     a.   Quality spreads are higher at economic peaks.

*   b.   Quality spreads are higher at economic troughs.

     c.   Another name for a quality spread is "horizon spread."

     d.   Quality spreads are similar, regardless of the state of the economy.

     e.   Both "b" and "c" are true statements.

7.   Which of the following statements about horizon spreads is (are) *true*?

     a.   They are unaffected by the state of the economy.

     b.   Another name for a horizon spread is "credit spread."

*   c.   They tend to shrink at the peak of the business cycle.

     d.   They tend to expand at the peak of the business cycle.

     e.   Both "b" and "c" are true statements.

8.   The term structure of interest rates depicts the relationship between

     a.   the quality of a bond and its yield-to-maturity.

     b.   the quality of a bond and its coupon rate.

     c.   the rate of inflation and the general level of market rates.

*   d.   the yield-to-maturity and years-to-maturity on bonds of the same risk class.

     e.   the default risk spread and the years-to-maturity on bonds of the same issuer.

9.   Which of the following statements regarding yield curves is *false*?

     a.   A yield curve created from zero-coupon bonds will differ from a yield curve created from coupon-paying bonds, even if the bonds have the same issuer.

*   b.   Yield curves do not change much over the short-term, but they can differ greatly over the long-term. That is, a yield curve that is constructed today will not look much different from one that is constructed in six to twelve months. However, it may look very different from one that is constructed three or five years from now.

     c.   All Treasury securities will not necessarily plot on a yield curve constructed using Treasury security data.

     d.   Separate yield curves can be constructed for different default-risk categories, and these curves will be approximately parallel.

     e.   All of the above statements are true.

10. The proponents of which of the following yield curve theories would contend that the yield curve will normally always be upward sloping?

   a. segmentation theory
   b. expectations theory
   c. Fisher theory
 * d. liquidity premium theory
   e. none of the above

11. Which of the following yield curve theories suggests that the yield curves are determined by differing supply and demand conditions in the various market segments?

 * a. segmentation theory
   b. expectations theory
   c. liquidity premium theory
   d. horizon premium theory
   e. Fisher theory

12. Which of the following yield curve theories asserts that long-term interest rates are the average of the short-term interest rates that are expected to prevail between the current period and the maturity date of the bonds?

   a. segmentation theory
 * b. expectations theory
   c. liquidity premium theory
   d. horizon premium theory
   e. Fisher theory

13. Irving Fisher's theory about interest rates is best summarized by which of the following statements?

   a. Real rates of return and rates of inflation will be negatively correlated because the nominal rates respond sluggishly to changes in the inflation rate.
   b. Market interest rates tend to move inversely with the rate of inflation.
   c. Market interest rates have historically had a small, positive correlation with the rate of inflation.
 * d. Market interest rates vary directly with the inflation rate in almost a one-to-one correspondence.
   e. Market interest rates are solely a function of supply and demand created by various market players.

14. Yield spreads can best be described by which of the following?

     a.   They are risk premia.
     b.   Yield spreads grow larger at the troughs in economic activity.
     c.   Yield spreads grow larger at the peaks in economic activity.
*   d.   both "a" and "b"
     e.   both "a" and "c"

15. How might you expect the yield curve for U.S. Treasury securities to compare to the yield curve for AAA corporate bonds, given the same observation dates?

     a.   The corporate yield curve should lie above the Treasury yield curve.
     b.   The Treasury yield curve should lie above the corporate yield curve.
     c.   The corporate yield curve differs from the Treasury yield curve by the amount of the appropriate risk premium.
     d.   both "b" and "c"
*   e.   both "a" and "c"

16. The segmentation theory about the term structure of interest rates might result for all of the following reasons *except*

     a.   legal restrictions on investors, such as "legal tests" of approved instruments
     b.   expertise in certain segments of bond investing
     c.   hedging of fixed liabilities with offsetting investment assets
*   d.   expectations that a certain segment of the yield curve represents underpriced bonds
     e.   All of the above are reasons underlying the segmentation theory.

17. A ten-year bond has a yield-to-maturity of 8% and a nine-year bond has a yield-to-maturity of 7.8%. If the expectations theory is correct, what is the implied one-year expected spot rate at the start of year 10?

     a.   1.86%
     b.   1.10%
*   c.   9.82%
     d.   9.11%
     e.   none of the above

18. Suppose that the yield on a Treasury bill is currently 4.5% and that the following rates are expected on one-year Treasury bills in future years:

Years from now	Expected yield on a one-year T-bill
1	4.8%
2	5.1%
3	5.4%
4	5.5%

If the expectations theory is correct, what yield would you expect to observe on a five-year Treasury security today?

   a.   5.55%
* b.   5.06%
   c.   4.50%
   d.   3.43%
   e.   none of the above

19. You observe that a Treasury bond with four years to maturity has a yield-to-maturity of 5.5%. The real risk-free rate has averaged 2% in recent years, and the expected one-year rates of inflation over the next three years are 2.5%, 2.2%, and 1.8% respectively. What does this data imply about the expected rate of inflation in year four?

   a.   13.5%
   b.   1.0%
* c.   7.5%
   d.   15.5%
   e.   none of the above

20. Assume the following spot rates exist for zero-coupon bonds:

Bond maturity	Yield-to-maturity
1 year	7.0%
2 years	7.5%
3 years	8.0%
4 years	9.0%

What is the implied expected spot rate on a 3-year bond at the beginning of year two?

   a.   9.00%
   b.   6.19%
   c.   12.96%
* d.   9.67%
   e.   none of the above

II.   SHORT ANSWER QUESTIONS

1.   True or false: The nominal market interest rate always moves directly with large changes in the inflation rate. Explain.

2.   Would you expect the yield spread between AAA-rated corporate bonds and U.S. Treasury bonds of the same maturity to be higher or lower during an economic trough? Why?

3.   Define the horizon premium theory of the term structure of interest rates and provide four reasons why the theory may be invalid.

4.   You observe the following data on zero-coupon Treasury bonds:

Time to maturity	Price	Yield-to-maturity
1 year	$956.94	4.5%
2 years	$903.58	5.2%
3 years	$890.00	6.0%

a.   What is the implied spot rate on a one-year bond issued at the beginning of year two?

b.   Assume that, instead of the answer calculated in part (a), you expect that the spot rate on the one-year bond issued at the beginning of year two will be 6.5%. How could you earn arbitrage profits if your expectations are correct?

5.   An investor observes the following term structure of interest rates:

Years to maturity	Yield-to-maturity
1	6%
2	7%
3	7.5%
4	8.5%

She decides to invest in the four-year bond, stating that by doing so, she is able to "lock in" the higher return of 8.5% a year. How would a proponent of the expectations theory respond to her statement?

CHAPTER TWENTY: SOLUTION GUIDELINES

Multiple Choice

1.   **b**:   The Fisher effect suggests an expected rate of inflation of 3.2%: $r = rr + E(INF)$, so $E(INF) = r - rr = 5.4\% - 2.2\% = 3.2\%$.

2.   **d**:   The realized real risk-free rate may be positive or negative. Because market rates are based on expected inflation levels, if the actual inflation level is greater than what was expected, investors may earn a negative real return. This results when the actual inflation rate is greater than the nominal risk-free rate. If the actual inflation rate is less than the nominal risk-free rate, the realized real risk-free rate will be positive although it may not adequately compensate investors for their loss of purchasing power.

3.   **d**:   The general level of market interest rates is affected by monetary and fiscal policy, both of which affect the supply and demand of the money supply. An example of fiscal policy is borrowing by the federal government; this affects the total demand. The business cycle also affects general market rates since it also affects the supply and demand for funds. During an economic expansion, businesses borrow more money, which causes interest rates, in general, to rise. While the length of time to maturity on a bond affects the required rate of return on that specific debt instrument, it does not affect the general level of market interest rates.

4.   **a**:   During an economic expansion, the unemployment rate falls as business activity is stimulated. Firms borrow money to finance their working capital needs and to build larger plants and purchase more equipment. This increased demand for funds results in higher interest rates.

5.   **b**:   This is the manner in which a quality spread, which reflects the default risk premium, is measured.

6.   **b**:   Quality spreads, or default risk premiums, vary over the business cycle. Quality spreads are higher at economic troughs for two reasons. First, risk-aversion is higher during recessions since unemployment fears increase, so most investors will demand larger risk premiums to induce them to buy riskier bonds. Secondly, corporate bond issuers typically experience reductions in sales and profits during recessions and are more subject to bankruptcy, so investors require greater risk premiums for this reason as well.

7.   **c**:   The horizon spread reflects the maturity risk premium. Maturity risk premiums tend to shrink at the peak of the business cycle because expectations are that both inflation and market interest rates will decline as the economy begins its downturn.

8.   **d**:   This is the definition of the term structure of interest rates.

9.   **b**:   It is true that separate yield curves can be constructed for different default-risk categories and that the resultant curves will be approximately parallel. Yield curves created using zero-coupon bonds will differ from those created using coupon-paying bonds; this difference is referred to as the coupon bias. All Treasury securities will not necessarily lie on a yield curve constructed using Treasury security data because some of the issues differ with respect to coupon rate, call provisions, and tax status. Yield curves do change over the short-term, however. They continuously shift position to reflect current market conditions. On days when significant news is reported, the yield curve may change dramatically.

10.   **d**:   The liquidity premium theory asserts that investors prefer to invest short-term rather than long-term and, therefore, that borrowers must pay a premium to induce investors to invest long-term. The proponents of this theory believe that the normal yield curve will be upward sloping due to this.

11.   **a**:   The segmentation theory asserts that the yield curve is composed of a series of independent maturity segments and that the supply and demand for investments by the players in each of these individual segments determines the interest rates for investments of the various maturities.

12.   **b**:   The expectations theory asserts that long-term yields are the average of the short-term yields expected to prevail during the intervening period. Thus, the yield curve is based on investor expectations.

13.   **d**:   Fisher observed that all market interest rates tend to rise and fall in a one-to-one correspondence with the rate of inflation. His theory is validated by significant positive correlations that can be observed between the inflation rate and nominal interest rates.

14.   **d**:   Yield spreads represent risk premia. All risk premiums tend to be larger at economic troughs.

15.   **e**:   A yield curve constructed using corporate bond data will lie above a yield curve constructed using Treasury security data since corporate bonds are riskier than Treasury securities, and investors demand a higher rate of return for the higher risk level. The amount by which the corporate yield curve differs from the Treasury yield curve reflects the risk premium demanded.

16.   **d**:   Regulations called "legal lists" limit the types of investments that certain institutional investors may make, thereby affecting the supply and demand of investments in different maturity sectors. Too, the high cost of gaining and maintaining information leads different investors to specialize in a particular market segment to minimize information costs. The fixed maturity structure of the liabilities that the various bond investors have mandates that they hedge these

liabilities with assets of equivalent maturity, creating a demand in a particular maturity segment. The segmentation theory asserts nothing about over-priced or under-priced bonds.

17.   **c**:   The forward rate is the implied expected one-year spot rate at the beginning of year ten:

$$1 + {}_9F_{10} = \left[\frac{(1 + {}_0S_{10})^{10}}{(1 + {}_0S_9)^9} \right]^{1/1}$$

$${}_9F_{10} = \frac{(1.08)^{10}}{(1.078)^9} - 1.0 = 9.82\%$$

18.   **b**:   The expectations theory asserts that the interest rate on the longer-term Treasury bond will be the average of the short-term interest rates that are expected to prevail between the current period and the maturity date of the longer-term bond. Given the current 1-year Treasury bill rate and the expectations of future one-year Treasury bill rates, the rate that a proponent of the expectations hypothesis would expect to observe on a Treasury security that matures in five years is:

$$\sqrt[5]{(1.045)(1.048)(1.051)(1.054)(1.055)} - 1 = 5.06\%$$

19.   **c**:   The expected rate of inflation in year four is 7.5%, calculated as follows:

$$5.5\% = 2\% + \frac{2.5\% + 2.2\% + 1.8\% + x}{4}$$

$$3.5\% = \frac{2.5\% + 2.2\% + 1.8\% + x}{4}$$

$$14\% = 2.5\% + 2.2\% + 1.8\% + x$$

$$x = 7.5\%$$

20.   **d**:   The implied expected spot rate on a 3-year bond at the beginning of year two is the forward rate on a 3-year bond issued in year two and maturing at the end of year four:

$$(1.07)(1 + {}_1F_4)^3 = (1.09)^4$$

$$(1 + {}_1F_4)^3 = \frac{(1.09)^4}{(1.07)}$$

$${}_1F_4 = \sqrt[3]{\frac{(1.09)^4}{(1.07)}} - 1 = 9.67\%$$

Short Answer

1. False. While the level of nominal market interest rates tends to vary directly with large changes in the general price level, there having been short-run periods of several months to a year when the level of market interest rates has not responded at all to changes in the inflation rate. Upon occasion, interest rates might even move inversely with movements in the inflation rate. One reason for this is that market rates tend to be based on expected levels of inflation; the actual rate of inflation may be different from what was expected.

2. The yield spread between AAA-rated corporate bonds and U.S. Treasury bonds represents the default risk premium on the corporate bonds. During an economic trough, you would expect the default risk premium to increase. For one thing, the corporations that issue bonds typically experience reductions in their sales and profits during recessions and are more subject to bankruptcies. Furthermore, bond investors are faced with high unemployment levels and the threat of lost jobs during economic troughs; therefore, they become more risk averse in their investments and demand larger risk premiums to induce them to buy riskier bonds.

3. The horizon premium, or liquidity premium, theory of the term structure of interest rates asserts that, on average, the yields from long-term bonds should be higher than the yields from similar short-term bonds since investors demand a premium for lending funds for a longer period of time. However, short-term rates may be higher than long-term rates for any one of the following four reasons:

    (1) Over time, short-term rates fluctuate continuously in an unpredictable manner. Investors in short-term maturities face reinvestment risk as these interest rates fluctuate.
    (2) Investors in short-term maturities must pay transactions costs to reinvest their funds when the instrument matures. There is also the additional cost of obtaining information before they reinvest. These costs reduce the net returns earned.
    (3) Investors in long-term bonds can always reduce their risk by hedging.
    (4) If investors are expecting lower inflation and, therefore, lower interest rates, the yield curve could be downward sloping to reflect these expectations.

4a. The implied spot rate on a one-year bond issued at the beginning of year two is:

$$_1F_2 = \frac{(1.052)^3}{(1.045)} - 1 = 5.9\%.$$

b. If you expected the spot rate on the one-year bond issued at the beginning of year two to be 6.5% rather than the 5.9% implied by the current term structure of interest rates, you could borrow money for two years at 5.2% and invest in one-year bonds:

Today	**End of one year**	**End of two years**
Borrow $100 at 5.2%: (+$100)		Pay back debt plus interest: $[-\$100(1.052)^2] = -\$110.67$
Lend $100 for one year at 4.5%: (-$100)	Receive $100(1.045) = +\$104.50$	
	Lend $104.50 at 6.5% for one year: (-$104.50)	Receive $104.50(1.065) = +\$111.29$

Note that the total cash flows for today and at the end of one year are zero. At the end of year two, you would make a net profit of $0.6225 from the combined transactions. If the actual one-year rate at the end of year one had been the 5.9% calculated in part (a), net profit would be zero, since $104.50(1.059) = $110.67.

5.   The expectations theory asserts that long-term rates are simply the average of the short-term rates that are expected to prevail between the current period and the maturity date of the bonds. Furthermore, the yield-to-maturity on a bond is the promised *average* annual yield that the investor will get. She is not promised 8.5% a year. If the expectations theory is valid, she is no better off investing in one four-year bond than if she were to invest in a series of four one-year bonds, transactions costs and information costs not included. Her assertion, therefore, that she is "locking in" the higher return is incorrect.

CHAPTER TWENTY-ONE: HORIZON RISK AND INTEREST RATE RISK

I. MULTIPLE CHOICE QUESTIONS

1. Calculate the price of a bond that has a $1,000 face value, pays a coupon rate of 8%, with annual interest payments, and matures in seven years if its yield-to-maturity is 10%.

   a. $1,000.00
   * b. $ 902.63
   c. $1,104.13
   d. $ 861.58
   e. $ 950.16

2. The amount by which a bond's price will fluctuate with changes in its yield-to-maturity is dependent on

   a. the coupon rate on the bond.
   b. the number of years the bond has to maturity.
   c. the default risk of the bond.
   d. all of the above.
   * e. "a" and "b" only.

3. A bond will always sell at a discount from its par value

   a. if it has a credit rating below BBB.
   b. if its yield-to-maturity is less than its coupon rate.
   * c. if it is a zero coupon bond.
   d. the first few years after it is originally issued.
   e. if it has any amount of default risk.

Use the following information to answer questions 4 & 5:

A bond has a $1,000 par value, a 12% coupon rate, makes annual interest payments, and matures in 5 years. Its yield-to-maturity is 9%.

4. The bond's Macaulay duration (MAC) is

   * a. 4.09 years.
   b. 2.62 years.
   c. 3.01 years.
   d. 1.52 years.
   e. none of the above.

5. The bond's modified duration (MOD) is

    a.   2.76 years.
    b.   2.34 years.
    c.   2.60 years.
    d.   1.39 years.
*   e.   3.75 years.

6. Which of the following bonds will experience the greatest price fluctuation for a given change in interest rates?

    a.   a 5% coupon bond with 10 years to maturity.
    b.   an 8% coupon bond with 10 years to maturity.
*   c.   a 5 % coupon bond with 12 years to maturity.
    d.   an 8% coupon bond with 12 years to maturity.
    e.   It cannot be determined with the information provided.

7. A portfolio manager of an actively managed bond mutual fund expects interest rates to increase in the near future. Which of the following bonds would he be most likely to include in his portfolio, based on his expectations?

    a.   a zero-coupon bond with 10 years to maturity.
    b.   a 10% bond with 10 years to maturity.
*   c.   a 12% bond with 5 years to maturity.
    d.   a 10% bond with 5 years to maturity.
    e.   a 12% bond with 10 years to maturity.

8. Which of the following statements regarding Macaulay duration is *true*?

*   a.   The Macaulay duration will always be less than the time to maturity if the bond pays coupons.
    b.   The Macaulay duration will be less than the time to maturity if the bond pays coupons and sells at a discount from its face value; the Macaulay duration will be greater than the time to maturity if the bond pays coupons and sells at a premium.
    c.   A bond's Macaulay duration will be unaffected by changes in market interest rates.
    d.   A bond's Macaulay duration will be shorter, the longer the bond has to maturity.
    e.   Given the same maturity, a bond with a lower coupon will have a shorter Macaulay duration than a bond that pays a higher coupon.

9. Which of the following bonds has the *least* reinvestment risk?

    a.   a bond that pays a 10% coupon and has 30 years to maturity
    b.   a bond that pays a 10% coupon in perpetuity
    c.   a bond that pays a 5% coupon and has 30 years to maturity
*   d.   a 30-year zero coupon bond
    e.   a 12-month Treasury bill

10. A bond is currently selling for $948.12 and has a yield-to-maturity of 8% and a Macaulay duration of 5.72 years. If the yield-to-maturity on this bond increases by 0.25%, to 8.25%, what will the new price of the bond be, all other factors the same?

     a. $ 961.68
     b. $ 946.76
     c. $1,002.35
*   d. $ 934.56
     e.   It cannot be determined with the information given; the coupon rate and time to maturity on the bond need to be provided.

11. A method of immunization that gives the manager some discretion to engage in active management so long as the portfolio earns a return that exceeds some safety net return is called

     a.   horizon analysis.
     b.   maturity matching.
     c.   duration matching.
*   d.   contingent immunization.
     e.   laddering immunization.

12. Which of the following statements regarding interest rate risk and horizon risk is (are) *correct*?

     a.   A bond's horizon risk refers to the fact that, other factors held constant, its interest rate risk usually decreases with the length of time remaining to maturity.
     b.   A bond's horizon risk will increase at an increasing rate as the time to maturity increases.
*   c.   For any given maturity, a decrease in the yield-to-maturity results in a price rise that is larger than the price decrease that would result from an equal increase in the yield-to-maturity.
     d.   Only zero-coupon bonds have no interest rate risk.
     e.   Both "c" and "d" are correct statements.

13. Which of the following bonds would be most likely to have negative convexity?

*   a.   a bond issued by the Federal National Mortgage Association (Fannie-Mae)
     b.   a non-callable Treasury strip
     c.   an OID (original issue discount) bond that has two years to maturity and no embedded options
     d.   a 10-year bond that pays a 10% coupon rate and has no embedded options
     e.   "c" and "d" only

14. If a bond has positive convexity, then when interest rates increase

    a.   the bond's duration will also increase, which will cause the bond's price to increase at a decreasing rate.

    b.   the bond's duration will also increase, which will cause the bond's price to increase at an increasing rate.

*   c.   the bond's duration will decrease, which causes the bond's price to fall at a decreasing rate.

    d.   the bond's duration will decrease, which causes the bond's price to fall at an increasing rate.

    e.   the bond's duration will also increase, which causes the bond's price to fall at an increasing rate.

15. Which of the following statements regarding zero coupon bonds is *true*?

    a.   A zero coupon bond exposes investors to a high degree of both reinvestment risk and price fluctuation risk.

    b.   A zero coupon bond has no price fluctuation risk, but exposes investors to a high degree of reinvestment risk.

    c.   Investors in zero coupon bonds enjoy low exposure to both price fluctuation risk and reinvestment risk.

*   d.   Investors in zero coupon bonds face no reinvestment risk, but they are exposed to more price fluctuation risk than investors in bonds that have the same maturity as the zero coupon bond, but make coupon payments.

    e.   none of the above

16. Which of the following statements is (are) *true*?

    a.   Interest rate elasticity is a good benchmark of interest rate risk only, while the Macaulay duration is the better measure of a bond's total risk.

    b.   Interest rate elasticity and the Macaulay duration are both equally good measures of a bond's interest rate risk and its total risk.

    c.   Both a bond's elasticity and the Macaulay duration indicate the size of the percentage price change that is expected to occur with a change in the bond's yield-to-maturity.

    d.   "a" and "c" only

*   e.   "b" and "c" only

17. The manager of the bond portfolio for the Assurance Insurance Company currently has the following five bonds in his portfolio:

Bond	Face Value	Current Market Value	Duration
A	$10,000,000	$ 9,800,000	5.21 years
B	$12,000,000	$13,200,000	6.15 years
C	$25,000,000	$22,500,000	8.67 years
D	$10,000,000	$12,800,000	7.48 years
E	$13,000,000	$11,900,000	9.36 years

The duration of this bond portfolio is

*   a.   7.61 years.
        b.   7.70 years.
        c.   7.37 years.
        d.   6.92 years.
        e.   It cannot be determined without knowing the coupon rates of the bonds.

18. A bond pays a 10% coupon and is selling for its face value of $1,000. Calculate its MACLIM.

        a.   10 years
*   b.   11 years
        c.   12 years
        d.   15.2 years
        e.   There is insufficient information provided to answer this question.

19. A measure of duration that incorporates each time period's forward interest rate into the calculation is the

        a.   modified duration.
*   b.   Fisher-Weil duration.
        c.   Cox, Ingersoll, and Ross duration.
        d.   Two-factor duration model.
        e.   Three-factor duration model.

20. If a bond has positive convexity, then

        a.   its duration will lengthen with an increase in its yield to maturity.
*   b.   its duration will shorten with an increase in its yield to maturity.
        c.   it will experience a greater price increase for a given percentage change in its yield to maturity.
        d.   it is necessarily a callable bond.
        e.   its modified duration will always be greater than its Macaulay duration.

II.   SHORT ANSWER QUESTIONS

1.   What are the two components of interest rate risk? How is each affected by a change in interest rates?

2.   What are the two assumptions on which Macaulay duration relies?

3.   Discuss the three factors that determine the duration of a bond. Describe what effect each of the factors has on a bond's duration.

4.   Because of regulations, the portfolio manager of an actively managed bond mutual fund needs to invest some of the excess cash held by the fund immediately. She is considering one of the following four bonds for investment. All are non-callable and have similar default risks, resulting in similar yields to maturity. If she anticipates an increase in interest rates in the near future, which bond would be her best choice? Explain, in detail, why your selection is better than the other three bonds.

Bond	Coupon	Maturity
A	12%	12 years
B	zero	15 years
C	5%	12 years
D	12%	15 years

5.   Explain what happens to the duration of each of the following bonds if their yields to maturity increase. (Assume positive convexity.)

(a)   a $1,000 bond that pays a 10% coupon and matures in 10 years
(b)   a $1,000, zero-coupon bond that matures in 10 years

CHAPTER TWENTY-ONE: SOLUTION GUIDELINES

Multiple Choice

1.   **b**: $\text{Price} = \$80 \sum_{t=1}^{7} \dfrac{1}{(1.10)^t} + \$1,000 \left[\dfrac{1}{(1.10)^7} \right] = \$902.63$

2.   **e**:   A bond's duration determines the percentage change in the bond's price for each percentage change in its yield-to-maturity. The duration, in turn, is a function of the bond's coupon rate and its time to maturity. The default risk of the bond plays no role unless, of course, it were to change, which would then affect the yield-to-maturity on the bond.

3.   **c**:   A bond will sell at a discount from its par value if its yield-to-maturity is greater than its coupon rate. This condition is independent of the bond's credit rating or on the issue date of the bond. However, a zero-coupon bond will always sell at a discount from its par value as long as it has time left to maturity since its yield-to-maturity must always be greater than its non-existent coupon rate.

4.   **a**:   The following table illustrates the calculation of the bond's Macaulay duration (MAC):

Year (t)	Cash flow (CF)	PV of CF @ 9%	PV of CF/ Price	t-weighted PV of CF/Price
1	$ 120	$110.09	0.0986	0.0986
2	$ 120	$101.00	0.0904	0.1808
3	$ 120	$ 92.66	0.0830	0.2490
4	$ 120	$ 85.01	0.0761	0.3044
5	$1,120	$727.92	0.6519	3.2595
		Price = $1,116.68		MAC = 4.0923 years

5.   **e**:   MOD = MAC/(1 + YTM) = 4.09/1.09 = 3.75 years.

6.   **c**:   The greatest price fluctuation will occur in the bond with the longest duration. Bond (c) has a longer duration than Bond (d) since, given the same maturity, it has the lower coupon. It also has a longer duration than Bond (a), since it has the same coupon, but a longer maturity. Bond (b) necessarily has a shorter duration than Bond (c) since it has bond a higher coupon and a shorter maturity than Bond (c).

7.   **c**:   If interest rates increase, then bond prices will decrease, so the portfolio manager will want the bond that will experience the smallest price decrease, i.e., the bond with the shortest duration. The bond with the shortest duration is Bond (c) since it has a higher coupon than that of Bonds (a), (b), and (d). It also has a shorter duration than Bond (e) since it has the same coupon, but a shorter maturity.

8. **a**: A bond's Macaulay duration will always be less than the time to maturity of the bond if a bond pays coupons since some of its cash flow is received prior to maturity. The Macaulay duration of a bond will decrease with an increase in market interest rates if the bond has positive convexity; it will increase with an increase in market interest rates if the bond has negative convexity. The Macaulay duration will be longer, the longer the bond has to maturity, given the same coupon rate; it will be longer, the lower the coupon, given the same maturity.

9. **d**: Any bond that pays a coupon has reinvestment risk since the interest rate at which the bondholder will be able to reinvest the coupon payments is unknown. Zero-coupon bonds have no reinvestment risk because the only cash flow comes at the maturity of the bond. A 12-month Treasury bill has no periodic cash flows either, but it has more reinvestment risk than a 30-year zero-coupon bond because of its much shorter term to maturity.

10. **d**: Percentage change in price = 5.72(0.25%) = 1.43%. Since the yield-to-maturity has increased, the bond price will decrease by this amount.
$948.12(1 - 0.0143) = $934.56.

11. **d**: This is the definition of contingent immunization.

12. **c**: Horizon risk refers to the fact that, all else equal, a bond's interest rate risk usually increases with the time remaining to maturity. As the time remaining until maturity increases, a bond's interest rate risk increases at a diminishing rate. Zero-coupon bonds have no reinvestment rate risk, but they do have price risk, which is one of the two components of interest rate risk. It is true that for any given maturity, a decrease in the yield-to-maturity results in a price rise that is larger than the price decrease that would result from an equal increase in the yield-to-maturity, assuming that yields change from the same starting value whether the movement is up or down.

13. **a**: Bonds that are callable may have price-yield curves that are concave rather than convex; that is, the bonds have negative convexity. Bonds issued by Fannie-Mae are mortgage-backed bonds that are likely to be redeemed prior to maturity. Therefore, they are the most likely of the bonds listed to have negative convexity.

14. **c**: If a bond has positive convexity, its price-yield curve is convex, rather than concave. As the yield-to-maturity increases, the duration of a bond with positive convexity will shorten, which means that while its price will fall due to the interest rate change, it will fall by a lower percentage.

15. **d**: Zero-coupon bonds have no reinvestment rate risk since there are no interim cash flows to reinvest. They do, however, have higher levels of price risk than a same maturity, coupon-paying bond since their duration is longer.

16. **e**: In general, a bond's Macaulay duration is mathematically equivalent to the bond's interest rate elasticity. Both indicate the percentage price change that is expected to occur with a change in the bond's yield-to-maturity, and both are fairly good measures of

both a bond's interest rate risk and of its total risk since systematic fluctuations in market interests rates affect all bonds simultaneously and are the main source of price fluctuation risk in default-free and high-quality bonds.

17. **a**: The duration of a bond portfolio is a market-value weighted average of the durations of the individual bonds held in the portfolio.

Bond	Face Value	Current Market Value	Duration	Percent, %
A	$10,000,000	$ 9,800,000	5.21 years	13.96
B	$12,000,000	$13,200,000	6.15 years	18.81
C	$25,000,000	$22,500,000	8.67 years	32.05
D	$10,000,000	$12,800,000	7.48 years	18.23
E	$13,000,000	$11,900,000	9.36 years	16.95
	Total	$70,200,000		

$MAC_p = 0.1396(5.21) + 0.1881(6.15) + 0.3205(8.67) + 0.1823(7.48) + 0.1695(9.36) = 7.61$ years

18. **b**: Since the bond is selling for its par value, its yield-to-maturity is equal to its coupon rate of 10%. $MACLIM = 1/0.10 + 1.0 = 11$ years.

19. **b**: The Fisher-Weil Duration measure (FWD) incorporates forward interest rates into the model, which was first proposed by Macaulay as an alternative model. Modified duration measures the percentage change in a bond's price that results from a *percentage* change in the market interest rates. The Cox, Ingersoll, and Ross duration measure employs stochastic calculus, making it more difficult to compute, but does not incorporate forward interest rates. Two factor models usually have a short-term and a long-term interest rate as factors, but not forward rates; three factor models also do not incorporate forward rates.

20. **b**: A bond with positive convexity has a convex price-yield curve. Therefore, its duration will shorten when the yield-to-maturity increases. It will, therefore, experience a lower percentage price *decrease*. A bond's modified duration will always be less than its Macaulay duration. A callable bond will often have negative convexity.

Short Answer

1. The two components of interest rate risk are price fluctuation risk and reinvestment risk. Each of these elements reacts opposite to the other when interest rates change. When interest rates increase, the prices of existing bonds fall, but investors are able to reinvest the cash flows from their bond investments at higher rates. When interest rates decrease, the prices of existing bonds increase, but investors are faced with reinvesting the cash flows from their bond investments at lower rates.

2. The two implicit assumptions on which Macaulay duration is based are: (1) The yield curve is horizontal at the level of the bond's YTM, and (2) The yield curve experiences only parallel shifts.

3. The three factors that determine the duration of a bond are the bond's coupon rate, its term to maturity, and its yield-to-maturity. The higher the coupon rate, the shorter is the bond's duration since the investor receives a greater proportion of the bond's cash flows in earlier years. The longer the term to maturity on a bond, the longer its duration is since an investor must wait longer for the receipt of the bond's cash flows. If a bond has positive convexity, the higher a bond's yield-to-maturity, the shorter the bond's duration. This is because when the bond's cash flows are discounted at higher interest rates, the more distant cash flows represent a smaller fraction of a bond's total market value than when a lower discount rate is used.

4. If interest rates increase as the portfolio manager anticipates, bond prices will fall. She will, therefore, want to invest in the bond that will experience the least price decrease, which will be the bond with the shortest duration. Bond A has the shortest duration of the bonds listed. Its duration is something less than 12 years since it has twelve years to maturity, but also pays coupons. Bond B is a zero-coupon bond, so its duration is the same as its time to maturity, fifteen years. Bond C has the same maturity as Bond A, but pays a lower coupon, so its duration will be longer than that of Bond A. Bond B pays the same coupon as Bond A, but has a longer maturity, so its duration will also be longer than that of Bond A.

5. The duration of the 10%, 10-year bond will fall since the coupon payments received earlier will become a greater percentage of the bond's new (lower) price at the higher interest rate. The duration of the zero-coupon, 10-year bond will not change. The duration of a zero-coupon bond is always equal to the bond's time to maturity.

CHAPTER TWENTY-TWO: CREDIT RISK

I.   MULTIPLE CHOICE QUESTIONS

1.   Which of the following statements regarding corporate bankruptcy is *true*?

    a.   A bankruptcy judge will force the liquidation of any firm that is found to be insolvent.

*   b.   If investors in a firm did not enjoy limited liability, the prices of a firm's securities would not respond so dramatically to bankruptcy news.

    c.   If a firm's assets are liquidated at a bankruptcy, consumer claims have a priority claim to employees' back wages.

    d.   If a firm's assets are liquidated at a bankruptcy, preferred shareholders have the same priority as general creditors, but secured creditors have priority over both.

    e.   Bankruptcies affect the price of a firm's unsecured debt more than it does the price of its preferred stock, which remains largely unaffected.

2.   Arrange the following according to the absolute priority rule, from the greatest priority to the least priority:

    I   preferred shareholders
    II   unsecured creditors
    III   past-due contributions to employee pension plan
    IV   consumer claims
    V   secured creditors

    a.   V, II, III, IV, I
    b.   III, IV, V, I, II

*   c.   III, IV, V, II, I
    d.   IV, III, V, I, II
    e.   IV, V, II, III, I

3. According to research, which of the following statements about the effect of bond rating changes on a firm's securities' prices is *true*?

   a. Bond prices are significantly affected in the month in which a rating is changed, but the stock price of the firm remains relatively unchanged.

   b. The prices of both the bonds and the stock of a firm are significantly affected in the month in which a bond rating change takes place.

   c. Most of the price reaction to a bond rating change takes place in the three months following the rating change announcement for both the stock and bonds of the firm.

   * d. Most of the price reaction to a bond rating change takes place in the year prior to the announcement of the rating change for both stocks and bonds of the firm. Bond prices show no significant price reaction during the month in which the rating is changed, and stock price reactions are only marginally significant in the month of the rating change.

   e. Most of the bond price reaction takes place prior to the rating change announcement, but the majority of the stock price reaction takes place in the month of the announcement.

4. Which of the following statements regarding junk bonds is *correct*?

   a. Junk bonds are defined as those bonds that are rated CCC or lower.

   b. Junk bonds are all original issue discount bonds.

   c. An investor should never knowingly invest in a junk bond since it has a high probability of default.

   d. Junk bonds are defined as bonds issued by firms that have already filed for bankruptcy and are not currently making the interest payments on the bonds.

   * e. A junk bond is defined as a bond that has a credit rating lower than BBB.

5. Which of the following ratios is *not* a ratio that bond rating analysts *primarily* use in establishing a rating for a firm's bond issue?

   a. EBIT interest coverage ratio

   * b. average collection period

   c. times-fixed-charges-earned ratio

   d. operating income-to-sales ratio

   e. All of the above ratios are typically used by bond rating analysts.

6. Which of the following accounts would *not* be considered part of the capitalization of a firm when computing the long-term debt to capitalization ratio?

   * a. accrued wages

   b. preferred stock

   c. common stock

   d. long-term debt

   e. Neither "a" nor "b" would be included.

7.   Which of the following provisions stipulates that any additional assets acquired by a firm after the issue of a first mortgage bond will automatically become part of the collateral supporting that bond?

      a.   sale-and-leaseback provision
      b.   put option
      c.   negative pledge clause
*   d.   after-acquired property clause
      e.   adjustable collateral provision

8.   A bond is considered to be "investment grade" if it has a rating of

      a.   AA or higher.
      b.   A or higher.
*   c.   BBB or higher.
      d.   BB or higher.
      e.   AAA only.

9.   A put bond

*   a.   allows the bondholders to sell the bond back to the issuing firm at a prespecified price.
      b.   will sell at a lower price than an identical bond that does not have the embedded option.
      c.   allows the bond issuer to retire the bond early.
      d.   pays a coupon that is indexed to some economic benchmark.
      e.   both "a" and "b"

Use the following information to answer Questions 10 through 14:

Freedom Air, Incorporated has 4.5 million common shares outstanding. At the end of 20XX, the firm's common stock was selling for $6.75 per share. Freedom's income statement and balance sheet are supplied below:

Freedom Air, Incorporated
Income Statement
for the year ending December 31, 20XX
(in thousands of dollars)

Revenues	$75,800
Operating expenses:	
Flight operations	23,260
Aircraft and traffic servicing	16,300
Maintenance	12,800
Promotion and sales	15,400
General and administrative	3,600
Depreciation and amortization	540
EBIT	$ 3,900
Interest expense	2,300
Earnings before tax	$ 1,600
Tax	640
Net income	$ 960

Freedom Air, Incorporated
Balance Sheet
as of December 31, 20XX
(in thousands of dollars)

Current assets		Current liabilities	
Cash and equivalents	$10,000	Accounts payable	$ 4,000
Trade receivables	7,400	Accrued maintenance	4,300
Maintenance deposits	7,000	Other accrued expenses	3,600
Prepaid expenses	3,500	Notes payable	8,000
Inventories	1,000	Total current liabilities	$19,900
Total current assets	$28,900		
		Long-term debt	$ 5,000
Fixed assets	$ 4,400	Total liabilities	$24,900
Total assets	$33,300	Common equity	
		Common stock	$ 3,000
		Retained earnings	5,400
		Total liabilities and equity	$33,300

10. Calculate Altman's Z-score for Freedom Air, Incorporated.

	a.	2.2899
*	b.	4.2432
	c.	5.0241
	d.	3.7632
	e.	-0.0374

11. Freedom's EBIT interest coverage ratio is

    a.   0.59.
    b.   0.70.
    c.   1.44.
    d.   2.40.
*   e.   1.70.

12. Freedom's EBITDA interest coverage ratio is

    a.   1.46.
    b.   0.46.
    c.   0.65.
*   d.   1.93.
    e.   1.28.

13. Freedom's funds from operations-to-total debt ratio is

*   a.   11.5%.
    b.   3.2%.
    c.   10.8%.
    d.   30.0%.
    e.   34.2%.

14. Freedom's long-term debt-to-capitalization ratio is

    a.   9.7%.
*   b.   37.3%.
    c.   62.5%.
    d.   15.0%.
    e.   39.0%.

15. Altman's multiple discriminant analysis (MDA) model is *best* described by which of the following statements?

    a.   Financial ratios from each of the respective corporations being analyzed were used as the explanatory variables.
    b.   The model correctly classified 52 of the 66 corporations in the sample.
    c.   The model predicted over half the changes in the corporations' bond credit ratings before they were announced to the public.
    d.   all of the above
*   e.   "a" and "b" only

16. Which of the following is *not* considered by Standard & Poor's bond raters when assessing the financial condition of a corporation?

    a.   the level and trend of the issuer's coverage ratios
    b.   the level and trend of the issuer's financial leverage ratios
    c.   the significance and size of the issuer
*   d.   the opinion of the issuer's bankers
    e.   Neither "c" nor "d" are considered by the bond raters.

17. The Hand, Holthausen, and Leftwich study of bond quality rating changes resulted in which of the following conclusions?

    a.   The prices of investment grade bonds reacted more to rating changes than did the prices of speculative grade bonds.
    b.   The stock price changes associated with bond rating changes were similar in size to the bond price changes when the bonds were being upgraded.
    c.   The stock price changes associated with bond rating changes were similar in size to the bond price changes when the bonds were being downgraded.
    d.   News warnings regarding rating changes caused larger price changes than did the actual bond rating changes.
*   e.   Both "c" and "d"

18. The Datta, Datta, and Patel study on bond IPOs resulted in which of the following conclusions?

    a.   Speculative grade bonds tend to be overpriced in their initial public offerings while investment grade bonds tend to be underpriced.
    b.   Bond IPOs tend to be underpriced, regardless of the bond rating.
    c.   In contrast to equity IPOs, bond IPOs tend to be overpriced, regardless of the bond rating.
*   d.   Investment grade bonds tend to be overpriced in their initial public offerings while speculative bonds tend to be underpriced.
    e.   The less prestigious the underwriters of a bond issue, the more likely it is that the bond IPO will be overpriced.

19. Which of the following statements about coverage ratios is (are) *true*?

    a.   Coverage ratios indicate the percentage of debt that a firm has.
    b.   The average collection period is one of the more widely used coverage ratios.
    c.   An EBIT interest coverage of 6 or better is necessary for a cyclical corporation to receive a top "investment grade" rating.
    d.   Coverage ratios are viewed by some bond analysts as being the single most important category of financial ratios in determining the quality rating of a bond issue.
*   e.   both "c" and "d"

20.   Credit risk is best defined as

*   a.   the portion of an investment's total variability resulting from changes in
             the financial condition of the borrower.
      b.   the portion of an investment's total variability resulting from changes in
             the degree of operating leverage of the borrower.
      c.   the portion of an investment's total variability resulting from the sales volatility of
             the borrower.
      d.   the portion of an investment's total variability resulting from changes in the
             volatility of the earnings of the borrower.
      e.   the portion of an investment's total variability resulting from changes in the
             general economic conditions of the nation.

II.   SHORT ANSWER QUESTIONS

1.   What is a sinking fund provision? How does it protect the bondholders?

2.   True, false, or uncertain: It is in the best interest of a firm's investors if an insolvent firm
       is liquidated. Explain.

3.   Discuss how the fact that a firm's investors have limited liability affects the prices of the
       firm's stocks and bonds when a firm declares bankruptcy.

4.   What are the three most important categories of information considered when assigning a
       quality rating to a bond issue?

5.   Discuss the findings of Hite and Warga in their study that examined bond upgrades and
       downgrades from 1985 through 1995.

CHAPTER TWENTY-TWO: SOLUTION GUIDELINES

Multiple Choice

1. **b**:   A firm should be liquidated only if the proceeds from a bankruptcy auction would exceed the present value of the firm as a continuing operation. In the event that a firm is liquidated, employees will receive their back wages (up to a maximum of $2,000 per worker) prior to the settlement of consumer claims. General creditors will be paid after senior creditors, but before any preferred shareholders' claims will be satisfied. The prices of a firm's securities are in line with the absolute priority rules. The value of its preferred stock falls more than that of the unsecured debt of the firm. The fact that a firm's investors enjoy limited liability increases the price fluctuations when a firm announces that it is declaring bankruptcy. If a firm's creditors were able to file a claim against the personal assets of the firms' investors in the event that the firm declared bankruptcy, the prices of the firm's securities would not respond so dramatically to the news.

2. **c**:   The absolute priority rule specifies that past-due contributions to the employee pension plan be paid before any of the other selections listed. Next paid is consumer claims. All creditors have priority over preferred shareholders, with the secured creditors having priority over the unsecured creditors since they receive the proceeds when their collateral is liquidated.

3. **d**:   The combined results of the research detailed in the chapter indicates that bond prices appear to react to a rating change during the year preceding the rating change announcement. Weinstein found that bond prices experienced only a statistically insignificant price reaction in the month in which the rating change occurred. A study by Griffin and Sanvicente found that most of the stock price reaction to bond rating changes occurred in the 11 months prior to the rating change announcement. Stock price reactions in the month that the rating change occurred were only marginally significant.

4. **e**:   Junk bonds are those that have a credit rating of BB or less. They may be junk when originally issued, or they may be "fallen angels"--bonds that were investment grade when issued, but that experienced downgrades in their ratings. Whether or not an investor should invest in a junk bond depends on his risk/return preferences. While junk bonds are very risky investments, they also offer higher expected returns.

5. **b**:   While bond rating analysts may look at a firm's asset management ratios, these ratios do not tend to have a direct influence on bond quality ratings. Coverage ratios, financial leverage ratios, and profitability ratios are the dominant categories that affect quality ratings.

6.   **a**:   Capitalization refers to a firm's permanently committed capital funds. Conservatively, it would be the sum of the firm's long-term debt, preferred stock, and common shareholder's equity. Liberally, it could also include the firm's permanently-maintained current liabilities, such as continuously revolving accounts payable. Accrued wages would not fall into this category.

7.   **d**:   This is the definition of the after-acquired property clause.

8.   **c**:   This is the definition of investment grade bonds.

9.   **a**:   A put bond allows the bondholders to sell the bond back to the issuing firm at a prespecified price. Because it offers protection to the bondholder, a put bond would sell at a higher, not a lower price, than an identical bond that does not have the embedded option.

10.   **a**:

$$Z_i = 0.033\left[\frac{EBIT}{Total\ assets}\right]_i + 0.999\left[\frac{Sales}{Total\ assets}\right]_i + 0.006\left[\frac{Aggregate\ market\ value\ of\ all\ equity}{Book\ value\ of\ debt}\right]_i$$

$$+\ 0.014\left[\frac{Retained\ earnings}{Total\ assets}\right]_i + 0.012\left[\frac{Net\ working\ capital}{Total\ assets}\right]_i + e_i, \text{ where the expected value}$$

of e_i is zero.

The market value of Freedom's equity is $6.75 x 4.5 million shares = $30,375,000. In calculating net working capital, notes payable were not included as part of the current liabilities since interest-bearing short-term debt is typically not included in the calculation.

$$Z_{Freedom} = 0.033\left[\frac{\$3,900}{\$33,300}\right] + 0.999\left[\frac{\$75,800}{\$33,300}\right] + 0.006\left[\frac{\$30,375}{\$24,900}\right] + 0.014\left[\frac{\$5,400}{\$33,300}\right]$$

$$+\ 0.012\left[\frac{\$17,000}{\$33,300}\right] = 0.033(11.71) + 0.999(2.28) + 0.006(122) + 0.014(16.2) + 0.012(51.5)$$

$$=\ 4.2432.$$

11.   **e**:   The EBIT interest coverage ratio $= \dfrac{\text{Earnings from continuing operations before interest and taxes}}{\text{Gross interest incurred before subtracting capitalized interest and interest income}}$

Freedom's interest coverage ratio is $\dfrac{\$3,900}{\$2,300} = 1.70$.

12.   **d**:   The EBITDA interest coverage ratio is calculated as follows:

$$\frac{\text{Earnings from continuing operations before interest, taxes, depreciation, and amortization}}{\text{Gross interest incurred before subtracting capitalized interest and interest income}}$$

Freedom's EBITDA interest coverage ratio is $\dfrac{\$3,900 + \$540}{\$2,300} = 1.93$.

13.   **a**:   The funds from operations-to-total debt ratio is calculated as follows:

$$\frac{\text{Net income from continuing operations plus depreciation, amortization, deferred income taxes, and other noncash items}}{\text{Long - term debt plus current maturities, commercial paper, and other short - term borrowings}}$$

Freedom's funds from operations-to-total debt ratio is $\dfrac{\$960 + \$540}{\$5,000 + \$8,000} = 11.5\%$.

14.   **b**:   The long-term debt-to-capitalization ratio is calculated as follows:

$$\frac{\text{Long - term debt}}{\text{Long - term debt + preferred stock + common shareholder's equity}}$$

Freedom has no preferred stock. Its long-term debt-to-capitalization ratio is $\dfrac{\$5,000}{\$5,000 + \$8,400} = 37.3\%$.

15.   **e**:   Altman's Z-score is calculated using financial ratios of the firms as explanatory variables. In testing the model on 33 bankrupt firms and 33 non-bankrupt firms, Altman classified 52 of the 66 firms correctly.

16.   **d**:   The three major categories of information that a credit analyst considers when assigning a quality rating are the level and trend of the issuer's financial ratios, the issuer's size and significance, and the protective provisions in the bond indenture contract. The credit analyst does not solicit the opinion of the issuer's bankers.

17.   **e**:   Hand, Holthausen, and Leftwich found that the stock price changes associated with bond rating changes were similar in size to the bond price changes for bond downgrades, but were smaller than the bond price changes associated with bond upgrades. They also discovered that warnings regarding rating changes caused greater price reactions than the actual bond rating changes.

18. **d**: Datta, Datta, and Patel found that speculative grade bonds tend to be underpriced in their initial public offerings while investment grade bonds tend to be overpriced. Investment grade bonds are more likely to be handled by prestigious investment banking firms.

19. **e**: Coverage ratios indicate the amount of profits that a firm has to cover its fixed charges, such as its interest expense. They are viewed by some bond analysts as being the single most important category of financial ratios in assigning the quality rating of a bond issue. In order for a cyclical corporation to receive a top investment grade rating, the EBIT interest coverage must be 6 or better.

20. **a**: This is the definition of credit risk.

Short Answer

1. A sinking fund provision requires the issuing firm to make scheduled payments into an account that is typically controlled by a third party, such as a commercial bank. The third party then uses the funds to repurchase the issuer's debt. Since the debt is periodically retired, the remaining bondholders' chance for repayment increases with the passage of time.

2. Uncertain. It depends on whether or not the value of the firm when liquidated is greater than the value of the firm as a going concern. If the liquidation value does not exceed the value of the firm as a going concern, then a reorganization is in the investors' best interest. Insolvency simply means that a firm is currently unable to meet its obligations. This may be a temporary condition.

3. Limited liability insures that investors in a bankrupt firm are not responsible for the debt incurred by the firm. Therefore, a firm's creditors cannot file a claim against the personal assets of a firm's investors. If there were no limited liability laws, security prices would not react so strongly to bankruptcy news since the creditors could obtain the investors' personal assets in addition to the assets of the bankrupt firm in order to satisfy their claims.

4. The three most important categories of information considered when assigning a quality rating to a bond issue are the level and trend of the issuer's financial ratios, the issuer's size and significance, and the protective provisions in the bond indenture contract.

5. Hite and Varga reported four major findings when they studied upgrades and downgrades from 1985 through 1995.

   (1) Bond prices experience larger price adjustments when downgraded than when upgraded.
   (2) Upgrades into the investment grade category and downgrades that remove the bond from the investment grade category are more significant than other rating changes.

(3) Samples of rating changes that are not contaminated by other rating changes within six months revealed that the market reacts reliably as much as six months before the rating change and continues to react for six months after the rating change in the anticipated direction.

(4) Moody's and Standard & Poor's tend to rate bonds similarly although split ratings occur occasionally.

CHAPTER TWENTY-THREE: EQUITY VALUATION - A MICROVIEW

I.   MULTIPLE CHOICE QUESTIONS

1.   Which of the following statements about *growth* firms is (are) *true*?

*   a.   If not for legislation that regulates the investments made by some
                institutional investors, growth firms would maximize their values by maintaining
                a dividend payout ratio of zero.
        b.   The required rate of return of a growth firm will always be greater than the firm's
                ROE.
        c.   In order to maximize their values, growth firms should maintain the highest
                dividend payout ratio possible since investors prefer stocks that pay high
                dividends.
        d.   Dividend policy is irrelevant for growth firms.
        e.   Both "b" and "c" are true statements.

2.   Which of the following statements about the dividend policy of *normal* firms is (are)
        true?

        a.   Normal firms should strive to pay out the highest dividends possible since
                investors prefer stocks that pay high dividends.
        b.   Normal firms should adopt a dividend payout policy of zero. This strategy allows
                them to reinvest 100% of their earnings, giving them a competitive advantage. It
                also allows them to avoid giving the market negative signals in the future if
                earnings fall since they will not be faced with reducing or eliminating dividend
                payments.
        c.   The higher the dividend payout ratio of a normal firm, the higher will be its price-
                earnings ratio.
*   d.   The price of a normal firm's stock will be unaffected by its dividend
                payout ratio.
        e.   Both "a" and "c" are true statements.

3.   Which of the following does *not* affect the price of a stock?

        a.   the expected growth rate of dividends
        b.   the riskiness of the firm
        c.   the risk-free interest rate
*   d.   the investor's expected holding period
        e.   All of the above affect the price of a stock.

4.   All else equal, which of the following would be most likely to cause a stock's price to *increase*?

      a.   The Federal Reserve raises interest rates.
*   b.   Investors become more confident about the economy, and their risk
            aversion decreases.
      c.   The expected dividend growth rate of the firm decreases.
      d.   The firm's equity beta increases due to its entry into a new, riskier venture.
      e.   The difference between the expected growth rate and the required rate of return
            on the firm's stock widens.

5.   The expected growth rate of dividends will be greater,

      a.   the lower the dividend payout ratio.
      b.   the greater the return on equity.
      c.   the lower the return on equity.
      d.   the higher the dividend payout ratio.
*   e.   Both "a" and "b" will cause the expect growth rate of dividends to be
            greater.

6.   Liquidators, Inc. currently pays a dividend of $6.50 per share; however, these dividends
      are expected to decline by 1% each year. If the required rate of return on this stock is
      8%, what is its fair market value?

      a. $92.86
      b. $93.79
      c. $91.93
*   d. $71.50
      e. $72.22

7.   Decimal Instruments, Inc. currently pays a dividend of $1.00 per share, and its dividends
      are expected to grow at a rate of 5% a year indefinitely. If investors require a 10% return
      on the firm's stock, what is its fair market value?

      a. $1.00
      b. $20.00
*   c. $21.00
      d. $22.00
      e.   none of the above

8.   The constant growth dividend discount model, $P_0 = \dfrac{DIV_1}{k-g}$, assumes that

   a.   dividends will remain constant at DIV_1 forever.
   b.   the firm's retention rate is zero.
* c.   dividends grow at the constant rate of "g" forever.
   d.   the required rate of return on the stock is less than the expected dividend growth rate.
   e.   the firm's most recent dividend payment was DIV_1.

9.   The dividends of Erratic Corporation are projected to be as follows:

Year	Dividends per share
1	$1.10
2	$1.15
3	$1.18
4	$1.20

   After year 4, dividends are expected to grow at a constant rate of 6% indefinitely. If investors require a 12% return on Erratic's stock, what is the value of a share of its stock?

   a. $13.47
   b. $12.03
* c. $16.97
   d. $15.53
   e.   none of the above

10. Simms Valley Electric currently pays a dividend of $2.00 a share. These dividends are expected to grow at a rate of 5% for the next three years, after which the dividend is expected to remain constant (i.e., zero growth). If investors require a 12% return on the firm's stock, at what price should it sell?

* a. $19.01
   b. $ 5.28
   c. $24.57
   d. $30.00
   e. $28.57

11.   Teltek stock pays no dividends. Its price-earnings ratio is 86, and its average cost of equity capital is 36%. Teltek's earnings per share growth rate is 30%. What is Teltek's imputed payout ratio?

*   a.   516.0%
       b.   143.3%
       c.   238.9%
       d.   116.3%
       e.   none of the above

12.   The Germinix Corporation had earnings per share this year of $4.30 and paid a dividend per share of $1.29. The firm's growth rate is expected to be 6%, and its cost of equity capital is estimated to be 12%. If Germinix is expected to maintain its current dividend payout ratio, what is its price-earnings ratio?

*   a.   5.0X
       b.   11.67X
       c.   5.3X
       d.   12.37X
       e.   none of the above

13.   In order to use the dividend discount model to determine the fair market value of a stock, cash dividends must be estimated with a great degree of accuracy

       a.   for at least 50 years into the future, which is why the model has come under criticism.
*   b.   for 10 years into the future; cash dividend payments beyond that need only be forecast within no more than 40% of their actual values.
       c.   indefinitely, which is why the model is impossible to apply to the real world. Its value lies in the theoretical study of the factors affecting stock prices.
       d.   for 5 years into the future since cash dividend payments beyond that have very negligible present values.
       e.   for at least 30 years into the future, after which the present value of the dividends becomes negligible.

14. The following information is available for the Avalone Corporation:

Most recent year's EPS = $3.15   Most recent year's DPS = $1.26
ROE = 12%   Beta = 1.4

The relevant risk-free rate is 6%, and the expected return on the market is 15%.
Calculate the value of a share of Avalone stock, assuming that Avalone maintains its
current payout ratio.

        a. $11.05
        b. $ 8.73
        c. $ 9.13
        d. $16.15
*   e. $11.85

15. The following information is supplied for four firms:

Firm	ROE	Retention rate	Beta
A	12%	0.4	0.7
B	18%	1.0	1.8
C	8%	0	0.3
D	24%	0.6	1.5

The relevant risk-free rate is 5%, and the expected return on the market is 15%. Which
of the four firms would be considered a growth firm?

        a.   A
        b.   B
        c.   C
*   d.   D
        e.   None of the firms would be classified as a true growth firm.

16. Observations of the S&P 500 Index and the S&P 500 price-earnings ratio from 1935 to
2000 indicate that

        a.   both the S&P 500 Index and the S&P 500 price-earnings ratio trended upward
              during the period.
        b.   after large moves up, the S&P 500 price-earnings ratio tends to revert toward its
              long-term mean, but after a large move down, the ratio tends to remain depressed
              for a number of years.
*   c.   although the S&P 500 Index trended upward during the period, the S&P
              500 price-earnings ratio fluctuated without any trend.
        d.   Neither the S&P 500 Index nor the S&P 500 price-earnings ratio seemed
              to follow any trend; both moved randomly.
        e.   Both "b" and "c" are true statements.

17.   A firm that is classified as "normal" has a beta of 1.1 and pays a dividend of $0.75 a share. The relevant risk-free rate is 6.2%, and the expected return on the market is 15%. The firm's price-earnings ratio is

     a.   6.67X.
     b.   18.0X.
*   c.   6.30X.
     d.   8.25X.
     e.   21.2X.

18.   The M. J. Malis Corporation has a return on equity of 15%. Next year, the firm is expected to pay $1.70 a share in dividends. Earnings are expected to be $5 million, and there are 2.2 million shares outstanding. What is the expected growth rate of the dividends, based on this information?

     a.   20.00%
     b.   11.25%
     c.   7.49%
     d.   5.80%
*   e.   3.75%

19.   The Wiebract Corporation currently pays a dividend of $1.20 a share, and dividends are expected to grow at an annual rate of 8.5% indefinitely. If Wiebract's stock is currently selling for $22.25, what is its cost of equity capital?

     a.   13.9%
     b.   8.6%
*   c.   14.4%
     d.   9.0%
     e.   none of the above

20.   The Henley-Triad Corporation currently pays a dividend of $1.00. This is expected to grow at a rate of 15% a year for the next five years, after which the growth rate is expected to drop to 5% a year indefinitely. If investors require a 12% return on their investment in Henley-Triad, what is the value per share of its stock?

     a. $20.69
*   b. $22.52
     c. $28.73
     d. $50.00
     e. $32.47

II.   SHORT ANSWER QUESTIONS

1. The Dedisse Company currently pays a dividend of $0.50 and is selling for $15.00 a share. Dividends are expected to grow at an annual rate of 20% for the next two years and at a constant rate of 10% indefinitely beyond that point. If you believe the stock needs to offer a return of 14% to compensate investors for the risk involved, is the stock fairly priced at its current price of $15.00 a share? Explain.

2. A firm has a return on equity of 15%, and this is expected to continue into the future. Its earnings are expected to be $10 million next year, and it is expected to pay dividends of $3.5 million. The same dividend payout ratio is expected to continue in future years. There are 1 million shares outstanding. If similar risk investments are yielding 18%, at what price should the stock of this firm sell?

3. Recently, the economy has been showing signs of weakening. This has increased the risk aversion of investors. Explain how this will affect stock prices in general by discussing how this affects the variables in the capital asset pricing model (CAPM) and the dividend discount model (DDM).

4. Discuss the factors that affect a *normal* stock's price-earnings ratio.

5. Explain how a firm's investment decisions directly affect the price of its stock.

CHAPTER TWENTY-THREE: SOLUTION GUIDELINES

Multiple Choice

1. **a**: A growth firm is one in which the return on equity is greater than the required rate of return on the stock. Because of this, the value of a growth firm would normally be maximized if it reinvested 100% of its earnings in the business. However, because laws exist that require institutional investors such as life insurance companies, banks, and pension funds to invest only in stocks that pay stable cash dividends, some growth firms pay dividends rather than reinvesting 100% of their earnings in order to be included on the "legal list."

2. **d**: A normal firm is one in which the return on equity is exactly equal to the required rate of return on the stock. Since this is true, its price is simply equal to the expected earnings per share divided by the required rate of return. The dividend policy of the firm does not affect the firm's value.

3. **d**: The risk level of the firm affects the required rate of return, which, in turn, affects the stock price. The required rate of return is also affected by the risk-free interest rate since it is equal to this risk-free rate plus a risk premium. The expected growth rate of dividends affects the expected future cash flows of the firm, and, thus, its value. The investor's expected holding period, however, does not affect the price of a stock. The estimated price at the end of the holding period implicitly incorporates the expected dividend stream from that point forward.

4. **b**: An increase in interest rates will increase required rates of return and cause stock prices to decrease, not increase. An increase in a firm's equity beta has the same effect. If the expected dividend growth rate decreases, the value of the stock will also decrease since expected future cash flows are lower. If the difference between the expected growth rate and the required rate of return widens, the stock price will drop since the denominator of the fraction, $\dfrac{DIV_1}{k-g}$, increases. However, as investors become less risk averse, the market risk premium ("$E(r_m)$ - RFR" in CAPM) decreases, which decreases the required rate of return on stocks, resulting in an *increase* in stock prices.

5. **e**: The growth rate is equal to the ROE times the retention rate. Therefore, the higher the ROE, the greater the expected dividend growth rate. The lower the dividend payout ratio, the greater the retention rate, and the greater the growth rate.

6. **d**: $P_0 = \dfrac{\$6.50(1-0.01)}{0.08-(-0.01)} = \dfrac{\$6.435}{0.09} = \$71.50$.

7. **c**: $P_0 = \dfrac{\$1.00(1.05)}{0.10-0.05} = \$21.00$.

8. **c:** DIV_1 represents the firm's next expected dividend, not its most recent dividend payment. The model assumes that dividends will grow at a constant rate of "g" forever, not that the dividend will remain constant forever (which would mean that "g" would always equal zero). The model does not assume that the firm's retention rate must be zero; in fact, a firm that pays out 100% of its earnings would be unlikely to grow at a constant rate indefinitely. For the model to be useful, the required rate of return on the stock must exceed the expected dividend growth rate. Otherwise, the price of a stock that is experiencing rapid growth would be negative, which makes no sense.

9. **c:** Erratic's expected price at the end of the fourth year can be determined by applying the constant growth dividend discount model:

$$P_4 = \frac{DIV_5}{k-g} = \frac{\$1.20(1.06)}{0.12-0.06} = \$21.20.$$

Erratic's current price is equal to the present value of its cash flow stream:

$$P_0 = \frac{\$1.10}{(1.12)^1} + \frac{\$1.15}{(1.12)^2} + \frac{\$1.18}{(1.12)^3} + \frac{\$1.20}{(1.12)^4} + \frac{\$21.20}{(1.12)^4} = \$16.97.$$

10. **a:** Simms Valley Electric's future dividend stream is calculated as follows:

$DIV_1 = \$2(1.05) = \$2.10$
$DIV_2 = \$2(1.05)^2 = \$2.205$
$DIV_3 = \$2(1.05)^3 = \$2.31525$
$DIV_4, DIV_5, \ldots = \$2.31525$

The price at the end of the third year can be calculated using the expected dividend at the end of year 4 and the assumption of zero growth:

$P_3 = \$2.31525/0.12 = \$19.29375$

Simms Valley Electric's current price is equal to the present value of its expected cash flow stream:

$$P_0 = \frac{\$2.10}{(1.12)^1} + \frac{\$2.205}{(1.12)^2} + \frac{\$2.31525}{(1.12)^3} + \frac{\$19.29375}{(1.12)^3} = \$19.01.$$

11. **a:** $P/EPS = \dfrac{\text{imputed payout ratio}}{k-g}$, so $86 = \dfrac{\text{imputed payout ratio}}{0.36-0.30}$. Solving the

equation, we get imputed payout ratio $= 86(0.06) = 5.16 = 516\%$.

12.   **a**: $$P/EPS = \frac{\text{payout ratio}}{k - g} = \frac{\frac{\$1.29}{\$4.30}}{0.12 - 0.06} = \frac{0.3}{0.06} = 5X.$$

13.   **b**:   In order to use the dividend discount model, it is only essential to forecast cash dividends accurately for the first ten years because only the first decade of cash flows has a significant present value. Dividends expected for years 11 through 30 need only be forecast within 40% of their actual values due to their small present values, and dividends expected to be paid beyond 30 years into the future have a very negligible present value and, thus, very little effect on the current stock price.

14.   **e**:   Avalone's retention rate is $[1 - \frac{\$1.26}{\$3.15} =] 0.60$. Its sustainable growth rate = RR x ROE = 0.60 x 12% = 7.2%. The required rate of return on Avalone's stock can be calculated by using CAPM. $E(r_A) = 6\% + 1.4(15\% - 6\%) = 18.6\%$. Therefore, its value per share is $11.85, calculated as follows:

$$P_0 = \frac{\$1.26(1.072)}{0.186 - 0.072} = \$11.85.$$

15.   **d**:   A growth firm is one for which ROE is greater than the required rate of return on the stock. Using CAPM to calculate the required rate of return on each of the four stocks, we get the following:

Firm	ROE	Retention rate	Beta	*Required rate of return, k*
A	12%	0.4	0.7	5% + 0.7(15% - 5%) = 12%
B	18%	1.0	1.8	5% + 1.8(15% - 5%) = 23%
C	8%	0	0.3	5% + 0.3(15% - 5%) = 8%
D	24%	0.6	1.5	5% + 1.5(15% - 5%) = 20%

Only Firm D has an ROE that exceeds the required rate of return on the stock.

16.   **c**:   Figure 25-3B in the chapter illustrates that while the S&P 500 Index trended upward during the period from 1935 to 2000, the price-earnings ratio did not seem to follow any sort of trend.

17.   **c**:   The required return on the stock is calculated using CAPM:

$E(r_i) = k = 6.2\% + 1.1(15\% - 6.2\%) = 15.88\%$. The price-earnings ratio of a normal firm = 1/k = 1/0.1588 = 6.30X.

18.   **e**:   The growth rate is equal to the firm's return on equity times its retention rate. M.J. Malis' earnings per share is expected to be $5 million/2.2 million shares = $2.27. Its retention rate is [1 - $1.70/$2.27 =] 0.25. Therefore, its growth rate = 15% x 0.25 = 3.75%.

19.   **c**:   The constant growth DDM is solved for "k," the required rate of return:

$$\$22.25 = \frac{\$1.20(1.085)}{k - 0.085}$$

$$\$22.25(k - 0.085) = \$1.302$$

$$k = \frac{\$1.302}{\$22.25} + 0.085 = 14.4\%.$$

20.   **b**:   The Henley-Triad Corporation's expected future dividend stream is first calculated:

$DIV_1 = \$1.00(1.15)^1 = \$1.15$
$DIV_2 = \$1.00(1.15)^2 = \$1.3225$
$DIV_3 = \$1.00(1.15)^3 = \$1.5209$
$DIV_4 = \$1.00(1.15)^4 = \$1.7490$
$DIV_5 = \$1.00(1.15)^5 = \$2.0114$
$DIV_6 = \$2.0114(1.05)^1 = \$2.1120$

The dividend at the end of year 6 can be used to calculate a price at the end of year 5 since the firm is then expected to grow at a constant rate:

$$P_5 = \frac{\$2.112}{0.12 - 0.05} = \$30.17$$

Henley-Triad's price today is the present value of all of these cash flows:

$$P_0 = \frac{\$1.15}{(1.12)^1} + \frac{\$1.3225}{(1.12)^2} + \frac{\$1.5209}{(1.12)^3} + \frac{\$1.7490}{(1.12)^4} + \frac{\$2.0114}{(1.12)^5} + \frac{\$30.17}{(1.12)^5} = \$22.54.$$

Short Answer

1.   Dedisse's stock is actually underpriced at its current price of \$15.00 a share. Expected cash flows are as follows:

$DIV_1 = \$0.50(1.20) = \$0.60$
$DIV_2 = \$0.60(1.20) = \$0.72$
$$P_2 = \frac{\$0.72(1.10)}{0.14 - 0.10} = \$19.80$$

The fair market value is the present value of these cash flows, using 14% as the discount rate.

$$P_0 = \frac{\$0.60}{(1.14)^1} + \frac{\$0.72 + \$19.80}{(1.14)^2} = \$16.32$$

2. The dividend payout ratio is \$3.50/\$10 = 35%. The implied growth rate is, therefore, 15%(1 - 0.35) = 9.75%. The next expected dividend per share is \$3.50, so using the constant growth DDM, the price is calculated as follows:

$$P_0 = \frac{\$3.50}{0.18 - 0.0975} = \$42.42.$$

3. An increase in the risk aversion of investors will cause the market risk premium, $E(r_m)$ - RFR, in the CAPM to increase. This, in turn, causes the required rates of return on all stocks to rise. A weakening economy also results in slower growth rates for firms. The combined effect is a widening of the "k-g" term in the constant growth DDM. As this difference gets larger, stock prices decrease.

4. In equilibrium, the price-earnings ratio of a normal stock is determined by the risk-adjusted discount rate of the firm and the growth rate of the firm. By examining the formula for the price-earnings ratio, we can determine the effect each of these factors has on the price-earnings ratio of a normal firm:

$$P/EPS_1 = \frac{\text{payout ratio}}{k - g}.$$

As the risk-adjusted discount rate, "k," increases, the price-earnings ratio will fall. Since the growth rate, "g," is subtracted from "k," the greater the growth rate, the lower the denominator of the fraction, and the higher the price-earnings ratio will be. Thus, the price-earnings ratio moves inversely with a firm's risk-adjusted discount rate and directly with a firm's growth rate. Although the "payout ratio" also appears in the formula, it has no effect on the price-earnings ratio of a normal firm. Since a normal firm's ROE is equal to its risk-adjusted discount rate, we can show that the price-earnings ratio of a normal firm is simply 1/k:

$$P/EPS_1 = \frac{\text{payout ratio}}{k - g} = \frac{1 - RR}{k - g}, \text{ and since } g = RR \times ROE,$$

$$\frac{1 - RR}{k - g} = \frac{1 - RR}{k - [RR \times ROE]}. \text{ But because } ROE = k,$$

$$\frac{1 - RR}{k - [RR \times ROE]} = \frac{1 - RR}{k(1 - RR)} = 1/k$$

5. The dividend discount model (DDM) can be restated to express the value of a firm in terms of its earnings per share as follows:

$$P_0 = \frac{EPS_1(1 - RR)}{(1 + k)^1} + \frac{(EPS_1) + (ROE)(RR)(EPS_1)}{(1 + k)^2} + \dots$$

248

The earnings can be separated into two categories: the perpetual annual earnings on old assets, denoted EPS_1, and the perpetual annual earnings on new assets, denoted $(ROE)(RR)(EPS_1)$. Therefore, the price per share of a firm is equal to the present value of the earnings from its old assets *plus* the net present value of new assets in which the firm invests. If a firm invests in projects that have a positive net present value, the value of the firm will be increased by that net present value. (Its price per share rises by the net present value per share of the project.) However, if a firm invests in projects with negative net present values, the value of the firm will decrease by those amounts. Projects that have zero net present values will neither increase nor decrease the price of a firm's stock.

CHAPTER TWENTY-FOUR: MEASURING EARNING POWER

I.   MULTIPLE CHOICE QUESTIONS

1.   John Lintner's study of corporate cash dividend payments revealed that

      a.   a corporation's board of directors tends to establish a fixed dividend payout ratio. This is applied to the annual earnings to determine dividends, so dividend payments will fluctuate directly as earnings vary.

*   b.   short-term changes in a corporation's earnings usually have little impact on its cash dividend payments because most firms tend to use a "smoothed" dividend policy whereby cash dividends follow the long-run trend in the firm's earnings.

      c.   most firms tend to increase their cash dividend payments annually, but decreases in the cash dividend payments are rare.

      d.   both "a" and "b"

      e.   both "b" and "c"

2.   In their study of cash dividend payments, Paul Healy and Krishna Palepu discovered that

      a.   the announcement of a commencement of dividend payments produced an increase in the firm's stock price, while the announcement of an increase in existing dividend payments had no effect on the firm's stock price.

      b.   dividend announcements have no effect on a firm's stock price.

      c.   while the announcement of a regular cash dividend omission tended to result in a decrease in the stock price of the firm, the announcement of the initiation of a regular cash dividend payment had no effect on the stock price of the firm.

*   d.   the announcement of a regular cash dividend omission tended to result in an abnormal decrease in the firm's stock price, and the announcement of an increase in a cash dividend payment resulted in an abnormal increase in the firm's stock price.

      e.   both the announcement of a regular cash dividend omission and the announcement of an increase in cash dividend payments result in abnormal stock price changes, but the announcement of the increase in dividends tends to cause a much greater change in the stock price than does the announcement of an omission of dividends.

3. Financial economists who have studied the earnings forecasts provided by different securities' analysts have concluded that the forecasters

* a. tend to over-estimate earnings per share.
    b. tend to under-estimate earnings per share.
    c. issue many more sell than buy recommendations.
    d. have a tendency to present more negative news about security issuers than they do positive news.
    e. both "c" and "d"

4. The study of standardized unexpected earnings (SUE) by Foster, Olsen, and Shevlin found that

* a. abnormal stock returns that resulted from earnings surprises continued for two months after the earnings announcement was made.
    b. stock prices tended to increase *prior* to the announcement date when earnings were much better than expected and tended to decrease only after the announcement date when earnings were much worse than expected.
    c. earnings announcements tended to have no effect on stock prices, regardless of whether they were much better or worse than expected.
    d. stock prices tended to increase prior to the announcement date when earnings were much better than expected and decrease prior to the announcement date when earnings were much worse than expected; after the announcement date, however, no abnormal returns were to be had by investing in stocks that had surprisingly good or surprisingly bad earnings announcements.
    e. only the announcement of earnings that were much worse than expected had any effect on the price of a firm's stock; better than expected earnings seemed to have no effect.

5. Which of the following statements regarding the LIFO and FIFO inventory valuation methods is *true*?

    a. In times of inflation, FIFO results in less taxable income than LIFO.
* b. FIFO incorporates capital gains or losses on inventory into regular income, while LIFO does not.
    c. LIFO will often result in more volatile profits than FIFO.
    d. In times of inflation, the ending inventory balance will be higher if FIFO is used than if LIFO is used.
    e. None of the above is a true statement.

6. Which of the following statements regarding the choice of a depreciation method is (are) *true*?

    a. There are five depreciation methods available for computing the taxable income payable to the Internal Revenue Service: straight-line, units of production, double declining balance, sum-of-the-digits, and MACRS.

*   b. Only straight-line or MACRS depreciation methods may be used when computing the taxable income payable to the Internal Revenue Service.

    c. Regardless of whether accelerated depreciation or straight-line depreciation is used, the value of the firm is unchanged since the total cost of the depreciable asset is fully depreciated by the end of its useful life.

    d. Both "a" and "b" are true statements.

    e. Both "b" and "c" are true statements.

7. Which of the following statements regarding defined benefit and defined contribution plans is *true*?

    a. Regardless of whether the plan is a defined contribution plan or a defined benefit plan, the employer's cost is deducted as a current business expense for the year.

    b. Regardless of whether the plan is a defined contribution plan or a defined benefit plan, the employer's contribution is recorded as a liability on the firm's balance sheet if the plan is under-funded.

    c. The majority of the defined benefit pension plans in the U.S. are under-funded-- i.e., the funds are said to have a pension deficit.

*   d. The employer is not responsible for making up any losses incurred by its pension fund manager in a defined contribution plan; however, losses must be covered by the employer in a defined benefit plan.

    e. Both "b" and "c" are true statements.

8. Which of the following would be classified as an extraordinary item on the income statement, according to GAAP?

    a. goodwill resulting from the merger of two firms

*   b. the destruction of a plant by a hurricane

    c. a loss incurred due to the depreciation of the U.S. dollar relative to the euro

    d. a substantial gain on the sale of a subsidiary of the firm

    e. All of the above would be classified as extraordinary items.

9. Which of the following would be recorded as a "cash flow from investing activities"?

      a.   cash received from the issue of a bond
*   b.   cash received from the sale of a building that the firm no longer uses
      c.   cash received from the sale of inventory
      d.   dividends paid to a firm's shareholders
      e.   cash paid for foreign exchange transactions

10. Which of the following adjustments are made to convert accounting income to cash flow?

      a.   add any increase in accounts receivable
      b.   subtract any increase in accounts payable
*   c.   subtract any increase in inventories
      d.   subtract the amortization of good will
      e.   both "a" and "b"

11. Which of the following would be recorded as a "cash flow from financing activities"?

*   a.   cash paid for the repurchase of some of the firm's stock
      b.   dividends received on stock owned in another corporation
      c.   an increase in accounts payable
      d.   cash paid for foreign exchange transactions
      e.   both "a" and "c"

12. The price per share of any firm can be determined by finding the present value of the firm's

      a.   expected cash flows from operations, on a per share basis.
      b.   expected cash flows from investing activities, on a per share basis.
      c.   expected earnings per share.
*   d.   expected leverage-free cash flows, on a per share basis.
      e.   expected cash flows from financing activities, on a per share basis.

13. The following information has been collected on the earnings of the Venus Corporation and Galaxy Industries:

	Forecasted EPS$_{2000}$	Actual EPS$_{2000}$	Standard deviation of forecast errors
Venus	$3.15	$4.00	$0.30
Galaxy	$1.10	$2.50	$1.20

Based on this information, which of the following statements is (are) correct?

*
    a. Investors in Venus were more pleasantly surprised than investors in Galaxy by the actual earnings reported.
    b. Investors in Galaxy were more pleasantly surprised than investors in Venus by the actual earnings reported.
    c. Venus' earnings are more volatile than Galaxy's.
    d. Galaxy experienced the greater growth rate in EPS from the previous year.
    e. Both "b" and "d" are correct statements.

14. A firm's economic income is

    a. equal to the firm's fully diluted earnings per share.
    b. equal to the firm's cash flow from operations.
    c. equal to the net cash flow from investing activities.
    d. the same as a firm's accounting income; the terms are synonymous.
*
    e. equal to the cash flow available to the firm's shareholders.

The following information is to be used to answer Questions 15 and 16:

The Palex Corporation, a retailer of glassware, made the following purchases from its supplier in 200X:

Quarter	Units purchased	Cost per unit
1	5,000	$3.00
2	5,000	$3.25
3	5,000	$3.40
4	0	

Palex sold 12,000 units in 200X.

15. Calculate Palex's ending inventory balance and COGS if it used FIFO inventory valuation.

   a. Ending inventory = $9,000; COGS = $38,050
   b. Ending inventory = $9,000; COGS = $39,250
 * c. Ending inventory = $10,200; COGS = $38,050
   d. Ending inventory = 0; COGS = $48,250
   e. none of the above

16. Calculate Palex's ending inventory balance and COGS if LIFO inventory valuation was used.

   a. Ending inventory = $9,000; COGS = $38,050
 * b. Ending inventory = $9,000; COGS = $39,250
   c. Ending inventory = $10,200; COGS = $38,050
   d. Ending inventory = 0; COGS = $48,250
   e. none of the above

17. A firm is said to have a "high quality of earnings" if

   a. it has reported a steadily growing EPS in the last five years.
   b. its EPS has been a positive number in the last five years.
 * c. its EPS has been either positive or negative, but has accurately reflected the firm's true economic income.
   d. and only if its EPS has been a positive number in the last five years *and* it has been an accurate reflection of the firm's true economic income.
   e. Both "a" and "c" are true statements.

The following information is to be used for Questions 18, 19, and 20:

Truax Corporation
Income Statement
for the year ending December 31, 20X2

Sales	$690,000
Cost of goods sold	500,000
Gross profit	$190,000
General selling and administrative expenses*	140,000
Earnings before interest and taxes	$ 50,000
Interest expense	10,000
Earnings before tax	$ 40,000
Taxes (@ 15%)	6,000
Net income	$ 34,000

*includes depreciation expense of $30,000

Truax Corporation
Balance Sheet
as of December 31,

ASSETS	20X1	20X2
Cash	$ 8,500	$ 10,000
Accounts receivable	$ 80,000	$ 90,000
Inventory	$250,000	$260,000
Total current assets	$338,500	$360,000
Gross plant, property, and equipment	$500,000	$610,000
- accumulated depreciation	$100,000	$130,000
Net plant, property, and equipment	$400,000	$480,000
Total assets	$738,500	$840,000
LIABILITIES AND EQUITY		
Accounts payable	$ 80,000	$ 83,000
Notes payable	0	$ 35,000
Accruals	$ 15,000	$ 12,000
Total current liabilities	$ 95,000	$130,000
Long-term debt	$187,500	$220,000
Total liabilities	$282,500	$350,000
Stockholders' equity	$456,000	$490,000
Total liabilities and equity	$738,500	$840,000

Truax retains all of its earnings.

18. Truax's cash flow from operations in 20X2 was a

     a. $ 64,000 inflow.
     b. $ 98,000 inflow.
     c. $104,000 inflow.
*   d. $ 44,000 inflow.
     e. $262,000 inflow.

19. Truax's cash flow from financing activities in 20X2 was a

     a. $102,500 outflow.
     b. $110,000 outflow.
     c. $ 77,500 outflow.
*   d. $ 67,500 inflow.
     e. $ 57,500 inflow.

20. Truax's cash flow from investing activities in 20X2 was

     a.   0.
*   b.   a $110,000 outflow.
     c.   a $120,000 outflow.
     d.   a $ 80,000 outflow.
     e.   a $ 10,000 outflow.

II.   SHORT ANSWER QUESTIONS

1. What are "whisper earnings," and how accurate do they seem to be?

2. True, False, or Uncertain: Studies regarding the movements of stock prices around dividend announcement dates refute Miller & Modigliani's theory of dividend irrelevance. Explain.

3. What four general conclusions were reached regarding earnings forecasts of securities' analysts by financial economists who studied them?

4. True, False, or Uncertain: The Foster-Olsen-Shevlin event study on the effect of earnings announcements on stock returns produced results that violate the semi-strong form of efficient markets. Explain.

5. Classify each of the following as a cash flow from operations, a cash flow from investing activities, or a cash flow from financing activities:

     a.   A firm buys a new piece of equipment.
     b.   A firm buys additional inventory, using cash.
     c.   A firm buys back shares of its common stock.
     d.   A firm pays off its accounts payable.

e. A firm retires some outstanding bonds three years before they were due to mature.

f. A firm pays dividends on its common stock.

CHAPTER TWENTY-FOUR: SOLUTION GUIDELINES

Multiple Choice

1.   **b**:   Lintner's study revealed that firms tend to develop long-run target cash dividend payout ratios and smooth their dividend payments so that they follow the long-run trend in a corporation's earnings. As a result, short-term changes in a corporation's earnings usually have little impact on its cash dividend payments. Dividend decreases are very unpopular, and only small, *infrequent* increases are popular.

2.   **d**:   The Healy & Palepu study found that the announcement of a regular cash dividend omission tended to result in an average abnormal decrease of 9.5% in the firm's stock price, while the announcement of an increase in a cash dividend payment tended to result in an average abnormal increase of 4%.

3.   **a**:   Financial economists who studied the earnings forecasts made by different securities' analysts found that the analysts tended to over-estimate earnings per share, issued many more buy than sell recommendations, and seemed to be reluctant to say negative things about the security issuers.

4.   **a**:   The study of standardized unexpected earnings that was conducted by Foster, Olsen, and Shevlin found that stock prices tended to increase prior to the announcement date when earnings were much better than expected and decrease prior to the announcement date when earnings were much worse than expected. Furthermore, they observed that the abnormal stock returns continued to occur for two months after the announcement date.

5.   **b**:   In times of inflation, FIFO results in more taxable income than LIFO since the COGS is less under FIFO than LIFO. FIFO results in a higher ending inventory balance than LIFO in times of inflation since the inventory purchased at higher prices is used to calculate the ending inventory balance. FIFO often causes profits to be more volatile than LIFO because FIFO incorporates inventory capital gains or losses into regular income, while LIFO does not.

6.   **b**:   The Internal Revenue Service requires that only straight-line depreciation or MACRS be used when calculating depreciation expense for reporting taxable income to the agency.

7.   **d**:   Under a defined contribution plan, the contributions that are to be made are defined. Benefits are determined at the point of retirement. The employer's cost is simply deducted as a current business expense from each year's income and expense statement. Under a defined benefit plan, the benefits to be received at retirement are

defined in the plan. Therefore, any losses due to poor investment management decisions must be made up by the employer in order to insure that the funds will be available to pay the benefits. The benefits under a defined benefit plan are accounted for as liabilities on the employer's balance sheet.

8.   **b**:   Accounting Principles Board (APB) Opinion No. 30 states that to be classified as extraordinary, an item must be both unusual in nature and not expected to recur in the foreseeable future. The destruction of a plant by a hurricane meets both these requirements. A substantial gain on the sale of a subsidiary of the firm would not be considered to be unusual in nature; nor would a loss due to foreign exchange fluctuations. Furthermore, the foreign exchange fluctuations can also be expected to recur in the future. Goodwill is not even an income statement item, only the amortization of good will appears on the income statement.

9.   **b**:   Cash flows from investing activities result from the purchase or sale of plant, property, and equipment owned by the firm as well as from the purchase or sale of investments in stocks and/or bonds of other issuers.

10.   **c**:   An increase in inventory is a cash outflow since any cash payments for the inventory is not reflected in the COGS account under accrual accounting. Similarly, an increase in accounts receivable would be subtracted, not added, since credit sales are included in the revenue income of a firm under accrual accounting although no cash was received. The COGS account includes the cost of goods that may have been purchased on credit; therefore, an increase in the accounts payable account would be added back to adjust for actual cash flow. The amortization of goodwill is not a cash flow, but it is deducted as an expense, so it should be added back, not subtracted.

11.   **a**:   Cash flows from financing activities include the payment of dividends to shareholders, the issue of new equity or the repurchase of shares by the firm, and the issue of new debt or the retirement of existing debt.

12.   **d**:   The price per share of a firm is equal to the present value of the expected future cash flows. Cash flows from operations do not consider cash flows such as those made for the repayment of debt or for capital expenditures. Therefore, the cash flows from operations do not measure the cash flows that are available to the shareholders of a firm. Earnings per share is an accounting number and, as such, does not measure the cash flows that are available to the shareholders of the firm.

13.   **a**:   The standardized unexpected earnings for the two firms are calculated below:

$$\text{SUE}_{Venus} = \frac{\$4.00 - \$3.15}{\$0.30} = 2.83$$

$$\text{SUE}_{Galaxy} = \frac{\$2.50 - \$1.10}{\$1.20} = 1.17$$

These numbers indicate that the Venus investors were more pleasantly surprised than were the Galaxy investors. This occurred because Venus' earnings are less volatile than Galaxy's earnings, as indicated by the lower standard deviation of the forecast error, so the large increase was less expected. Galaxy's actual EPS represents a slightly greater percentage increase over what was forecast than does the actual EPS for Venus, but this percentage increase is not a measure of the growth rate in EPS from the previous year.

14.   **e**:   The economic income of a firm during a given period equals the maximum amount of consumption opportunities that can be withdrawn from the firm during the period without diminishing the consumption opportunities available in the future. This is measured by the cash flow available to the shareholders. The cash flow from operations must be adjusted for debt servicing costs, tax effects arising from the borrowed funds, and any net cash flows arising from increases or decreases in the debt of the firm to determine the cash flow that is available to the shareholders.

15.   **c**:   Under FIFO, the cost of the inventory items that were purchased earliest is used in the calculation of the cost of goods sold for Palex:

> 5,000 units @ $3.00 = $15,000
> 5,000 units @ $3.25 = $16,250
> 2,000 units @ $3.40 = $ 6,800
> Total COGS = $38,050

Only 3,000 units are left in inventory, at a cost of $3.40 a unit, so the ending inventory balance is $10,200.

16.   **b**:   Under LIFO, the cost of the inventory items that were purchased last is used in the calculation of the cost of goods sold for Palex:

> 5,000 units @ $3.40 = $17,000
> 5,000 units @ $3.25 = $16,250
> 2,000 units @ $3.00 = $ 6,000
> Total COGS = $39,250

Only 3,000 units are left in inventory, at a cost of $3.00 a unit, so the ending inventory balance is $9,000.

17.   **c**:   A firm is said to have a high quality of earnings if the earnings per share is an accurate reflection of the firm's true economic income, even if those earnings are negative.

18.   **d**:   The cash flow from operations for Truax is calculated below:

Cash inflows	
Sales	$690,000
minus the increase in accounts receivable	10,000
Net cash inflows from operations	$680,000

<u>Cash outflows</u>

Cost of goods sold	($500,000)
Operating expenses	(140,000)
add back depreciation expense	30,000
minus interest expense	(10,000)
minus increase in inventory	(10,000)
minus decrease in accruals	(3,000)
plus increase in accounts payable	3,000
minus taxes	(6,000)
Net cash outflows	($636,000)
Net cash flow from operations	$ 44,000

19.　**d**:　Truax's cash flow from financing activities is calculated below:

Increase in notes payable	$35,000
Increase in long-term debt	$32,500
Total cash flow from financing activities	$67,500*

*Note that interest expense has been included in the cash flow from operations.

20.　**b**:　Truax's cash flow from investing activities is simply a cash outflow from its additional investment in plant, property, and equipment of $110,000.

Short Answer

1.　Whisper earnings are forecasts of earnings per share that circulate among securities' analysts and traders on web sites, television programs, and in the financial press. These are unofficial forecasts that reflect the expectations of various market participants. A study by Bagnoli, Beneish, and Watts found that, on average, whisper forecasts are more accurate than surveys of institutional forecasts and that abnormal profits could be earned by trading on the "whispers."

2.　False. The M&M dividend irrelevance theory states that the cash dividend policy of a normal firm has no impact on the value of its stock. However, the theory does not address the effect that the information content of a cash dividend payment announcement may have on the effect of stock price. Thus, findings, such as those by Healy and Palepu, that some types of dividend announcements *do* affect stock prices does not refute the M&M theory.

3. Financial economists who analyzed the I/B/E/S and Zacks databases to study the earnings forecasts of many different securities' analysts reached four general conclusions: (1) The forecasters tended to over-estimate earnings per share. (2) The forecasters tended to revise their forecasts downward to improve their accuracy as the earnings announcement date drew closer. (3) The forecasters seemed to be reluctant to say negative things about the security issuers. (4) The forecasters issue many more buy than sell recommendations.

4. True. Foster, Olsen, and Shevlin used standardized unexpected earnings from quarterly earnings announcements in their event study to measure the effect of earnings announcements on stock returns. They found that stock prices tended to increase prior to the announcement date that earnings were much better than expected and decrease prior to the announcement date if earnings were much worse than expected. This finding alone does not refute the efficient markets theory since it provides evidence that, on average, the stock market correctly incorporates anticipated earnings changes in the prices of the stocks. However, the researchers also found that the abnormal returns continued to exist for two months after the announcement date. This suggests that an investor could earn an abnormal return by utilizing the quarterly earnings announcements in the *Wall Street Journal*. This violates the semi-strong form efficient markets theory, which states that the markets quickly and accurately incorporate all publicly available information into current stock prices. An investor should not, therefore, be able to earn an abnormal return by studying publicly available information.

5. The classifications are as follows:

a.	A firm buys a new piece of equipment	**Cash flow from investing activities**
b.	A firm buys additional inventory, using cash	**Cash flow from operations**
c.	A firm buys back shares of its common stock	**Cash flow from financing activities**
d.	A firm pays off its accounts payable	**Cash flow from operations**
e.	A firm retires some outstanding bonds three years before they were due to mature	**Cash flow from financing activities**
f.	A firm pays dividends on its common stock	**Cash flow from financing activities**

CHAPTER TWENTY-FIVE: STOCK VALUATION ISSUES

I.   MULTIPLE CHOICE QUESTIONS

1.   According to empirical data, which of the following statements is *true* regarding the real returns on stock and the rate of inflation?

      a.   The U.S. stock market's highest real returns occurred during periods of extraordinary deflation and extraordinary inflation.

      b.   The U.S. stock market's highest real returns occurred during periods of extraordinary inflation.

*   c.   The U.S. stock market's highest returns occurred during periods of extraordinary deflation.

      d.   On average, the highest real total stock market returns occurred when inflation was rapidly increasing.

      e.   Both "b" and "d" are true statements.

2.   Which of the following may be considered to be a *buy* signal?

      a.   The dividend yield on the S&P 500 Index falls below 5%, indicating that more returns can be had from price appreciation.

      b.   The S&P 500 Index price/earnings ratio is less than 8.0.

      c.   The dividend yield on the S&P 500 Index is greater than 5%.

      d.   The S&P 500 Index price/earnings ratio is greater than 8.0.

*   e.   Both "b" and "c" are buy signals.

3.   The 1994 study by Bakshi and Chen, which was based on the life cycle theory of savings, concluded which of the following?

      a.   A raging bull market would begin in the year 2012, when the oldest baby boomers begin to retire and start spending their retirement savings.

*   b.   A bull market would begin in the year 1995 when the oldest baby boomers reached 49 years old and start saving more towards retirement.

      c.   A bear market would begin in the year 1995 when the oldest baby boomers reach 49 years old and begin exercising their early retirement options.

      d.   Repurchases of common stock by corporations, not the life cycle theory, contributed to a bull market beginning in 1995.

      e.   A bull market would begin in 1995, but would be short-lived, and would end when the oldest baby boomers started to retire in the year 2000.

4.   Which of the following are characteristics associated with the emerging growth stage of the product-life cycle?

    a.   high price per unit; net losses by producers; no cash dividends
    b.   competitive pricing; producer profits declining gradually; growing dividend payments
    c.   high, but falling, price per unit; producer profits declining gradually; zero or very small dividend payments
*   d.   high, but falling, price per unit; rapidly rising producer profits; zero or very small dividend payments
    e.   high price per unit; rapidly rising producer profits; growing dividend payments

5.   Which of the following is *not* a reason for the bull market experienced in the latter half of the 1990s?

    a.   Stock market purchases increased as a result of increased savings by the baby boomers and stock repurchases by issuing firms.
*   b.   The risk aversion of investors increased, resulting in higher equity risk premiums.
    c.   Interest rates dropped sharply during the 1980s and 1990s.
    d.   Firms' earnings grew at a faster rate during the 1990s.
    e.   The productivity of labor increased in the U.S. during the last half of the 1990s.

6.   Which of the following is a correct statement?

    a.   Bricks-and-mortar companies strive to dominant their market because of the winner-take-all nature of the businesses in which they are involved.
    b.   The majority of the Dot.com companies are burdened by large fixed costs resulting from frequent large salary increases given to keep talented employees.
*   c.   Dot.com companies tend to use little or no debt, resulting in lower interest expense than the bricks-and-mortar companies.
    d.   The typical Dot.com company attempts to increase profits by cutting costs since significant price increases are not feasible.
    e.   Both "b" and "c" are true statements.

7.   The most desirable Internet stocks usually have a price/earnings-to-growth rate multiple of

    a.   1.0 to 1.5.
    b.   greater than 5.0.
    c.   greater than 20.0.
*   d.   2.4 to 2.6.
    e.   less than 1.0.

8.   The valuation of common stock as a call option is based on which of the following?

    a.   The company's creditors own a call option on the firm's assets with an exercise price equal to the book value of the assets of the firm; the common shareholders are the writers of the option.

    b.   The company's creditors own a call option on the firm's assets with an exercise price equal to the market value of the firm's common equity; the common shareholders are the writers of the option.

    c.   The company's common shareholders own a call option on the firm's assets with an exercise price equal to the book value of the assets of the firm; the firm's creditors are the writers of the option.

    d.   The company's common shareholders own a call option on the firm's assets with an exercise price equal to the market value of the equity of the firm; the company's creditors are the writers of the option.

*   e.   The company's common shareholders own a call option on the firm's assets with an exercise price equal to the face value of the firm's total debt; the company's creditors are the writers of the option.

9.   Which of the following would be associated with an over-priced stock?

    a.   high price to book value ratio and high return on equity
    b.   low price to book value ratio and low return on equity
*   c.   high price to book value ratio and low return on equity
    d.   low price to book value ratio and high return on equity
    e.   both "c" and "d"

10.   Price stability in the stock market is said to exist when the inflation rate is between

    a.   -1.00% and 3.99%.
*   b.   -0.99% and +0.99%.
    c.   1.00% and 3.99%.
    d.   4.00% and 7.99%.
    e.   less than -4.00%.

11. Which of the following statements regarding stock price movements and inflation is *true*?

    a. In the long-run, stock price changes move directly with inflation.

    b. In the short-run, stock price changes move directly with inflation, but they move inversely with inflation in the long-run.

    c. Stock price changes move inversely with inflation in the short-run, but directly with inflation in the long-run.

*   d. In the long-run, stock prices adjust to inflation so that their long-run average real returns and inflation-adjusted prices are unaffected by inflation.

    e. None of the above is a true statement.

12. Which of the following statements regarding the power law model is *false*?

*   a. It is a good tool for determining which Internet stocks are underpriced and which are overpriced.

    b. When it was applied in 1999, it was able to explain over half the variation in the total market value of the firms that it was used to evaluate.

    c. It has been successful in ranking various industry subgroups in the e-commerce industry.

    d. While it is able to explain the *relative* values of Internet firms, it cannot be used to determine whether the prices of all Internet firms are too high or too low.

    e. Selections "c" and "d" are both false.

13. *All else equal*, which of the following will cause the price to book value (PBV) ratio of a firm to *increase*?

    a. an increase in investors' required rate of return

    b. a decrease in the firm's return on equity

    c. the sale of new shares common stock

*   d. an increase in the growth rate of the firm

    e. a decrease in the amount of debt a firm uses

Use the following information to answer Questions 14, 15, 16, and 17:

Toledo Homebuilders Corporation is financed with a single issue of bonds that have a face value of $50 million and have two years remaining to maturity. The assets of the firm currently total $90 million and are pledged as collateral for the bond issue. The bond indenture prohibits the payment of cash dividends until the debt is repaid. There are 2 million shares of common stock outstanding.

14. When the firm's common stock is valued as a call option, the exercise price of the stockholders' call option is

        a. $0.
        b. $40 million.
*   c. $50 million.
        d. $90 million.
        e.   none of the above.

15. When the firm's common stock is valued as a call option, the intrinsic value of a share of Toledo Homebuilders' stock is

        a. $0.
        b. $10.
        c. $45.
*   d. $20.
        e. $25.

16. The market price of a share of Toledo Homebuilders' stock should be

        a. $0.
        b. $10.
        c. $20.
*   d.   greater than $20.
        e.   less than $20.

17. If, two years later, when the bonds reach maturity, the value of Toledo Homebuilders' assets has fallen to $45 million, the value of the bonds would be

        a. $0.
        b. $50 million.
*   c. $45 million.
        d. $5 million.
e.   The value cannot be determined without knowing the coupon rate on the debt.

18. When AOL was the largest Internet firm with a market capitalization of $204,385, the market capitalization of the seventh largest Internet firm, CMGI, was $8,709. If b = 1.0124, the power rule model indicates that, at that point in time,

        a.   CMGI was correctly priced relative to AOL.
*   b.   CMGI was underpriced relative to AOL by $19,793.
        c.   CMGI was overpriced relative to AOL by $19,793.
        d.   both AOL and CMGI were overpriced stocks.
        e.   both AOL and CMGI were underpriced stocks.

Use the following information to answer Questions 19 and 20:

The following end-of-quarter data was collected for CMGI:

Revenues (3 months ending 7/31/00): $395 million
Shares outstanding: 285.4 million
Market price: $37.875

The firm's 5-year average net profit margin is 70.64%, but the firm has posted negative earnings in the last four quarters, so you have decided to use the industry average net profit margin of 31.4% as the largest plausible net profit margin for CMGI. You have also decided to use the firm's last positive earnings per share, $2.40, as an estimate of the firm's normal EPS.

19.   CMGI's practical price-earnings ratio is

        a.   6.84X.
*   b.   21.78X.
        c.   52.32X.
        d.   0.22X.
        e.   none of the above.

20.   Based on its practical price-earnings ratio, the market value per share of CMGI's stock should be

*   a. $52.27.
        b. $16.42.
        c. $37.88.
        d. $0.53.
        e.   none of the above.

II.   SHORT ANSWER QUESTIONS

1.   Discuss three reasons why the belief that inflation benefits corporations and, therefore, the stock market is erroneous.

2.   Discuss the six factors that contributed to the bull market of the 1990s.

3.   Match each of the following characteristics with one of the following four stages of the product-life cycle: Product Introduction, Emerging Growth, Mature Growth, Declining Growth.
        a.   decreasing number of competing producers
        b.   widely accepted product
        c.   no cash dividend payments
        d.   rapidly rising sales revenues

4. Discuss the effect that each of the following has on investment values:
   a. an increase in labor productivity
   b. the retirement of baby boomers
   c. the repurchase of common stock by issuing firms

5. Explain the "winner-take-all" nature of the Internet stocks. What is the underlying rationale for this belief? What potential problems face a firm that tries to capitalize on the "winner-take-all" possibilities?

CHAPTER TWENTY-FIVE: SOLUTION GUIDELINES

Multiple Choice

1. **c**: The empirical data indicates that stock market returns were average during years of moderate inflation, and real returns were far below average during the high inflation years. Average real returns were negative when the inflation rates were highest. The highest average real returns were recorded when inflation was rapidly decelerating.

2. **e**: Some investors believe that when the cash dividend yield on the S&P 500 Index rises above 5%, the U.S. stock market is underpriced. Similarly, they believe that when the stocks in the S&P 500 Index are selling at less than 8 times earnings, the stock market is underpriced. Therefore, both of these events are interpreted as buy signals by some investors.

3. **b**: The Bakshi-Chen study was based on the life cycle theory of savings. The two researchers hypothesized that baby boomers would allocate an increasing portion of their income to savings and stock market investments upon reaching the age of 49. This cash inflow to the markets would contribute to a bull market that would begin in 1995, the year when the oldest baby boomers would be 49 years old. They predicted that the bull market would continue until about 2012 when the youngest baby boomers would reach the age of 65 and retire, resulting in net cash withdrawals from the markets.

4. **d**: The emerging growth stage of the product-life cycle is characterized by a high, but falling, price per unit as new competition enters, attracted by the rapidly rising profits. Cash dividends are typically zero, or very small.

5. **b**: The risk aversion of investors decreased, not increased, during the 1990s. This resulted in lower discount rates, which helped to spur the bull market. An increase in investors' risk aversion would have resulted in higher discount rates, causing stock prices to fall.

6. **c**: Dot.com companies strive to dominate their market because of the winner-take-all nature of the businesses in which they are involved. They do not tend to concentrate on cost reduction programs because they are able to increase their prices to cover their costs, due to the high demand for their products. They tend to reward their employees with stock options in lieu of the frequent large salary increases used by the brick-and-mortar companies and are not burdened by the associated fixed costs of the large salaries. They also tend to use little or no debt, and have lower interest expense than the brick-and-mortar companies.

7. **d**: According to Mr. Chip Morris, the portfolio manager of the T. Rowe Price Science and Technology mutual fund, the most desirable Internet stocks trade at 2.4 to 2.6 times their underlying growth rate.

8. **e**:   The valuation of common stock as a call option assumes that the common stockholders own a call option on the firm's assets with an exercise price equal to the face value of the firm's total debt. The option is written by the company's creditors. The call option will have no value unless the value of the firm's assets exceeds the face value of the firm's debt.

9. **c**:   A normal-priced stock would have a high price to book value ratio if it offered a high ROE and a low price to book value ratio if its ROE was low. If the stock has a low ROE *and* a high price to book value ratio, it would be considered to be overpriced.

10. **b**:   Price stability is said to exist when the inflation rate is near zero--between -0.99% and +0.99%.

11. **d**:   Examination of the historical stock market returns indicates that, in the short-run, stock price changes move inversely with inflation. However, in the long run, stock prices appear to adjust to inflation so that their long-run average real returns and inflation-adjusted prices are unaffected by inflation.

12. **a**:   The power law model is able to explain the relative values of Internet firms, but it does not give any indication about whether Internet stocks as a whole are underpriced or overpriced.

13. **d**:   The PBV ratio can be expressed as $\dfrac{(\text{Payout ratio})(1+g)(\text{ROE})}{k-g}$. In this format, one can see that an increase in the investors' required rate of return, k, will cause a decrease in the ratio, as will a decrease in the firm's ROE. A decrease in the amount of debt a firm uses will decrease the firm's ROE, all else equal, since it will decrease the sustainable growth rate of the firm. The sale of new shares of common stock will increase the book value of the firm's equity, and, all else equal, P/BV will fall. An increase in the growth rate of the firm will increase the PBV ratio; ROE will increase with an increase in the growth rate and the "k-g" spread will decrease, all else equal.

14. **c**:   The exercise price is equal to the face value of the firm's debt, $50 million;

15. **d**:   The intrinsic value of a share of the firm's stock is determined by the formula $P = \dfrac{\text{MAX}[0,(A-D)]}{N}$. In this case, the intrinsic value is equal to $\dfrac{\text{MAX}[0,(\$90\text{ million} - \$50\text{ million})]}{2\text{ million}} = \dfrac{\$40\text{ million}}{2\text{ million}} = \$20.$

16. **d**:   Because there are two years remaining to maturity on the bond, the market value of the firm's stock will exceed its intrinsic value of $20, due to the time value of the option.

17. **c**:   The value of the bonds equals MIN[D, A] = MIN[$50 million, $45 million] = $45 million.

18.   **b**:   The power law model indicates that the value of CMGI's stock should have been $204,385/(7)^{1.0124} = \$28,502$. Since the market capitalization of CMGI at that point in time was only $8,709, it was underpriced by $19,793 according to the model.

19.   **b**:   The practical price-earnings ratio for CMGI is calculated as follows:

Step 1: The market capitalization of CMGI at the end of July 31, 2000 was 285.4 million x $37.875 = $10,809.525 million.
Step 2: Annualized sales, based on the most recent quarter sales, are estimated to be $395 million x 4 = $1,580 million.
Step 3: The price to sales ratio is $10,809.525/$1,580 = 6.84X.
Step 4: This results in a practical price-earnings ratio of 6.84/0.314 = 21.78X.

20.   **a**:   The market price of CMGI is found by multiplying the practical price-earnings ratio by the normal EPS estimate: 21.78 x $2.40 = $52.27.

Short Answer

1.   People who believe inflation is good for the stock market believe that corporations benefit by raising the prices of their products. However, this reasoning ignores three issues. First, consumers tend to resist price increases. Secondly, corporations may have entered into long-term contracts to sell their products at fixed prices, so inflation will hurt them. Thirdly, generally accepted accounting principles do not contain inflation adjustments for depreciation allowances, so the cash flows from the tax savings due to depreciation are inadequate to pay for equipment renewal during inflationary periods.

2.   *Interest rates dropped* sharply during the 1980s and 1990s, resulting in lower required rates of returns on stocks. This, in turn, increased stock prices. *Equity risk premiums also decreased* as investors' risk aversion lessened as a result of the booming economic conditions. This, too, lowered the required rates of return on stocks, increasing stock prices even more. *Firms' earnings grew at increasing rates during the 1990s*, and increased growth in earnings increases stock prices. Additionally, the *increased investments of baby boomers* and *stock buybacks* caused an increase in demand, which increased prices. Finally, *labor productivity increased* in the U.S. during the last half of the 1990s. Increased labor productivity is anti-inflationary, and therefore, leads to higher stock prices.

3.   The stages of the product-life cycle that match the characteristics listed are as follows:

a.	decreasing number of competing producers	**Declining growth**
b.	widely accepted product	**Mature growth**
c.	no cash dividend payments	**Product Introduction or Emerging Growth**
d.	rapidly rising sales revenues	**Emerging Growth**

4.   An <u>increase in labor productivity</u> leads to reduced unit labor costs and is, therefore, anti-inflationary. This will tend to increase investment values, all else equal, since the highest average real total returns on stocks have historically occurred when the inflation rate was decreasing. The <u>retirement of baby boomers</u>, on the other hand, will result in the net withdrawal of funds from the markets, and could lead to lower stock prices. The <u>repurchase of common stock by issuing firms</u> creates an increased demand for stocks, which, all else equal, would serve to increase stock prices.

5.   The "winner-take-all" nature of the Internet stocks is based on the belief that the first firm to successfully enter a new niche on the world wide web will be capable of reaping great rewards, while latecomers may experience difficulty in obtaining any market share. This is based on the fact that the popularity of the first web site in any particular market niche is determined by the referrals to it that pass among friends, relatives, and acquaintances. Additionally, when an Internet user visits a web site, he or she is likely to return to it in an effort to minimize search costs. The result is that the most popular sites become even more popular, and the stock prices of the most popular web site companies get bid up by investors.

The problem with becoming the "winner" in this environment is that it is not an easy position to maintain. Rapidly changing technology can cause the current "winner" to lose its position to a new e-commerce firm. Projects undertaken by Internet firms need to be evaluated on the same basis as projects undertaken by a brick-and-mortar company--they must produce a positive net present value to increase the value of the firm.

In an effort to be the immediate "winner," some dot.com firms have opted to offer prices that do not cover their total costs (e.g., Amazon.com). While this may prove to be a good short-run strategy, if the volume of sales for these firms decreases or if a new technology proves superior and robs these firms of market share, it could result in perennial losses and falling stock prices for those firms.

CHAPTER TWENTY-SIX: TECHNICAL ANALYSIS

I.   MULTIPLE CHOICE QUESTIONS

1.   Which of the following is *not* an assumption underlying technical analysis?

       a.   Chart patterns tend to repeat themselves.
       b.   Changes in a trend are caused by shifts in supply and demand.
       c.   Shifts in supply and demand, no matter what the cause, can be detected sooner or later by observing charts of market transactions.
*   d.   The marginal investor is a rational investor.
       e.   Market value is determined by the interaction of supply and demand.

2.   The Dow Theory involves

       a.   studying tertiary moves, which are the daily fluctuations in stock prices, to determine the best time to buy or sell stocks.
       b.   determining a percentage (filter) by which a stock's price must go up (or down) after a new low (or high) is reached before the stock should be bought (or sold).
*   c.   studying primary trends to identify bear or bull markets and secondary movements to identify market corrections.
       d.   studying the financial statements of a firm to determine if the firm is underpriced or overpriced.
       e.   calculating a confidence index to determine the size of the market risk premium to be used in the capital asset pricing model.

3.   Most Dow theorists believe that an emergence of a new primary trend is confirmed when
       a.   an abortive recovery occurs.
       b.   a pattern of ascending or descending tops occurs in the DJIA.
*   c.   the pattern of ascending or descending tops occurs in both the industrial and transportation stock price averages.
       d.   a trading range breakout point is identifiable.
       e.   the confidence index is greater than 1.0.

4.   A test of the Dow-theory based trading rules used by William Hamilton resulted in which of the following conclusions?

        a.   Use of the trading rules can produce large abnormal returns if an investor adheres to the rules religiously.
*   b.   While the Dow theory seemed to have power to predict returns in the post-sample period, trading frictions would prevent an investor from earning large abnormal returns by using the trading rules.
        c.   The trading rules were more likely to produce profits if the buy signals were used, but the sell signals seemed to provide mixed results.
        d.   The trading rules were more likely to produce profits if the buy and sell signals were used in conjunction with the calculation of a confidence index.
        e.   Investors could earn large abnormal returns if they sold their portfolios when the DJIA fell after reaching a new high in the last 52 weeks.

5.   In a head and shoulders top pattern, the right shoulder designates

*   a.   a moderate rally that lifts the price somewhat but fails to push prices as high as the top of the head before another decline begins.
        b.   a period of heavy buying that pushes the price up to a new peak before a lull in trading allows the price to slip back down.
        c.   a spurt of buying activity that bids the price up to a new high, followed by a lull in trading that allows the price to fall back below the top of the left shoulder.
        d.   a point at which the price falls below the neckline.
        e.   none of the above.

6.   In a head and shoulders top pattern, the neckline

        a.   is a straight line that is tangent to the bottoms (or tops) of the left and right shoulders.
        b.   is used to determine when to sell a stock; if the price drops below the neckline, it is considered to be a sell signal.
        c.   is a straight line that is tangent to the left shoulder and the head.
        d..   both "b" and "c."
*   e.   both "a" and "b."

7.   A support level is

        a.   a market price at which one may expect an increase in the supply of a
                security or commodity offered for sale.
        b.   the highest price at which a security or commodity is expected to sell.
*   c.   a price at which an increase in demand for a security or commodity is
                expected to exist.
        d.   a range of prices in which a particular security's or commodity's price seems to
                fluctuate trendlessly.
        e.   the price at which the lowest volume of trading for a security or commodity seems
                to occur.

8.   Which of the following is (are) considered to be *buy* signals by technical analysts?

        a.   A trading range breakout penetrates the support line.
        b.   The price of a security falls below the neckline of a head and shoulders top
                pattern.
*   c.   The DJIA recovers after a recent decline.
        d.   The confidence index declines in value.
        e.   both "a" and "c."

9.   Which of the following is considered by technical analysts to mark the *end* of a bull
        market?
        a.   The S&P 500 Index rises above the neckline in a head and shoulders
                pattern.
        b.   A trading range breakout occurs that penetrates the resistance line.
        c.   A selling climax occurs.
*   d.   A speculative blowoff occurs.
        e.   Both "c" and "d."

10.   The confidence index is the ratio of

*   a.   high-grade bond yields to low-grade bond yields.
        b.   AAA-rated corporate bond yields to U.S. treasury bond yields.
        c.   the rate of return on the DJIA to U.S. treasury bond yields.
        d.   the rate of return on the S&P 500 Index to the rate of return on the NASDAQ
                Composite Index.
        e.   the rate of return on the S&P 500 Index to AAA-rated bond yields.

11.   A rising confidence index

        a.   occurs when the yield spread between high- and low-quality bonds widens.
        b.   occurs when the yield spread between high- and low-quality bonds narrows.
        c.   is an interpreted as an indication that stock prices will rise.
        d.   both "a" and "c."
*   e.   both "b" and "c."

12.   Moving average analysts recommend buying a stock when

      a.   actual prices are above the moving average, but the difference is narrowing.

*   b.   the price of a stock temporarily falls below a moving average line that is rising.

      c.   a stock's price temporarily rises above a moving average line that is declining.

      d.   a stock's price falls downward through the moving average line and turns around to rise, but then falls again before penetrating the moving average line from below.

      e.   both "a" and "c."

13.   Empirical tests of moving average rules concluded that

      a.   moving averages that were calculated over very short time spans of only a few days resulted in more profitable trades than those that were calculated over a longer time period, such as 150 days.

      b.   trading rules based on moving averages yielded significant profits, even after transactions costs were considered.

*   c.   trading rules based on moving averages seemed to produce profitable results before accounting for transactions costs, but not after.

      d.   both "a" and "b."

      e.   both "a" and "c."

14.   With which of the following statements would a technical analyst most likely agree?

*   a.   Shifting prices are the result of gradual shifts in supply and demand.

      b.   Stock prices tend to move randomly with the random arrival of new information.

      c.   When a security's price moves in the same direction for several days, it is the result of a series of independent changes in supply or demand, which coincidentally happen to move the price in the same direction.

      d.   The only way to increase returns is to accept higher levels of risk.

      e.   both "a" and "b."

15.   Which of the following technical analysis tools has seemed to be able to produce large excess returns, even after transactions costs and market frictions are considered?

      a.   Dow Theory

      b.   moving averages

      c.   Elliot Wave Theory

      d.   trading range breakout rules

*   e.   none of the above

16. In behavioral finance, when someone who is making a probabilistic inference ignores population statistics or insightful sample information, it is referred to as

* a. the base-rate fallacy.
  b. hindsight bias.
  c. overconfidence.
  d. irrational decision making.
  e. appeal to the wrong authority.

17. Some technical analysts chart the volume of shares traded

  a. because they believe trading volume is a better predictor of future stock prices than is the study of past and current stock prices.
  b. to help them better identify congestion areas.
* c. to help them predict possible penetrations of existing support and resistance levels.
  d. all of the above
  e. "a" and "b" only.

18. A high volume of selling near the end of a bear market is referred to as

  a. a speculative blowoff.
* b. a selling climax.
  c. a trough.
  d. bounded rationality.
  e. hindsight bias.

19. Which of the following is *not* a technical analysis tool?

  a. confidence index.
  b. Dow Theory
  c. point-and-figure charts
* d. financial ratio analysis
  e. All of the above are technical analysis tools.

20. Which of the following statements about the confidence index is (are) *true*?

  a. The confidence index has always led changes in the stock market by several months.
* b. The confidence index can never be greater than 1.0.
  c. The confidence index is based on the fact that as bond investors grow more confident about the strength of the national economy, they shift their holdings from low-grade to higher-grade bonds.
  d. all of the above
  e. "b" and "c" only.

II. SHORT ANSWER QUESTIONS

1. What are the criticisms that technical analysts have regarding fundamental analysis? Can you conclude, in light of these criticisms, that technical analysis is superior to fundamental analysis? Explain.

2. Explain how technical analysts use trading volume data.

3. Identify each of the following as a buy or a sell signal:

    a. A stock's price falls below the neckline that is identified in a head and shoulders pattern.
    b. A trading range breakout occurs, and the resistance line is penetrated.
    c. A stock's price temporarily falls below a moving average line that is rising.
    d. The confidence index has been moving closer to 1.0 in recent weeks.

4. What specific signal do technicians who use moving average analysis look for as a cause for action in general? Describe *two* buy signals and *two* sell signals that moving average analysts identify.

5. What are "tertiary moves?" What part do they play in the Dow Theory?

CHAPTER TWENTY-SIX: SOLUTION GUIDELINES

Multiple Choice

1. **d**: Technicians believe that changes in a trend are caused by gradual shifts in supply and demand, rather than instantaneous shifts. They believe that these shifts can be detected sooner or later by observing charts of market transactions. They also believe that some chart patterns tend to repeat themselves. They do not believe that investors are necessarily rational; some of their trading rules are based on the fact that some trades are emotion-driven.

2. **c**: The Dow Theory is based on studying primary and secondary trends. Tertiary moves are considered to be meaningless. While the filter rule and confidence indexes are tools of technical analysts, they are not part of the Dow Theory. Financial analysis is a fundamental analyst's tool.

3. **c**: Trading range breakout points and confidence indexes are not associated with the Dow Theory. While an abortive recovery signals a change in the direction of the market's primary movement, most Dow theorists do not believe that the emergence of a new primary trend has been confirmed until the pattern of ascending or descending tops occurs in both the industrial and transportation stock price averages.

4. **b**: When Brown, Goetzmann, and Kumar tested the Dow Theory, they concluded that, while the theory seemed "to have some power to predict returns in the post-sample period, normal trading frictions would preclude using the theory to generate large excess returns, particularly in the most recent period."

5. **a**: In a head and shoulders pattern, the right shoulder designates a moderate rally that lifts the price somewhat but fails to push prices as high as the top of the head before another decline begins. A period of heaving buying that pushes the price up to a new peak before a lull in trading allows the price to slip back down is designated by the left shoulder. A spurt of buying activity that bids the price up to a new high and is followed by another lull in trading that allows the price to fall back below the top of the left should is represented by the head of the pattern. The point at which the price falls below the neckline is the breakout.

6. **e**: The neckline is a straight line that is tangent to the bottoms (or tops) of the left and right shoulders. If the price drops below the neckline, it is considered to be a sell signal that precedes further price declines.

7. **c**: A support level is the price at which one may expect an increase in demand for a security or commodity. It is considered to be a level beneath which a price is not expected to fall, but not the highest price at which the security or commodity is expected to sell.

8.   **c**:   A trading range breakout that penetrates the support line is a sell signal since the price has fallen lower than expected. Similarly, if the price of a security drops below the neckline of a head and shoulders top pattern, it is considered to be a sell signal. A declining confidence index means that investors' optimism is waning and signals a bear market may be forthcoming. A recovery from a recent decline in the DJIA is considered a buy signal by Dow theorists.

9.   **d**:   When the S&P 500 Index rises above the neckline of a head and shoulders pattern and/or a trading range breakout penetrates the resistance line, prices are rising. A selling climax marks the end of a *bear* market; it occurs near the end of a bear market when there is a high volume of selling as the last of the bearish investors liquidate their holdings. A speculative blowoff occurs when a high volume of buying pushes prices up to a peak, exhausting the enthusiasm of bullish speculators, which makes way for a bear market to begin.

10.   **a**:   This is the definition of the confidence index.

11.   **e**:   A rising confidence index occurs when the yield spread between high- and low-quality bonds narrows. This happens because bond investors become more confident about the economic strength of the nation and shift from high-quality bonds to low-quality bonds. This drives the prices of the lower quality bonds up, and their yields down, thus narrowing the yield spread. It is interpreted by chartists as an indication that the managers of "smart money" are optimistic, and the chartists expect that the stock market will follow the lead of the "smart money" managers. Therefore, it is viewed as an indication that stock prices will rise.

12.   **b**:   Moving average analysts recommend buying a stock when the price of a stock *temporarily* falls below a moving average line that is rising. Since the moving average line is rising, it is expected that this stock's price will continue to rise. If the moving average line were flattening out, then the drop in the price would be viewed as a sell signal.

13.   **c**:   None of the studies on moving average trading rules reported high levels of profitability once transactions costs were considered. When short sample periods were studied, there were some sample periods that yielded significant profits, but others yielded significant losses.

14.   **a**:   Technical analysts believe that shifting prices are the result of gradual shifts in supply and demand rather than instantaneous shifts. They do not believe that securities' prices react immediately to random new information that enters the market. They also believe that studying charts of past prices can lead to excess returns.

15.   **e**:   Although some tests of technical analysis trading rules indicated that significantly large profits could be earned by adhering to the rules before the test results were adjusted for transactions costs and market frictions, once these items were considered there was no support for the belief that any of the trading rules would result in large excess returns.

16. **a**: This is the definition of the base-rate fallacy.

17. **c**: Technical analysts who chart the volume of shares traded also simultaneously chart stock prices. They do not look at the trading volume only. When a technical analyst views trading volume in conjunction with stock prices,
he may be observe a strong buying (or selling) surge that he may feel could work to drive the price beyond an existing resistance level (or below an existing support level).

18. **b**: This is the definition of a selling climax.

19. **d**: Although some security analysts study financial ratios in addition to performing technical analysis, financial ratio analysis is a tool of fundamental analysis, not technical analysis.

20. **b**: The confidence index has sometimes lagged changes in the stock market. If bond investors grow more confident about the strength of the economy they shift their holdings *to* low-grade bonds *from* high-grade bonds, which is the basis for the calculation of the index. Because the yields on high-grade bonds can never be as high as the yields on similar low-grade bonds, the index has an upper limit of 1.0.

Short Answer

1. Technical analysts believe that technical analysis is superior to fundamental analysis because it is easier, faster, and can be applied simultaneously to more stocks than fundamental analysis. They believe fundamental analysis is too troublesome to bother with; it is hard work. They also point out that even if a fundamental analyst does find an underpriced security, he must wait and hope that the market will recognize the security's true value and will bid its price up. Technical analysts cite the inadequacy of the accounting statements, on which much of fundamental analysis is based. They point out that the earnings growth rate forecasts, management evaluations, and price-earnings multiples used by fundamental analysts are often ambiguous.

   Even though these claims are true, it does not follow that technical analysis is superior to fundamental analysis. Only if technical analysis can be used to predict security prices better, or at least as well, as fundamental analysis, can it be considered to be superior.

2. Technical analysts study trading volume in conjunction with stock price movements. They believe that trading volume is an indication of the intensity of investors' feelings. They use trading volume to decide whether or not significant buying (or selling) pressure exists that could cause a stock's price to break through an existing resistance (or support) level. Technicians watch the volume closely when supply and demand are out of balance, resulting in price movements. If high volume occurs on days when prices move up, the market is considered to be bullish. If the high volume occurs when prices are falling, it is a bearish signal. If the same price changes had been coupled with low trading volume, technical analysts would have considered the price movements to be of less significance.

3.   a.   Sell signal
       b.   Buy signal
       c.   Buy signal
       d.   Buy signal

4.   When daily prices penetrate the moving average line, technical analysts view it as a signal to take action. A downward penetration of a flattened moving average is generally regarded as a sell signal, whereas an upward penetration of a flattened moving average is considered a buy signal.

    The textbook provides three buy signals used by moving average analysts: (1) the moving average line flattens, and the stock's price rises up through the moving average line, (2) the price of a stock temporarily falls below a rising moving average line, and (3) a stock's price that is above the moving average line falls but turns around and begins to rise again before it ever penetrates the moving average line from above.

    The three sell signals discussed in the textbook are: (1) the moving average line flattens out and the stock's price drops downward through the moving average line, (2) a stock's price temporarily rises above a declining moving average line, and (3) a stock's price falls downward through the moving average line and turns around to rise, but then falls again before penetrating the moving average line from below.

5.   In Dow Theory, tertiary moves are defined as little daily fluctuations. The theory asserts that these fluctuations are meaningless. However, the chartist must still plot the daily prices in an effort to identify the latest development in the primary trend, which is the main focus of Dow Theory.

CHAPTER TWENTY-SEVEN: FUTURES

I.   MULTIPLE CHOICE QUESTIONS

1.   Which of the following are *not* usually found in a trading room of a futures exchange?

      a.   commission brokers
      b.   locals
*   c.   specialists
      d.   floor brokers
      e.   All of the above hold positions on the trading floor of a futures exchange.

2.   If a commodity's price experiences a limit move,

      a.   trading in that commodity's futures contract is halted for one hour; when trading resumes, no trades may be conducted at prices that exceed the daily limit.
*   b.   trading in that commodity's futures contract is halted and, for the remainder of the day, trading cannot occur at any price that differs from the opening price by more than the daily limit.
      c.   trading in that commodity's futures contract is halted for the remainder of the trading week.
      d.   specialists who are making a market in the contract are forced to buy or sell against the market.
      e.   both "a" and "d."

3.   A person who enters a short position in a futures contract

      a.   will earn a profit if the price of the underlying commodity increases.
      b.   will let his contract expire if the price of the underlying commodity increases.
      c.   need not put up any initial margin requirement since he is agreeing to make delivery, not take delivery, of the underlying contract.
      d.   must take a long position in the same contract in order to close out his short position in the contract.
      e.   Selections "a," "b," and "c" are all true.

4.   Which of the following statements about the delivery and settlement of a futures contract is *true*?

      a.   The short seller must deliver the commodity to a warehouse that is owned by the futures exchange on which the trade took place.

      b.   The short seller must deliver the commodity by the Saturday following the third Friday of the month that is specified as the delivery month in the contract.

    *   c.   The short seller is provided with a few different warehouse locations and several different delivery dates in the delivery month from which to choose.

      d.   The buyer of a futures contract may choose to take delivery of the physical goods or may require a cash settlement instead.

      e.   Both "c" and "d."

5.   "Open interest " is

      a.   the term given to the method used by commission brokers and locals to signal their intention to transact business in a trading pit.

    *   b.   the number of futures contracts that are outstanding in a particular commodity for a specific delivery month.

      c.   the term given to a futures contract that has less than one month until delivery.

      d.   the amount of money that remains to be paid, i.e., contract price - initial margin, upon delivery of an underlying commodity.

      e.   the term given to a situation that occurs when the number of long positions exceeds the number of short positions in a particular futures contract.

6.   Which of the following futures exchanges uses the open outcry system for trading in the pits?

      a.   Deutsche Terminborse (DTB, or Eurex)

      b.   London International Financial Futures Exchange (LIFFE)

      c.   Sidney Futures Exchange

    *   d.   Chicago Board of Trade (CBOT)

      e.   Cantor Financial Futures Exchange (CFFE)

7.   The agency that currently has veto power over new stock or bond index futures contracts is the

      a.   Federal Reserve Board.

      b.   Chicago Board of Trade.

      c.   National Futures Association.

      d.   Commodity Futures Trading Commission.

    *   e.   Securities Exchange Commission.

8. The self-regulating trade group for the futures industry is the

* a. National Futures Association (NFA).
  b. National Association of Securities Dealers (NASD).
  c. Commodity Futures Trading Commission (CFTC).
  d. Chicago Board of Trade (CBOT).
  e. Futures Protection Insurance Corporation (FPIC).

9. A market for a storable commodity is said to be *normal* when

* a. the commodity's futures price exceeds its spot price by an amount that is sufficient to cover the carrying charges incurred to store the commodity for future delivery.
  b. the commodity's futures price is equal to its spot price.
  c. the commodity's spot price exceeds its futures price by an amount that is equal to the carrying charges required to store the commodity for future delivery.
  d. the number of speculators entering a futures contract in the commodity is equal to the number of hedgers since this indicates that the supply and demand factors are in equilibrium.
  e. Both "c" and "d" are necessary conditions for the market to be classified as "normal."

10. An inverted market is said to occur when

  a. the demand for a futures contract exceeds the supply.
* b. the futures price for a commodity is less than the spot price.
  c. the basis is a positive number.
  d. the futures price for a commodity is greater than the spot price.
  e. both "c" and "d"

11. Jo Evans has contracted to have a house built. The construction is due to be completed in nine months, at which time Jo will have to borrow the money to purchase the house. Unfortunately, Jo fears that interest rates will increase over the next few months. Jo wishes to use a futures contract to hedge her risk.
To do so she should

* a. sell a long-term Treasury bond or mortgage bond future.
  b. buy a long-term Treasury bond or mortgage bond future.
  c. buy an S&P 500 Index future.
  d. sell an S&P 500 Index future.
  e. sell a futures-option on GNMA bonds.

12. In order to create a perfect hedge, which of the following has to be *true*?

    a.   The units specified in the futures contract (or a multiple thereof) must exactly match the number of units being hedged.

    b.   The underlying asset of the futures contract must be identical to the asset being hedged.

    c.   The delivery date of the futures contract must match the date on which the underlying asset is needed.

    d.   The delivery location must be as close to the futures exchange on which the trade was conducted as possible.

*   e.   selections "a," "b," and "c," only

13. The theory that asserts that the futures price should slightly exceed the expected future spot price of a commodity is the theory of

    a.   basis convergence.

    b.   normal backwardation.

*   c.   contango.

    d.   unbiased expectations.

    e.   upward bias.

14. The discount rate that is to be used in estimating the value of a financial futures contract is

    a.   10%.

*   b.   the risk-free rate.

    c.   the average cost of debt for the industry.

    d.   the weighted average cost of capital for the short-seller.

    e.   the weighted average cost of capital for the buyer of the contract.

15. Which of the following statements regarding perfect hedges is (are) *true*?

    a.   If a perfect hedge can be constructed, the investor will be able to maximize his profits.

    b.   Perfect hedges serve both to reduce risk and maximize the potential for speculative profits.

    c.   Perfect hedges are easy to construct in normal markets, but are much more difficult to construct in inverted markets.

    d.   All of the above are true.

*   e.   None of the above is true.

16. Which of the following statements regarding futures options is (are) *true*?

   a. The *buyer* of a futures options contract has the option to purchase a call, but not a put, option in the underlying asset if he so chooses.

   b. The *seller* of a futures options contract is obligated to purchase a call option in the underlying asset unless he does a reversing trade prior to the delivery date of the futures option contract.

   c. The *seller* of a futures options contract has the right, but is not obligated, to exercise the put or call option on which they have sold the futures contract.

* d. The *buyer* of a futures options contract has the right, but is not obligated, to exercise the put or call option that they purchased.

   e. both "c" and "d."

17. Which of the following statements regarding commodity exchanges is *false*?

   a. Floor brokers are those who execute trades at commodity exchanges on behalf of those who are not members of the exchange.

   b. "Locals" refers to exchange insiders who trade only on their own accounts.

   c. The open outcry system is used on all commodities futures exchanges to conduct trades.

* d. Specialists act as market makers in assigned commodities.

   e. Both spot contracts and futures contracts are traded together at futures exchanges.

18. Dante Albercino purchased a futures contract on May corn for $2.3125 a bushel in November 2000. He did a reversing trade in February 2001 when May corn was selling at $2.28125 a bushel. His rate of return, ignoring transactions costs and taxes was

   a. -0.92%.

* b. -1.35%.

   c. +1.37%.

   d. +1.35%.

   e. This cannot be determined without knowing the risk-free rate at the time of purchase.

19. In November 2000, the price of December 2000 oats (1 contract = 5000 bushels) was $1.0075 per bushel. The monthly carrying cost was $0.03 per bushel. The best estimate of the price of the December 2001 oats contract is

   a. $1.0375 per bushel.

   b. ≥ $1.3675 per bushel.

   c. ≤ $1.0375 per bushel.

* d. ≤ $1.3675 per bushel.

   e. none of the above.

20.   The initial margin requirement on most futures contracts is

       a.   100%.
       b.   50%.
       c.   less than 1%.
*   d.   between 3% and 10%.
       e.   greater than 50%.

II.   SHORT ANSWER QUESTIONS

1.   Robert has noted that the S&P 500 Index is currently at 1450 while the risk-free
       rate is 5%. If the dividend yield on the S&P 500 Index is 3%, what is the fair
       market value of the futures contract with a delivery date 12 months from now?

2.   Assume that the S&P 500 Index is trading at 1340 and is expected to pay a dividend of
       $10 at the end of one year. The price of a futures contract on the S&P 5000 Index for
       delivery at the end of one year is 1400. What does this imply about the risk-free rate of
       interest? If, in actuality, the risk-free rate is 5%, demonstrate how you could earn
       arbitrage profits. (For simplicity, ignore the Index multiplier.)

3.   What comprises the carrying cost of a futures contract? To what is the carrying cost of a
       financial futures contract equal?

4.   What role does the carrying cost play in the price of a futures contract for storable
       commodities? Explain thoroughly and specifically.

5.   Define the convergence principal. Explain how arbitrage profits could exist if the
       convergence principal was not upheld. Provide explanations for both the normal market
       and the inverted market scenarios

CHAPTER TWENTY-SEVEN: SOLUTION GUIDELINES

Multiple Choice

1.   **c**:   Commission brokers, also known as floor brokers, execute trades at commodity exchanges for people who are not members of the exchange. Locals trade only on their own accounts. Most commodity futures exchanges do not use specialists or other market makers to consummate trades.

2.   **b**:   If a commodity's price experiences a limit move, the rule is that trading in that commodity's futures contract is halted. Trading resumes as usual the next day, but the price cannot change the next day by more than the daily limit or trading will be halted again.

3.   **d**:   A person who enters a short position in a futures contract will profit if the price decreases. He must make an initial margin requirement as well as the individual that enters the long position. An investor in a futures contract does not have the option of letting a contract expire; he must actively do a reversing trade in order to close out his position.

4.   **c**:   Short sellers are given several delivery dates and several warehouse locations from which to choose. Commodity contracts are always settled by the delivery of physical goods, but many financial futures contracts are settled in cash. The buyers of the contracts, however, do not have the option to choose between these settlement procedures.

5.   **b**:   This is the definition of open interest.

6.   **d**:   The Chicago Board of Trade still uses the open outcry system. The other selections either initiated the electronic trading system or have since converted to it.

7.   **e**:   While the Commodity Futures Trading Association has the authority to license futures exchanges and approve futures contracts, the SEC retains final veto power over new stock or bond index futures contracts.

8.   **a**:   The NFA was established in 1982 as a self-regulating trade group of the futures industry.

9.   **a**:   This is the definition of a normal market for a storable commodity.

10.   **b**:   This is the definition of an inverted market.

11.   **a**:   If interest rise, the prices of mortgage bonds will fall, and Jo will profit in the futures market by entering a short position in (i.e., selling) a futures contract on a similar asset, such as T-bonds, or preferably, mortgage bonds, such as those issued by GNMA or FMNA. The sale of a futures option contract does not provide her with an option to do

anything. The seller is committed to assume a long or short position in the futures market at the exercise price on the option if the buyer exercises the futures option.

12. **e**: In order to be a perfect hedge, the units of the futures contract must match the units being hedged, the underlying asset must match the asset being hedged, and the delivery date of the futures contract must match the date on which the underlying asset is needed (or is needed to be sold). The delivery location must be convenient, but that does not mean that it must be as close to the futures exchange as possible, which may, in fact, be inconvenient.

13. **c**: C.O. Hardy, the proponent of the contango theory, asserted that the futures price should be at a slight premium from the expected future sport price to account for the gambling fee. The normal backwardation theory asserts that the futures prices for storable commodities should be slightly less than expected future spot prices. The unbiased expectations theory asserts that expected spot prices should be equal to futures prices. There are no theories bearing the names of "basis convergence" or "upward bias."

14. **b**: Financial futures do not incur physical storage costs, so the discount rate is simply the interest rate for a loan to finance the inventory underlying the contract. The clearing house's guarantee removes default risk from futures contracts, so the risk-free rate is the appropriate discount rate for a financial futures contract.

15. **e**: Perfect hedges are constructed to eliminate risk; therefore, the investor can expect to earn only the risk-free rate, not to maximize profits. Perfect hedges can be constructed under both normal and inverted market conditions so long as a contract that meets the underlying asset, contract size, delivery date, and delivery location requirements is available.

16. **d**: The buyers of put and call options on futures have the right, but not the obligation, to exercise the option they purchase. Whether a call or a put option is purchased depends on whether the futures option was on a call or a put. However, the writer of a futures option contract is committed to assume a long or a short position (from a call or a put, respectively) in the futures market at the exercise price if the buyer exercises the futures option.

17. **d**: Specialists are not part of the futures markets trading structure.

18. **b**: $r = \dfrac{\$2.28125 - 2.3125}{2.3125} = -1.35\%.$

19.　　**d**:　　The estimated price is calculated below:

$$\text{Price} \leq \begin{bmatrix} \text{Price of} \\ \text{December 2000} \\ \text{contract} \end{bmatrix} + (\begin{bmatrix} \text{Carrying cost per} \\ \text{item per month} \end{bmatrix} x \begin{bmatrix} \text{number of months difference} \\ \text{between expiration of the} \\ \text{two contracts} \end{bmatrix})$$

$$\leq \$1.0075 + [0.03 \times 12] = \$1.3675$$

20.　　**d**:　　The initial margin requirement on most futures contracts is between 3% and 10%.

Short Answer

1.　　The price of a futures contract on the S&P 500 Index is determined using the following formula:

$$\begin{bmatrix} \text{Price of futures contract} \\ \text{on the S\&P 500 Index today} \end{bmatrix} = \begin{bmatrix} \text{Spot price of underlying} \\ \text{stock index today} \end{bmatrix} \left[1 + \left(\frac{\text{RFR} - \text{Cash dividend}}{\text{dividend yield on S\&P 500}} \right) \right]^{YEARS}$$

$$\text{Price} = (250 \times 1450)(1.02)^1 = \$369,750$$

2.　　Since $FP_t = SP_t(1 + RFR) - DIV$, it follows that

$$\frac{FP_t + DIV - SP_t}{SP_t} = RFR, \text{ so}$$

$$\frac{1400 + 10 - 1340}{1340} = 5.2\%.$$

If the risk-free rate is only 5%, then the futures price should be 1340(1.05) - $10 = 1397. Since the actual price is 1400, it is overpriced. An investor can short the overpriced futures contract and buy the underpriced stock portfolio, using money borrowed at 5% as follows:

Event	Cash flow today	Cash flow on delivery date, (T)
Borrow $1,340, repay with interest	+$1,340	-$1,340(1.05) = - $1,407
Buy stock	- $1,340	$10 dividend + SP_T
Enter short position (FP$_t$ = 1400)	0	$1400 - SP$_T$
Arbitrage profit	0	$3.00

293

3.   The carrying cost rate for a futures contract represents the interest expense that is incurred to finance the inventory, warehousing costs, and any other relevant costs. Because financial futures do not involve warehousing costs or any other such costs that are relevant to most commodity futures, the carrying cost for financial futures is equal to the interest rate on the loan used to finance the underlying inventory. Because clearing houses at the futures exchanges guarantee the contracts, the default risk is zero; therefore, this interest rate is equal to the risk-free rate.

4.   Under normal conditions the futures price at time "t" of a storable commodity must be less than or equal to the spot price at time "t" plus the carrying cost of the commodity. This means that under normal conditions futures prices cannot rise above the current spot price plus the carrying cost since by paying the carrying cost, current inventories can be carried into future months. If this were not true, then arbitrage profits would exist. An arbitrageur could purchase the asset at its current price and simultaneously take a short position in a futures contract on the asset at the current futures price. If the current futures price was greater than the cost of the asset plus the carrying cost of the asset, he would earn a certain profit when he delivered the asset at the specified future delivery date.

5.   The convergence principle states that as a futures contract approaches its expiration date, the futures price draws closer, and finally converges, on the underlying asset's spot price. If this were not true, arbitrage profits would exist.

        Under a normal market situation, when futures prices exceed spot prices, a trader could earn arbitrage profits by selling the futures contract and simultaneously buying the physical commodity. At maturity of the futures contract, the trader would deliver the physical commodity. Ignoring carrying and transactions costs, arbitrage profits would be earned since the price paid for the physical asset exceeds the price set in the futures contract. Additionally, continued short selling of the contract will have driven the futures price further downward in the meantime.

        Under an inverted market situation, when spot prices exceed futures prices, an arbitrageur would take a long position in the futures contract and wait for the delivery date. By the delivery date, the long position will be profitable as similar purchases by other profit-seekers will result in an increase in the futures price of the contract.

CHAPTER TWENTY-EIGHT: OPTIONS

I.   MULTIPLE CHOICE QUESTIONS

1.   Which of the following statement about the price of a call option is *true*?

      a.   The price of the option will be lower, the greater the risk of the underlying asset.
      b.   The price of the option will be lower, the longer the time to expiration of the option.
      c.   The price of the option will be lower, the higher the risk-free rate of interest.
*   d.   The price of the option will be lower, the higher the exercise price on the option.
      e.   The price of the option will be lower, the lower the price of the underlying asset.

2.   Which of the terms in the Black-Scholes option pricing model represents the amount by which the price of an option will change for each dollar change in the price of the optioned asset?

*   a. $N(x)$
      b. $\ln(P_0/XP)$
      c. XP
      d. $\sigma d^{0.5}$
      e. $N(y)$

3.   If the hedge ratio for a call option is determined to be 0.5 and you own 100 shares of the underlying stock, which of the following would result in a risk-free hedge?

      a.   Buy 200 calls on the same stock.
*   b.   Write 200 calls on the underlying stock.
      c.   Buy 50 calls on the same stock.
      d.   Write 100 calls on the same stock.
      e.   Write 50 puts on the same stock.

4.   Which of the following will cause the hedge ratio to change?

      a.   a change in the stock price
      b.   a change in the risk-free interest rate
      c.   a change in the variance of returns on the asset underlying the option
      d.   a change in the time to expiration
*   e.   all of the above

The following information is supplied for Questions 5, 6, and 7. Students will also need to be supplied with table of values for the area of the normal distribution both below and above the distribution mean.

A certain stock is currently selling for $22.88. The standard deviation of the returns on the stock is 60.5%. A call option on the stock that expires in four months has an exercise price of $40. The annual risk-free rate is 6.2%.

5. The Black-Scholes hedge ratio for the stock option is

     a.   -1.366.
     b.   0.9131.
     c.   0.0427.
*   d.   0.0853.
     e.   -1.715.

6. According to the Black-Scholes option pricing model, the fair market value of the call option on the stock is

*   a. $0.28.
     b. $0.11.
     c. $16.62.
     d. $2.75.
     e. $1.125.

7. Calculate the fair market value of the call if the stock is expected to pay a cash dividend per share of $1.10 at the end of one year.

     a. $15.62
     b. $0.125
*   c. $0.19
     d. $1.75
     e. $1.28

8. A call option on General Electric's stock that has 3 months to expiration is selling for $6.75 and has an exercise price of $50. GE's stock is currently selling for $53.38 a share. The annual risk-free rate is 6%. Assuming that the call option is fairly priced, the price of a put option on GE stock that has the same strike price and time to expiration is

     a. $0.54.
*   b. $2.65.
     c. $4.65.
     d. $7.12.
     e.   none of the above.

9. A call option on Intel's stock has an exercise price of $32.50 and expires in one month. The option is currently selling for $4.00 per optioned share. A put option on Intel that has the same exercise price and time to expiration is selling for $3.75. Intel is currently selling for $32.31 a share. The risk-free rate is 6.5%. According to the put-call parity model,

    a. the put option is overpriced relative to the call option by $0.27.
    b. the call option is underpriced relative to the put option by $0.27.
    c. The put and the call are correctly priced relative to one another, but we do not know whether either is fairly priced.
*   d. The put option is underpriced relative to the call of $0.27.
    e. The call option is underpriced relative to the put by $0.02.

10. If a stock pays cash dividends, then on the ex-dividend date,

    a. the values of both put and call options on the stock will increase.
    b. the values of both put and call options on the stock will decrease.
*   c. the values of any put options on the stock will increase, but the values of any call options on the stock will decrease.
    d. the values of any put options on the stock will decrease, and the values of any call options on the stock will increase.
    e. the values of any in-the-money options will increase while the values of any out-of-the-money options will decrease, regardless of whether the options are puts or calls.

11. Which of the following statements regarding the International Securities Exchange (ISE) is (are) *true*?

    a. It was established to conduct trades in options on foreign securities.
    b. Its trading floor is located in Chicago, Illinois.
    c. Both futures and options are traded on the ISE.
*   d. It lists options on most of the same stocks as those options traded on the CBOE, AMEX, PHIX, and PSE.
    e. All of the above are true statements.

12. A synthetic long position in an asset is created by

*   a. buying a call option on the stock and simultaneously writing a put option on the stock.
    b. buying a put option on the stock and simultaneously writing a call option on the stock.
    c. buying a put and a call with the same exercise price, but differing expiration dates.
    d. buying a put and a call with the same expiration date, but different exercise prices.
    e. buying a call option on a stock and simultaneously writing a call option on the stock with the same exercise price, but a different expiration date.

13. The writer of a covered call will experience the greatest gain from having written the call when

       a.   the price of the optioned stock increases greatly.

*   b.   the price of the optioned stock is the same as the option's exercise price and remains stable until expiration.

       c.   the price of the optioned stock drops.

       d.   either "a" or "b."

       e.   either "a" or "c."

14. A long straddle position is formed by

       a.   buying a call option on the stock and simultaneously writing a put option on the stock.

       b.   buying a put option on the stock and simultaneously writing a call option on the stock.

       c.   buying a put and a call with the same exercise price, but differing expiration dates.

       d.   buying a put and a call with the same expiration date, but different exercise prices.

*   e.   buying a put and a call on the same stock with the same exercise price and the same expiration date.

15. The writer of a straddle will profit if

       a.   the price of the optioned asset increases greatly.

       b.   the price of the optioned asset falls sharply.

       c.   the price of the optioned asset moves significantly, regardless of whether it is up or down.

*   d.   the price of the optioned asset does not vary significantly over the life of the option.

       e.   the price of the optioned asset increases above the exercise price of the put, but remains below the exercise price of the call.

16. A strategy that utilizes a combination of options that have both different expiration dates and different exercise prices is called a

       a.   butterfly spread

       b.   horizontal spread

       c.   vertical spread

*   d.   diagonal spread.

       e.   calendar spread.

17. An investor who expects the price of a stock to experience only a modest increase would be most likely to

   a. enter a long straddle position.
   b. enter a short butterfly spread position.
   c. enter a long call bear spread position.
   d. enter a long put bear spread position.
   * e. enter a long bull spread position.

18. Donna Gessup entered a short straddle position on a stock. The call option premium was $3 and the put option premium was $4. The exercise price on the options was $40. Which of the following statements is *true*?

   a. Donna's maximum loss is $7 and her break-even points occur at stock prices of $33 and $47.
   * b. Donna's maximum profit is $7 and her break-even points occur at stock prices of $33 and $47.
   c. Donna's maximum profit is $7 and her break-even points occur at stock prices of $43 and $37.
   d. Donna's maximum profit is $1 and her break-even points occur at stock prices of $41 and $39.
   e. none of the above

19. Which of the following would constitute a bear call spread? (Assume the options have the same expiration date.)

   a. the purchase of a call option with a $30 exercise price and the sale of a call option with a $40 exercise price
   b. the purchase of a call option with a $30 exercise price and the sale of a put option with a $40 exercise price
   * c. the purchase of a call option with a $30 exercise price and the sale of a call option with a $20 exercise price
   d. the sale of a call option with a $40 exercise price and the purchase of a call option with a $30 exercise price
   e. Either "b" or "c" could be used to form a bear call spread.

20. Which of the following statements regarding a long bull spread position is (are) *true*?

   a. The investor can experience unlimited losses if the price of the underlying asset falls below the lowest exercise price.
   b. The largest profits are realized if the price of the underlying asset moves above the higher of the two exercise prices.
   c. The investor benefits only from upward price moves that occur between the exercise prices of the two options.
   d. The investor's losses are limited to the cost of the option.
   * e. Both "c" and "d" are true.

II. SHORT ANSWER QUESTIONS

1. Evaluate the following claim: "By writing calls against a long position in the underlying stock, it is possible to both reduce the portfolio's risk and increase its expected rate of return." Is this statement true, false or uncertain? Explain.

2a. Explain how to create the economic equivalent of a short position (called a synthetic short position) by combining options.

b. Is the synthetic short position as desirable as the genuine short position? Explain.

3. The stock of the Inmar Corporation is currently selling at $36 3/8. Call premiums for an option on the stock with a $40 strike price are provided below:

Strike price	Month of expiration	
	September	December
$40	$7/8	$1 3/4

(a) Explain how an investor who expected a modest short-run price rise would form a horizontal spread, using the information given. (b) What is the net cost of this position? (c) Discuss what would happen if Inmar's stock price traded at or just below $40 in September. (d) What would happen if the stock price rose to $45 in September? (e) What would happen if the stock price dropped to $25 in September?

4. The price of GM common stock had been hovering around $50 per share for a long time, and Avner Wolf thought the stock was poised for a big move. So, Mr. Wolf considered purchasing a July call with a $50 exercise price for a premium of $3 per share in case the stock's price rose. He also considered purchasing a July put with an exercise price of $50 for a premium of $2 in case the stock's price fell. (a) What is the name of the position Avner is considering? (b) What would be the total cost of Avner's aggregate position? (c) Construct a table showing Avner's gains and losses from his put and call options at $10 stock price intervals for GM prices from $30 to $70 inclusive. (d) At what stock prices would Mr. Wolf break even on his combination of options?

5. What is the difference between a vertical spread and a horizontal spread? Under what set of circumstances would each be used?

CHAPTER TWENTY-EIGHT: SOLUTION GUIDELINES

Multiple Choice

1. **d**: The premium of a call option will be higher the greater the volatility of the underlying stock's returns since this increases the chance that the option will expire in the money. The premium will also be *higher* the *higher* the price of the underlying (more risk for the writer), the *lower* the exercise price (greater chance to expire in the money), the *longer* the time to expiration (more time to become more profitable for the owner), and the *higher* the level of market interest rates (greater opportunity cost).

2. **a**: N(x) in the Black-Scholes option pricing model is the hedge ratio, which represents the amount by which the price of an option will change for each dollar change in the price of the optioned asset.

3. **b**: A hedge ratio of 0.5 means that to establish a perfect hedge, an investor must sell 100 calls for every 50 shares of stock owned. Thus, if you own 100 shares of the underlying stock, you would have to write 200 calls.

4. **e**: The price of the underlying stock, the risk-free interest rate, the variance of the returns on the underlying stock, and the time to expiration of the option are all factors in determining the value of "x." A change in any one of them will, therefore, cause a change in "x," and in the hedge ratio, N(x).

5. **d**: The value of "x" is calculated first:

$$x = \frac{\ln(\$22.88/\$40) + [0.062 + 0.5(0.366)](0.333)}{(0.605)(0.333)^{0.5}} = \frac{-0.5586 + 0.0816}{0.3491} = -1.366.$$

Using a table of values for the area of the normal distribution below the distribution mean, we determine N(1.37) = 0.0853.

6. **a**: The value of "y" is calculated as follows:

y = -1.366 - (0.605)(0.333)$^{0.5}$ = -1.715.

N(-1.72) = 0.0427

COP$_0$ = P$_0$N(x) - XP[e$^{(-RFR)d}$]N(y) = 22.88(0.0853) - 40[e$^{(-0.062)(0.333)}$]0.0427
= 1.9517 - 1.6731 = \$0.28.

7. **c**: COP$_0$ = [P$_0$ - (DIV/1 + RFR)]N(x) - XP[e$^{(-RFR)d}$]N(y)
= [22.88 - (1.10/1.062)](0.0853) - 40[e$^{(-0.062)(0.333)}$](0.0427)
= 1.8633 - 1.6732 = \$0.19.

8.   **b**: $POP_0 = COP_0 + [XP/(1 + RFR)^d] - P_0$

$$= 6.75 + [50/(1.06)^{0.25}] - 53.38$$
$$= 6.75 + 49.28 - 53.38 = \$2.65.$$

9.   **d**:   According to the put-call parity model, the price of the put should be \$4.02:

$$4 + [32.50/(1.065)^{0.083}] - 32.31 = \$4.02$$

Since the put is selling for \$3.75, it is underpriced by \$0.27 (= \$4.02 - \$3.75).

10.   **c**:   On the ex-dividend date, the stock begins trading without the cash dividend attached, and its market price drops by the amount of the cash dividend payment. This serves to decrease the value of any call options on the stock since the price of the underlying has fallen. By similar argument, the price of any put options will increase.

11.   **d**:   The ISE is an electronic exchange and has no traditional open-outcry trading floor. It competes with the CBOE, AMEX, PHIX, and PSE by listing options on most of the same stocks listed on these traditional options exchanges.

12.   **a**:   An options trader who simultaneously writes a put and buys a call with the same exercise price and expiration date on the same underlying security will experience the same gains and losses as if he had entered a long position in the underlying asset.

13.   **b**:   Covered call writers gain the most from their call writing when the price of their optioned stock remains at its exercise price and the option expires unexercised because the writer then gets to keep the stock *and* the premium paid for the option. If the price of the optioned stock increases, the option owner will choose to exercise the option, and the call writer will have the stock "called away," at the exercise price. This results in an opportunity loss for the writer. If the price of the optioned stock decreases, the option will not be exercised; however, the writer will experience a loss due to his long position in the stock that is only partially offset by the option premium he received.

14.   **e**:   This is the definition of a long straddle position.

15.   **d**:   The straddle writer will profit if the price of the underlying stock does not move enough to wipe out the fees received for writing the two options. This requires that the price of the optioned asset not vary significantly over the life of the option. If the price moves significantly in either direction, the straddle owner will exercise one of the two options. (Selection "e" can be ruled out since a straddle involves options that have the same exercise price and the same maturity.)

16.   **d**:   This is the definition of a diagonal spread.

17.   **e**:   An investor will profit from a long straddle position only if the price of the underlying asset moves significantly in one direction or the other. The same is true of a short butterfly spread position. An investor will profit from a long bear spread position, regardless of whether it is a put bear spread or a call bear spread, if the price of the

underlying stock experiences only a modest decrease. A long bull spread position is profitable if the price of the underlying stock experiences a modest increase. The only price moves that are profitable are those between the exercise prices of the two options.

18.   **b**:   The only profits for the straddle writer is the income from the combined option premiums, or $7 in this case. If the price of the stock varies from the exercise price by more than this in either direction, the straddle writer will experience losses. The break-even points are, therefore, $33 and $47 (= $40 ± $7).

19.   **c**:   A bear spread is established in one of two ways: (1) writing a put and simultaneously buying a put with a higher exercise price, but the same expiration date, on the same asset or (2) writing a call and simultaneously buying a call with a higher exercise price, but the same expiration date, on the same asset. The exercise price of the long position must be higher than the exercise price of the short position in either case. Only selection "c" meets this qualification.

20.   **e**:   Losses on bull spreads are limited to the cost of the option. Investors in bull spreads experience gains only on stock price moves that occur between the exercise prices of the two options. Gains are unaffected if the stock price rises above the highest exercise price.

Short Answer

1.   Generally speaking, the statement is uncertain. The statement is true in a bear market, flat market, or slightly bullish market because writing covered call options against a portfolio of stocks can generate premium income. The premium income can increase the portfolio's rate of return above what it would have been without writing the calls. Writing covered calls also reduces the portfolio's risk because the premium income from writing covered calls can compensate for some losses if the price of the optioned stock declines. There is a cost to receiving these benefits, however. If market conditions become strongly bullish and the calls are exercised, the appreciating stocks are called away at the disadvantageous values of their lower exercise prices. Thus, if a bull market occurs, writing covered calls can decrease the portfolio's rate of return below what it would have been if the calls were not written.

2a.   The economic equivalent to a short position on the underlying stock can be created by writing (or selling) a call and buying a put on the same stock at the same exercise prices. The resulting combination of a put and a call equals a synthetic short position. If transactions costs are ignored, the synthetic short position produces the same gains and losses as the short sale of the asset.

 b.   The traditional short position has the advantages of being easier to understand and costing less in commission expenses. However, a synthetic short position can be more desirable than the short position that is obtained directly for three reasons. First, the option position is superior because the call that was sold brings in premium income from its time premium that exceeds what must be spent to pay for the time premium on the long put. A positive net cash flow results. A second advantage of the synthetic short sale is that it offers more financial leverage. Short sales require an initial margin of about 50 percent. The synthetic short position involves a smaller initial investment. The margin computations are below.

Deposit: Fifteen percent of the optioned stock's price plus the call premium received minus the put premium paid. This total will be less than 50% of the short position.

The third benefit is that the synthetic short seller does not have to pay cash dividends on the optioned stock from his own funds as does the short seller of the borrowed stock.

3a.   To construct a horizontal spread if an investor expected a short-run price rise for Inmar, he would buy the December calls and sell (write) the September calls.

b.   His net cost would be $1 3/4 - $7/8 = $7/8.

c.   If Inmar traded at or just below $40 in September, the September calls would expire worthless. The December calls would still have 3 months to run and be worth about $2 (due to their time value), in which case the investor's return would be over 100%: ($2 - $7/8)/$7/8 = 128%

d.   If Inmar traded at $45 in September, both the September and the December calls would increase in value. The difference in the two option prices may either increase or decrease slightly, producing little or no gain or loss.

e.   If Inmar's stock dropped to $25 a share, both the September and the December calls would decrease dramatically in value. If, in September, the December calls were still worth $3/8, due to their time value, the initial spread would narrow from $7/8 to $3/8. The losses incurred would be substantial, but limited. Adverse moves in the short position will be offset by favorable moves in the long position, and vice versa.

4a.   Mr. Wolf is considering purchasing a long straddle position.

b.   The long straddle is what brokers call a net debit transaction that costs ($3 + $2 =) $5 per share (or $500 total), plus commissions.

c.   The gains and losses from the straddle are as follows:

GM price	Call profit	Put profit	Straddle profit
$30	-$300	+$1,800	+$1,500
$40	-$300	+$800	+$500
$45	-$300	+$300	0
$50	-$300	-$200	-$500
$55	+$200	-$200	0
$60	+$700	-$200	+$500
$70	+$1,700	-$200	+$1,500

d. The break-even points on Avner's straddle occur at stock prices of $45 and $55, as shown in the table above.

5. A vertical spread involves entering both a long and a short option position at different exercise prices, but the same expiration date, whereas a horizontal spread involves entering both a long and a short option position with different expiration dates but the same exercise price. An investor who believes that the stock price will experience a *modest* upward movement can enter a bull spread, which both reduces his risk and allows him to experience increased gains if his belief holds true. (However, for *larger* favorable gains, the long position alone would prove to be more profitable.) If the investor anticipated a modest downward movement in price, he would execute a bear spread. Horizontal spreads would be used by investors who expect modest, *short-term* price swings.

CHAPTER TWENTY-NINE: ALTERNATIVE INVESTMENTS

I.   MULTIPLE CHOICE QUESTIONS

1.   Which of the following is *not* typically classified as a *business* real-estate investment?

      a.   apartment buildings
      b.   shopping centers
*   c.   farms
      d.   raw land
      e.   All of the above are usually considered to be business real-estate investments.

2.   Which of the following statements about real estate investment trusts (REITs) is (are) *true*?

      a.   They are a type of mutual fund that invests in real property.
      b.   Their shares trade on stock exchanges and in the over-the-counter market.
      c.   In order to be exempt from taxes, their cash dividend payout ratio must be greater than 95% of their annual income every year.
      d.   Their shares are bought and sold at net asset value.
*   e.   both "b" and "c"

3.   In analyzing the financial performance of real estate investments, appraised real estate values are often used because

      a.   they are more realistic estimates of the true economic value of the property.
      b.   using appraised values allows for a smoothing process that makes the interpretation of the statistics easier.
      c.   they result in lower standard deviations for real estate investment returns.
*   d.   market data is not readily available since residential, farm, and business real estate transactions occur infrequently.
      e.   all of the above

4.   Which of the following is *not* an advantage that may be enjoyed by real estate investors?

      a.   geographic diversification
*   b.   lower transactions costs than those incurred when investing in the stock market
      c.   inflation hedge
      d.   ability to utilize more financial leverage
      e.   All of the above are advantages of investing in real estate.

5.   Which of the following statements is (are) *true*?

*   a.   An investment in physical real estate is usually a good hedge against inflation, but
            the same cannot be said about an investment in real estate investment trusts
            (REITs).
      b.   The advantage of geographic diversification can be achieved only by investing in
            REITs; this advantage does not apply to investments in physical real estate.
      c.   Investments in real estate are usually good inflation hedges, regardless of whether
            one invests in the actual physical real estate or invests through an REIT.
      d.   Physical real estate investments have historically provided both higher returns and
            less risk than investing in the stock market.
      e.   both "b" and "c"

6.   Which of the following statements about hedge funds is (are) *true*?

      a.   They tend to be aggressively managed.
      b.   They are not regulated by the Investment Company Act of 1940.
      c.   Most of them are incorporated.
      d.   They are prohibited from investing in mutual funds.
*   e.   both "a" and "b"

7.   In which of the following ways does a domestic hedge fund differ from an off-
      shore hedge fund?

      a.   Domestic hedge funds are regulated by the Investment Company Act of 1940, but
            off-shore hedge funds are not.
*   b.   Domestic hedge funds must register with the SEC, but off-shore hedge funds do
            not have to register with the SEC and are largely unregulated.
      c.   Domestic hedge funds provide non-U.S. investors the opportunity to avoid
            taxation; non-U.S. investors in off-shore hedge funds receive no tax shelter
            benefits.
      d.   all of the above
      e.   "a" and "b" only

8.   A sister fund is

*   a.   an off-shore hedge fund that invests in the same securities as a domestic hedge
            fund.
      b.   a fund that invests in physical silver and is managed by the same individual or
            team that manages a fund invested in gold bullion.
      c.   a mortgage REIT that is directly affiliated with an equity REIT.
      d.   a domestic hedge fund that invests in the ADRs of the same companies in which
            an off-shore hedge fund is directly invested.
      e.   open only to non-U.S. investors.

9. Which of the following types of trades are prohibited to hedge fund managers?

    a. short sales
    b. the purchase of options
    c. a short position in a futures contract
    d. the purchase of shares of a unit investment trust
*   e. none of the above

10. A hedge fund that has a manager who simultaneously buys stock in a company being acquired and sells stock in its acquirers would be classified by Managed Account Reports (MAR), Inc. as a

*   a. risk arbitrage fund.
    b. long/short stocks fund.
    c. convertible arbitrage fund.
    d. short-sales fund.
    e. short-term fund.

11. Which of the following is a subcategory of a U.S. Opportunistic hedge fund?

    a. risk arbitrage fund
    b. distressed securities fund
    c. regional fund
    d. stock index arbitrage fund
*   e. short-term fund.

12. Based on historical statistics, which of the following categories of hedge funds has been an inferior performer?

    a. global macro funds
*   b. market neutral funds
    c. event driven funds
    d. U.S. opportunistic funds
    e. all of the above

13. A study of hedge funds by Brown, Goetzmann, and Ibbotson found that

      a.   the average beta of hedge funds exceeds 2.0.

      b.   the average hedge fund had both a higher average rate of return than the S&P 500 Index and a lower standard deviation than the S&P 500 Index over the period studied.

*   c.   the average hedge fund had both a lower average rate of return than the S&P 500 Index and a lower standard deviation than the S&P 500 Index over the period studied.

      d.   when risk and return are considered at the same time, the performance of the hedge funds is worse than that of the S&P 500 Index.

      e.   both "a" and "d"

14. In comparing the performance of hedge funds to mutual funds, Ackermann, McEnally, and Ravenscraft's study concluded that

      a.   mutual funds outperformed hedge funds by a large margin, based on the SHARPE performance measure.

      b.   hedge funds outperformed mutual funds by a large margin, based on the SHARPE performance measure.

      c.   mutual funds outperformed hedge funds, but only slightly, based on the SHARPE performance measure.

*   d.   hedge funds outperformed mutual funds, but only slightly, based on the SHARPE performance measure.

      e.   hedge funds outperformed not only the mutual funds, but also the eight market indexes that were used in the study.

15. Which of the following led to the demonetizing of silver in the U.S.?

      a.   The Federal Reserve Act of 1913

*   b.   The Coinage Act of 1965

      c.   The Securities Act of 1933

      d.   The Great Stock Market Crash of 1929

      e.   none of the above; silver continues to be used as a medium of exchange in the U.S. today.

16. Which of the following has historically provided the best long-run inflation hedge?

*   a.   common stocks

      b.   gold bullion

      c.   physical silver

      d.   REITs

      e.   both "b" and "c"

17. Which of the following is a potential problem associated with the demonetizing of gold?

    a.   The value of gold as a commodity decreases because the forces of supply and demand are upset.

    b.   The price of the nation's exports decreases.

* c.   It can lead to high levels of inflation if other devices are not put in place to control the nation's money supply.

    d.   Government spending is severely restricted, resulting in the elimination of social welfare programs.

    e.   all of the above

18. A major benefit of investing in gold bullion or physical silver is that

    a.   these investments have provided the best hedge against inflation over the long-run.

    b.   they provide higher returns and are more liquid than other similar-risk investments, such as money market securities.

    c.   they have value as catastrophe insurance.

    d.   they provide further diversification to a portfolio of financial securities.

* e.   both "c" and "d."

19. Which of the following statements about equity REITs is (are) *false*?

    a.   Investors in equity REITs receive rental income as well as income from capital appreciation if a piece of property is sold for a gain.

    b.   Their returns tend to be negatively correlated with inflation.

    c.   Investors in equity REITs receive rental income from the properties which the REIT manages and also receive interest income from the loans that the REIT makes to builders.

    d.   Equity REITs are less liquid than mortgage REITs.

* e.   Both "c" and "d" are false statements.

20. The high water mark of a hedge fund is

* a.   the total asset value that must be attained before the fund's manager receives any incentive fee.

    b.   the total asset value that must be attained before the investors in the fund can withdraw any of their investment monies.

    c.   the minimum amount of investment funds that the law requires investors in hedge funds to have before the hedge fund can accept their investments.

    d.   typically equal to the average net asset value of the fund in the trailing twelve months.

    e.   both "a" and "d."

II. SHORT ANSWER QUESTIONS

1. What three national objectives does having a gold standard accomplish? What is the potential major problem with the abolition of a gold standard?

2. Why are appraised, rather than market, values often used in compiling the statistics for real estate investments? What problems are caused by using appraised values instead of market values?

3. Consider the following information regarding the purchase of a $230,000 home:

   Down payment = $57,500
   Mortgage: 30-year, fixed rate loan at 7.5% interest
   Monthly mortgage payment: $1,206
   Average monthly interest payment for the first year: $1,078
   Expected annual price appreciation: 8%
   Monthly real estate taxes: $240
   Monthly home insurance: $67
   Gas, electricity, and water: $218
   Monthly estimate for repairs and upkeep: $100

   What is the net monthly cash payment required of a home buyer who is in the 28% marginal tax bracket?

4. About 20% of the existing hedge funds go out of business every year. What two forces are responsible for this high attrition rate?

5. What constitutes the *political risk* of real estate investment in the United States?

CHAPTER TWENTY-NINE: SOLUTION GUIDELINES

Multiple Choice

1.   **c**:   Farms are a separate category of real estate investment.

2.   **e**:   REITs are not mutual funds; they are patterned after closed-end investment companies. Like other closed-end investment companies, their shares are sold on stock exchanges and in the over-the-counter market, and their prices are set by supply and demand. Their prices, therefore, may be less than, greater than, or equal to their net asset value. In order to be exempt from taxes, one of the requirements is that their cash dividend payout ratio be greater than 95% of their annual income each year.

3.   **d**:   Appraised real estate values are often used because market data is not readily available. However, appraised values are often not good estimates of the true value of the property and tend to fluctuate less than the actual market values, which leads to a smoothing process that causes standard deviations to be downward biased. It would be preferable if market data were available.

4.   **b**:   Transactions costs are typically higher for real estate investments than for investments in financial securities. Real estate brokers often charge a flat 6% commission, which is higher than what a similar dollar investment in stocks would require. The cost of acquiring information is also higher since each piece of real estate is unique. However, real estate investment can provide investors with geographic diversification, serves as an inflation hedge, and allows investors to use more financial leverage since the down payments required are significantly less than the initial margin requirement in the stock market.

5.   **a**:   The market value of most physical real estate is positively correlated with the rate of inflation, which makes physical real estate a good inflation hedge. However, REITs tend to be negatively correlated with inflation, which means they are poor inflation hedges. Multiple investments in physical real estate can provide geographic diversification, even without substantial geographic distance between the properties purchased. Historical data reveals that real estate investment provided both lower returns than the stock market and less risk; however, the risk statistics are suspect due to the downward bias that occurs because appraised, rather than market, values are used.

6.   **e**:   Hedge funds are not regulated by the Investment Company Act of 1940, and they tend to be aggressively managed. Most of them are organized as limited partnerships. The law allows hedge funds to buy and sell a wide variety of financial assets, including shares of other investment companies.

7.   **b**:   Neither domestic nor off-shore hedge funds are regulated by the Investment Company Act of 1940, but domestic hedge funds must register with the SEC while off-shore hedge funds do not. Off-shore funds, set up as sister funds of domestic funds, provide non-U.S. investors the opportunity to avoid taxation.

8.   **a**:   This is the definition of a sister fund.

9.   **e**:   Hedge fund managers are allowed to engage in all of the listed trades.

10.   **a**:   This is the investment objective associated with the risk arbitrage fund as categorized by MAR, Inc.

11.   **e**:   Subcategories of the U.S. Opportunistic hedge fund category are value, growth, and short-term.

12.   **b**:   Based on historical statistics, the three categories of hedge funds that have been inferior performers are the fund-of-funds, market neutral, and short sales funds.

13.   **c**:   Brown, Goetzmann, and Ibbotson reported that over the seven-year sample period that they studied, the average hedge fund earned a lower average rate of return than the S&P 500 Index and also had a lower standard deviation of returns than the S&P 500 Index. They also found that the average betas for the hedge funds were low--less than 0.5, regardless of whether they used equal weighting or value weighting. When risk and return were considered together, the performance of the hedge funds was found to be better than that of the S&P 500 Index.

14.   **d**:   Ackermann, McEnally, and Ravenscraft found that the hedge funds were just modestly superior to mutual funds when they compared the two using the SHARPE performance measure. When they compared the hedge funds with eight different securities market indexes, they got mixed results. They concluded that hedge funds were unable to beat the market on a consistent basis.

15.   **b**:   The Coinage Act of 1965 was the first step toward demonetizing silver in the U.S.

16.   **a**:   Although stock prices are negatively correlated with inflation during sample periods of less than one year, they are uncorrelated with inflation over longer periods and have provided a better long-run inflation hedge than either gold or silver.

17.   **c**:   The demonetizing of gold allows political leaders to expand the nation's money supply in order to provide funds to support their favorite programs. This, however, can result in high levels of inflation, which means that the prices of that country's goods and services will increase, not decrease. When gold is demonetized, its value will fluctuate freely, based on the supply and demand for it.

18.   **e**:   Gold bullion and physical silver investments provide catastrophe insurance since they are portable stores of value and mediums of exchange that tend to be used in place of currency during periods of crisis. They also provide diversification to a portfolio that is invested in financial securities since they are not highly correlated with stock or bond prices. Common stocks, however, provide a better hedge against inflation over the long-run, and money market securities offer the same zero real returns as gold and silver, but provide investors with greater liquidity.

19.   **e**:   REIT returns tend to be negatively correlated with inflation. Equity REITs have most of their funds invested in equity positions in real estate. The shareholders receive rental income and income from capital appreciation if the property is sold for a gain. It is the mortgage REIT that lends money to builders; mortgage REIT investors are the ones who receive interest income from these loans. Equity REITs and mortgage REITs are equally liquid.

20.   **a**:   This is the definition of a high water mark.

Short Answer

1.   A gold standard serves to prevent a nation's money supply from expanding too rapidly. It also prevents a nation's politicians from spending too much since the politicians cannot simply print more money for their favorite uses. By preventing these two events, the gold standard also controls the nation's inflation rate. When the gold standard is eliminated, if constraints are not put on the money supply by some other means, it can expand too rapidly, which results in high inflation and an erosion of that nation's economic health.

2.   Appraised real estate values are used because they are more readily available. Residential, farm, and business real estate transactions occur infrequently, so investors are unable to obtain market data from actual transactions that can be observed at frequent intervals. Unfortunately, this results in a smoothing process that biases the statistical data for real estate investments because appraisers tend to ignore some realistic events and produce values that fluctuate much less than actual market values. This results in a downward bias in the calculation of standard deviations, making the SHARPE ratio a misleading measure of performance for real estate investments. It also results in serial correlations that are suspiciously high.

3.   The net monthly cash payment is the difference between the total monthly payments and the monthly tax savings due to interest expense and real estate taxes. While the price appreciation is like a savings program, it cannot be withdrawn and does not serve to reduce the monthly payments needed.

Total monthly payments = mortgage + real estate taxes + utilities + insurance + maintenance and repairs = $1,206 + $240 + $218 + $67 + $100 = $1,831

Monthly tax savings = 0.28($1,078 + $240) = $369

Net monthly cash payment = $1,831 - $369 = $1,462

4. First, when a hedge fund suffers large losses, it is difficult to keep old investors and also difficult to attract new investors. Additionally, because hedge fund managers receive incentive fees only if the total asset value of their fund is above the high water mark, many managers get discouraged and quit if their fund suffers large losses for one or two consecutive years.

5. The political risk of a real estate investment in the United States lies in the tax laws. Currently, real estate investors can deduct the interest expense on their mortgages and their real estate taxes when calculating taxable income. However, tax laws can be changed, and there is the possibility that these deductions may be disallowed in the future. In point of fact, the elimination of these tax benefits has been argued about among the nation's legislators from time to time.